HEALTH EDUCATION
AUTHORITY

A
SURVEY
of the
UK
POPULATION

PART 1

© Health Education Authority 1995

ISBN 0 7521 0460 8

First published 1995

Health Education Authority
Hamilton House
Mabledon Place
London WC1H 9TX

Typeset by BookEns Ltd, Royston, Herts.
Printed in Great Britain.

Contents

Acknowledgements

Health and Lifestyles Project Team:

Dominic McVey	Acting Head of Research	HEA
Rhiannon Barker	Researcher Manager	HEA
Keith Bolling	Research Manager	HEA
Kai Rudat	Director	MORI
Claire Ivins	Formerly Researcher at	MORI
Caroline Frith	Senior Research Executive	MORI

The HEA would like to thank everybody who contributed to the survey and the production of the report. Special thanks should go to Rosemary Pope, Jeannie McKenzie, Antony Morgan, Lesley Owen, Jacky Chambers, Rosemary Glass, Alan Glanz and Christine Callum who contributed much to the development of the survey.

Most importantly, the HEA would like to thank the thousands of individuals who agreed to take part in the survey and gave us so much of their time to be interviewed.

Introduction

With the publication in 1992 of the government's white paper *The Health of the Nation*, it became clear that health education was to play an important part in achieving the targets set in the five key areas: coronary heart disease and stroke, cancers, mental illness, HIV/AIDS and sexual health and accidents. To assess progress towards these targets the HEA commissioned a number of surveys of the health and lifestyles of people living in the UK.

The objectives of the studies were as follows:

- To provide standardised data sets to monitor key national targets identified in *The Health of the Nation*, that are relevant to the HEA's strategic and operational plans.

- To ascertain progress towards targets in terms of the work carried out through the HEA's programmes and service delivery settings.

- To examine the range of factors contributing to health status.

- To provide information to assess the needs of specific target groups, and the barriers that exist to the maintenance of good health.

- To collect data at a national level that will provide a frame of reference for data collected at a local level.

- To provide a reliable and valid research instrument – drawing on data from other sources.

This study is part of a programme of research commissioned by the HEA. Additional studies of black and minority ethnic communities have been conducted using similar questionnaires, and findings from this work are reported elsewhere (HEA, 1994).

This report presents the findings from the first study, conducted in 1992, of the health and lifestyles of over 5000 people aged 16–74.

The survey comprised modules of questions on smoking, sexual health, cancer, health concerns, health services and psychosocial health. Subsequent surveys will comprise different modules, but will retain a number of core questions common to each health and lifestyle survey. It is intended to repeat the modules over the years providing a comprehensive data set over time for each of the areas within *The Health of the Nation*.

Researchers from within the HEA and other organisations were given the data and commissioned to write chapters on the different survey modules.

The researchers have adopted various approaches to the analysis. Some have reported on most of the data within the module under discussion, whilst others have used a selected number of variables as the focus of their analysis.

It is beyond the scope of this book to report the findings on every variable contained within the questionnaire. The chapters have been written to reflect, in the author's view, the key areas of interest and concern. However, as some readers may require analysis of questions not covered in the report, the HEA has produced a set of data tables on electronic fiche. Appendix 2 contains information about the data disk available from the HEA.

Many of the questions asked of the general population will not be found in other surveys. Indeed there are few examples of surveys where respondents have been asked such a range of health-related knowledge, attitudes and behaviour questions. Whilst this report has concentrated on the analysis by topic area the data have considerable potential, using more sophisticated multivariate analysis, to link the attitudes and behaviours across different health areas, and to build a more comprehensive picture of the health and lifestyle of the individual. Further analysis of the data is already under way.

The HEA has a major commitment to improving the health and well-being of people in England. The findings contained within this report are currently informing the development of HEA work at national and local level. We hope it will prove to be a valuable source of information for NHS purchasers and providers, local authorities, voluntary organisations and others planning health promotion activities.

Dominic McVey
Acting Head of Research
Health Education Authority

Reference
Health Education Authority (1994) *Health and lifestyles. Black and minority ethnic groups in England.* HEA.

1. Background and methodology

Kai Rudat
Director
Market Opinion Research International
London

Background to the survey

In August 1991 the Health Education Authority commissioned MORI to carry out a programme of health and lifestyle research on its behalf. The programme was intended to consist of separate quantitative surveys among the general public in the UK, and among black and minority ethnic communities resident in the UK. The primary objective of the programme was to evaluate the HEA's key mission statement, that 'the people of England are more knowledgeable, better motivated and more able to acquire and maintain good health', by examining factors contributing to health status and assessing the needs, and the barriers to maintaining good health, of specific target groups. The research findings would inform the HEA's strategies for achieving Health of the Nation targets and for monitoring indicators.

Fieldwork methodology

MORI conducted a random probability survey, using a nationally representative sample of 334 points in England, 28 points in Scotland, 19 points in Wales and 9 in Northern Ireland (a total of 390 sample points). In Great Britain the sample points were Census enumeration districts (EDs); in Northern Ireland the sample points were postal sectors.

Within England the sample was stratified by Regional Health Authority, and within Great Britain the sample was stratified by country. Probability of selection of each ED was proportional to the size of the adult population within the ED. Within each ED a random sample of 30 addresses was drawn from the PAF (the Small Users' Postcode Address File). The sample of addresses in Northern Ireland was also drawn from PAF, but it was not possible to draw an ED-based sample because of the lack of commercially available census information relating to Northern Ireland. Nine postal sectors were selected, and from a random start within each sector every fifth residential address was selected, to a total of 30 addresses.

A letter was sent to each address included in the survey, to explain the purpose of the survey and to let people know that a MORI interviewer would be calling at their address.

Fieldwork was conducted between 14 April and 31 July 1992. The sample addresses were screened by interviewers, and those which were identifiable as invalid (non-residential, vacant, demolished, etc.) were eliminated from the sample.

Addresses were screened for multiple households, and if necessary a Kish grid was used to select one of the households resident at the address.

Selected households were then screened to obtain a listing of all adults eligible to take part in the survey (i.e. those aged between 16 and 74 and normally resident at the address). Households containing only people aged 75+ were eliminated at this stage.

Because of the intended sample structure of 4000 interviews with people aged 16–54 and 1000 interviews with people aged 55–74 – a lower proportion of 55–74 year olds than that found among the population at large – it was necessary to screen out some of the older people identified. One in two households containing only 55–74 year olds were eliminated from the sample, and in households containing both 16–54 year olds and 55–74 year, each younger person was given twice as great a chance of being selected as respondent as each older person in the household. In households where there was more than one potential respondent, the intended respondent was then selected using a Kish grid.

Response rate

A total of 11 508 addresses were used for this survey, of which 10 469 were thought to be valid (91%). Interviewers were able to screen households at 8312 of these (79%); at the remainder they were unable to screen either because of refusals, in 13% of cases, and because of being unable to make contact with anyone resident at the address after four or more calls, in 8% of cases. (It seems likely that a proportion of these 'non-contacts' were actually invalid addresses which the interviewer was unable to identify as such). At the addresses screened, 926 contained only people aged 75+, and a further 799 were excluded from the survey because the residents were all aged 55–74. At 249 addresses, residents were away or too ill to be interviewed during the fieldwork period, and at 76 addresses, the interviewer could not find an adult resident who spoke fluent enough English for screening to take place.

In total, 6262 addresses were identified as in scope and containing a person eligible to be interviewed (75% of those originally identified as valid). Eight hundred and forty-eight potential respondents refused to be interviewed, and in 323 cases, interviewers were unable to make contact with the potential respondent after repeated calls at the address. Interviews were conducted at 5007 addresses, giving a response rate of 80% at valid screened addresses.

Self-completion questionnaire

After completing the face-to-face interview, respondents who were aged 16 to 54 years (inclusive) were handed a self-completion questionnaire, together with an envelope. They were asked by the interviewer to fill in the questionnaire on their own, put it into an envelope and seal it before handing the envelope back to the interviewer. Interviewers did not look at the completed questionnaire at any stage, and therefore could not tell to what extent the respondent had actually filled it in.

The respondent's unique identifying number was written on the envelope. At the office, the identifying number was transferred to the questionnaire itself and some basic editing was carried out. It was at this stage that questionnaires which were mostly blank, or where there was a lack of internal consistency between responses, were identified. Self-completion questionnaires were then sent for data entry and matched back to the main questionnaire with which they belonged, via the unique identifying number.

The achieved sample of 5007 adults included 3959 in the age range 16 to 54. Of these, 3733 (94%) filled in a questionnaire which could be data entered, though 30 of these could not be matched back to a main questionnaire and therefore could not be included in the tabulations relating to the self-completion questionnaire.

Of the remainder:

214 did not accept the self-completion questionnaire from the interviewer:

    188 refused
     16 were unable to read
      5 were unable to write
      4 said there were parental or family objections to their completing it
      1 was visually impaired

  12 accepted questionnaires:

      6 were returned blank
      6 were completed either at random or in a deliberately misleading way, with contradictory answers or no internal logic.

Weighting of the data

Survey data used in this report have been edited, weighted proportional to household size of the respondent (to correct for the fact that the chosen survey methodology only selected one respondent per household, thereby lessening the chances of being selected for the survey of people belonging to larger households) and also weighted by age and sex within RHA (in England) and within country for Wales, Scotland and Northern Ireland, in line with population projections for 1992 obtained from Office of Population Census Surveys (for England) and from the Welsh Office, Scottish Office and Northern Ireland Office.

Sample design

The major stratification variable used in the design was the 14 Regional Health Authorities within England (as they were in 1992). Within each authority enumeration districts (EDs) were sampled with probability proportional to the number of households. In total 390 EDs were selected. Within each selected sampling point 30 households were selected systematically. Within each selected household, all individuals aged 16–74 were listed. In order to produce a sample of 4000 people aged 16–54 and 1000 people aged 55–74, in households containing people in both these age groups the people aged 16–54 were listed twice, doubling their chances of selection. In addition, where households containing only individuals aged 55–74 were identified, one in two of these households was discarded from the sample. Use of a Kish grid determined the individual required for interviewing purposes.

Sources of sampling error

The features of the sample design of relevance to estimates of sampling error, beyond those which would be expected by simple random sampling fluctuation, are:

(i) Disproportional sample of individuals within households

In a one-adult household, the person listed is certain to be selected. In a two-adult household, each listed person has a one in two chance of being selected, and so on. Given that the probability of each household being selected is equal, then clearly the probability of an individual being selected is

$$\frac{1}{\text{number of adults in household}}$$

and the inverse of this equation must be used at the corrective weighting level to equalise selection probabilities. As a general rule, disproportional selection of individuals within households will increase the error. (More will be said about this later.) However, this is the inevitable price to pay for using the most comprehensive list of addresses in the UK – the Postcode Address File.

(ii) Disproportional sampling of adults aged 16–54 relative to adults aged 55 +

The extent to which this affects the error is as follows:

(a) If there is greater variation in the statistic to be measured in the group which has been over-sampled relative to the under-sampled group, the error may well be reduced.

(b) If the variation in the statistic to be measured is the same in both the over-sampled and under-sampled group, the error will always be increased.

(c) If the variation is greater in the under-sampled group, the error will always be increased.

The extent to which the error will be affected depends largely on the degree of over-sampling conducted. In the case of the current survey, the disproportionality is slight and results were unlikely to be greatly affected by this. (Again, more will be said about this later.)

(iii) Clustering

The population from which interviews was taken were based in 390 selected small clusters defined by the boundaries of any enumeration district, rather than systematically spread over every corner of the UK. Clustering is an effective means of keeping down survey costs, but may have a detrimental effect on survey error. The major reason for this is that small areas tend to attract a similar type of person, e.g. wealthy, poor, intermediate income, and thus within an area persons are more similar than would be the case if they were assigned to areas randomly. This tends to increase errors in estimates relating to status, e.g. class estimates, newspaper readership, educational attainment. In general, if there is little correlation between the statistic measured and status, clustering effects tend to be minimal, but the higher the correlation with status, the greater (normally) the effect due to clustering. However, even when clustering effects occur, they can be considerably reduced by maximising the number of sampling points and minimising the number of interviews per cluster within the constraints of fieldwork and interviewer requirements. For the full sample, only about 13 interviews an average were obtained per cluster, and for 16–54 year olds (the sample for the self-completion section) less that 9 interviews were obtained per cluster. We would thus expect the clustering effects within the survey to be kept within reasonable bounds, even with status-correlated variables.

Methodology for error estimation

The standard error of a sample estimate, based on sample size n, is itself an estimate of the standard deviation of all-possible samples of size n which could be drawn from the population, i.e. it is a measure of the variation from sample to sample of all possible results. Many techniques for estimating the true standard error of statistics based on complex designs attempt to simulate this process by means of replicated sub-samples. In essence, the statistics required for examination are analysed by a series of sub-samples A to N. The data are then transformed into a further series of sub-samples of the form Total-A, Total-B, etc. The programme then examines the degree of data variation over these sub-samples and estimates the true standard error from them. This sub-sampling (using the Jackknife technique) thus attempts to recreate the underlying theoretical basis for the calculation of standard errors.

The key requirement is to divide the original sample in terms of sampling points in strata order, thus preserving the original design. Thus if 10 sub-samples are required points 1, 11, 21, etc. are assigned to sub-sample A, and so on.

The data on the following page shows standard errors estimated by the Jackknife of replicated sub-sample process, and are particularly effective in highlighting the clustering effects discussed above.

Base	Characteristic	%(p)	Sample size	Standard error of p	95% confidence interval	Design factor
All	Social class					
	I & II	23.8	5 007	0.67	1.30	1.11
	IIINM	16.5	5 007	0.60	1.18	1.14
	IIIM	15.6	5 007	0.53	1.03	1.03
	IV	11.2	5 007	0.58	1.13	1.30
	V	4.2	5 007	0.37	0.72	1.29
All	Visiting surgery on own behalf in last 12 months					
	No visit	26.1	5 007	0.57	1.12	0.92
	1–2 visits	32.1	5 007	0.91	1.78	1.38
	3–6 visits	28.1	5 007	0.95	1.86	1.49
	7+ visits	13.7	5 007	0.54	1.06	1.12
All	Had screening for any kind of cancer					
		38.5	5 007	0.65	1.27	0.93
All	Smoke cigarettes nowadays					
		31.1	5 007	0.95	1.86	1.45
16–54 year olds who filled in self-completion section						
	Used condoms on last occasion of vaginal sexual intercourse					
		20.9	3 733	0.79	1.54	1.18
As above						
	Number of sexual partners (vaginal intercourse) in last 12 months					
	0	4.0	3 733	0.27	0.53	0.85
	1	65.2	3 733	0.84	1.65	1.08
	2+	12.1	3 733	0.91	1.79	1.70

Observations

The standard error estimates above, and hence design factors are based on the combined influences of sample disproportionality and clustering effects. If we untangle some of the elements we find that, in general, the effect of disproportionality in terms of sampling individuals within households produces an average increase in sampling error of about 7 (design factor 1.07), whereas the effects of sampling disproportionality are small. The remaining influences on design may thus be assumed to be the clustering effect.

2. General health concerns

Isobel Bowler
Formerly Policy Officer
Health Education Authority
London

Self-reported general health status

Informants were asked to assess their general health for their age, choosing from one of the following four categories : 'very good', 'fairly good', 'fairly poor', or 'very poor'. Almost half (47%) of informants reported 'very good' health, 46% reported 'fairly good' health, 6% reported 'fairly poor' health and only 2% reported 'very poor' health.

Men and women reported similar levels of good and bad health. The proportion of informants who reported 'very poor' or 'fairly poor' health increased with age among both women and men (Table 2.1). Levels of poor health rose particularly sharply from the age of 55, with 18% of men and 12% of women aged 55–64 and 14% of men and 13% of women aged 65–74 reporting 'very poor' or 'fairly poor' health.

Table 2.1: Self-reported general health by age and gender

	16–24	25–34	35–44	45–54	55–64	64–74	All
Health status	%	%	%	%	%	%	%
Men							
Very good	46	48	50	48	47	37	47
Fairly good	50	49	46	44	36	49	46
Fairly poor	3	2	3	6	13	12	6
Very poor	<0.5	1	1	2	5	2	2
Women							
Very good	43	53	55	46	46	35	47
Fairly good	53	42	39	44	42	53	45
Fairly poor	3	4	5	8	9	9	6
Very poor	1	1	1	2	3	4	2
Bases							
Men	475	540	456	403	334	269	2477
Women	451	529	453	401	347	327	2507

Table 2.2: Self-reported general health by socio-economic status of head of household

Health status	I&II	IIINM	IIIM	IV&V	Unemployed	Sick	Home	Education
	%	%	%	%	%	%	%	%
Very good	55	49	42	45	40	26	42	52
Fairly good	41	45	50	47	47	41	49	45
Fairly poor	4	5	6	8	8	22	7	3
Very poor	<0.5	1	2	1	5	12	2	0
Base	1 385	555	1 283	629	307	170	178	57

This pattern of gender and age distribution is similar to the findings of the 1991 Health Survey for England (OPCS, 1993), although a direct comparison is not possible as that survey used a five-point assessment scale.

There was some relationship between socio-economic circumstances and self-reported health status. In the survey those reporting that they were long-term sick or disabled were classified separately. Not surprisingly, this group had the lowest levels of self-reported good health with 26% reporting 'very good' health compared with 12% who reported 'very poor' health. Those who were unemployed were also less likely to rate their general health as good with 13% reporting their health to be 'very poor' or 'fairly poor'.

Informants in the non-manual social classes were more likely than those in the non-manual classes to report their health as good. Thus, 96% of those in social classes I–II reported 'very good' or 'fairly good' health compared with 92% of those in social classes IIIM and IV–V.

Taking tenure as a proxy for social and economic circumstance also revealed differences in self-reported health. Those who lived in rented accommodation were almost twice as likely as those who were owner-occupiers to report their health as 'very poor' or 'fairly poor' (13% and 6% respectively). This pattern was true for both men and women (Table 2.3).

Looking separately at those aged under 55 and those aged over 55, in order to control for the relationship between age and tenure, the difference in self-reported health status remained. For example, among those aged over 55, 22% of renters reported 'very poor' or 'fairly poor' health compared with 12% of owner-occupiers in this age group. Similar differences between renters and owner-occupiers were found in those under 55 (Table 2.4).

Educational status also showed some relationship with self-reported health status. The classification used was the qualification attained, not years of schooling. The categories were 'no qualifications', 'GCE O level or equivalent', 'GCE A level or equivalent', 'higher than that but lower than a degree', 'degree level or above', 'other qualification'.

Table 2.3: Self-reported health by gender and tenure category

Health status	Women		Men		All adults	
	Own	Rent	Own	Rent	Own	Rent
	%	%	%	%	%	%
Very good	51	38	49	38	50	38
Fairly good	44	49	45	50	44	49
Fairly poor	5	10	5	9	5	9
Very poor	1	4	1	4	1	4
Base	1 869	553	1 824	637	3 693	1 190

Table 2.4: Self-reported health by age and tenure category

Health status	Age 16–54		Age 55–74	
	Own	Rent	Own	Rent
	%	%	%	%
Very good	51	41	45	28
Fairly good	45	49	43	51
Fairly poor	3	7	9	16
Very poor	1	3	3	6
Base	2 738	882	955	308

In general, informants with higher qualification levels were less likely to report 'very poor' or 'fairly poor' health. This was true for both men and women. Thus, for example, 14% of those with no qualifications reported 'very poor' or 'fairly poor' health compared with only 3% of those educated to degree level (Table 2.5).

Long-standing illness and limiting long-standing illness
Informants were asked if they had any long-standing illness, disability, or infirmity. If so, they were then asked if their illness or disability limited their activities in any way.

Almost three out ten informants (28%) reported that they had a long-standing illness. Similar proportions of men and women reported a long-standing illness (Table 2.6).

Table 2.5: Self-reported general health by educational qualification

	None	Other	GCE O or equivalent	GCE A or equivalent	Higher than A but lower than degree	Degree level or above
Health status	%	%	%	%	%	%
Very good	40	51	47	58	51	58
Fairly good	46	43	49	44	44	39
Fairly poor	10	5	3	3	4	2
Very poor	4	1	1	1	1	1
Base	1 647	327	1 340	572	448	463

Table 2.6: Self-reported long-standing illness, disability or infirmity by gender

	Women	Men	All
Long-standing illness	%	%	%
Yes	29	28	28
No	71	72	72
Base	2 493	2 469	4 962

About one in six (17%) women and one in seven (14%) men reported an illness or disability which limited their activities in some way (Table 2.7).

Not surprisingly, the proportion of informants who reported a long-standing illness was higher among the older age groups. The proportion of informants with a long-standing illness or disability was fairly constant up to about age 44 and then increased across age groups. Thus, 33% of those aged 45–54 reported a long-standing illness or disability compared with 44% of those aged 55–64 and 49% of those aged 65–74 (Table 2.8). The pattern for limiting long-standing illness was similar.

There was no strong relationship with socio-economic status. This might be expected because in this study those who reported that they were unable to work because they were sick or disabled were coded separately as long-term sick. However, the social dimension of illness was revealed when comparing the prevalence of limiting long-standing illness by housing tenure. Over one in five

Table 2.7: Self-reported limiting long-standing illness, disability or infirmity by gender

Limiting long-standing illness	Women	Men	All
	%	%	%
Yes	17	14	16
No	83	86	84
Base	2 477	2 356	4 833

Table 2.8: Self-reported long-standing illness by age

Long-standing illness	16–24	25–34	35–44	45–54	55–64	65–74	All ages
	%	%	%	%	%	%	%
Yes	17	18	22	33	44	49	28
No	83	82	78	67	56	51	72
Base	916	1 064	906	807	681	589	4 962

(22%) informants in rented accommodation reported a limiting long-standing illness compared with 13% of owner-occupiers. The pattern for men and women was similar (Table 2.9).

Looking separately at those aged under 55 and those aged over 55 to take account of the association between age and tenure showed similar differences. Among those aged under 55, 16% of renters reported a limiting long-standing illness compared with 9% of those living in owner-occupied accommodation. Among those aged 55 and over the proportions of renters reporting a limiting long-standing illness was 41% compared with 25% of owner occupiers (Table 2.10).

Health behaviours

Informants were asked if they did anything to improve or maintain their health. Those who said that they did were then asked what sort of things they did. Informants were further asked if there was anything they would like to do to keep themselves healthy but didn't do at the moment.

Over six out of ten (61%) informants reported that they currently did something

Table 2.9: Self-reported limiting long-standing illness by gender and tenure class

	Women		Men		All	
	Own	Rent	Own	Rent	Own	Rent
Limiting long-standing illness	%	%	%	%	%	%
Yes	14	23	13	21	13	22
No	86	77	87	79	87	78
Base	1 804	630	1 848	550	3 652	1 180

Table 2.10: Self-reported limiting long-standing illness by age and tenure class

	Age 16–54		Age 55–74	
	Own	Rent	Own	Rent
Limiting long-standing illness	%	%	%	%
Yes	9	16	25	41
No	91	84	75	60
Base	2 708	876	944	304

to improve their health, and a further two out of ten (19%) reported that although they currently did nothing they would like to do something. The remaining 20% of informants reported that they neither did anything to maintain or improve their health nor wanted to do anything. There were no significant differences between men and women (Table 2.11).

There were no age-related patterns in levels of participation in healthy activity, with 64% of those aged 16–24 reporting that they did something to improve their health compared with 63% of those aged 65–74. However, among non-participants the motivation to adopt healthy behaviour was lower among older age groups (Table 2.12).

The proportion of non-manual workers who reported adopting healthy behaviour was higher than among manual workers. Almost two-thirds (65%) of informants from social classes I–II reported participation in some form of healthy activity, compared with 56% of those in social classes IV–V. Correspondingly, a lower

Table 2.11: Proportion reporting behaviour to improve or maintain health by gender

Health behaviour	Women	Men	All adults
	%	%	%
Currently do	61	63	62
Don't do but would like to	20	18	19
Neither	19	21	20
Base	2460	2430	4890

Table 2.12: Proportion reporting behaviour to improve or maintain health by age

Health behaviour	16–24	25–34	35–44	45–54	55–64	64–74
	%	%	%	%	%	%
Currently do	64	64	59	58	62	63
Don't do but would like to	19	23	22	20	13	9
Neither	16	14	19	22	26	27
Base	912	1055	892	800	675	588

proportion of those in social classes I–II (15%) said they currently neither did anything nor wanted to do anything to improve their health compared with those in social classes IV–V (26%). Those who looked after the family or home were the most likely to do nothing, with almost three out of ten (29%) reporting that they currently neither did anything healthy nor wanted to do anything (Table 2.13).

There was also a difference in the proportion of owner occupiers compared with renters who reported currently adopting healthy behaviour. Thus, 63% of owner occupiers reported that they were currently doing something to maintain or improve their health compared with 56% of renters. This pattern was true for both men and women (Table 2.14).

Among those with no qualifications, just over half (54%) reported adopting some form of healthy behaviour compared with 71% of those with a degree. Correspondingly, those with no qualifications were more than three times as likely as those with a degree to report neither doing anything healthy nor wanting to do anything (30% and 9% respectively) (Table 2.15).

Table 2.13: Proportion reporting behaviour to improve or maintain health by socio-economic status of head of household

Health behaviour	I&II	IIINM	IIIM	IV&V	Unemployed	Sick	Home	Education
	%	%	%	%	%	%	%	%
Currently do	65	63	62	56	55	57	51	62
Don't do but would like to	19	21	19	18	21	20	20	23
Neither	15	16	20	26	25	23	29	15
Base	1 367	547	1 262	616	309	170	175	57

Table 2.14: Proportion reporting behaviour to improve or maintain health by gender and tenure category

Health behaviour	Women		Men		All adults	
	Own	Rent	Own	Rent	Own	Rent
	%	%	%	%	%	%
Currently do	63	55	63	57	63	56
Don't do but would like to	20	20	16	20	18	20
Neither	17	25	20	23	18	24
Base	1 795	633	1 848	549	3 643	1 182

Types of behaviour

On the whole informants participated in activities which fit with traditional health promotion, such as eating a healthy diet, taking regular exercise and trying to quit smoking. However, there were also a small number of informants who interpreted the question as 'taking medication' (1% of sample) or 'attending a health clinic' (< 1%). It is also important to remember that the question was not qualified to restrict reports to activities undertaken on a regular basis. Consequently some responses (e.g. skiing < 1% of sample) are more likely to be occasional activities rather than regular.

Table 2.15: Proportion reporting behaviour to improve or maintain their health by educational qualification

	None	Other	GCE O or equivalent	GCE A or equivalent	Higher than A but lower than degree	Degree level or above
Health behaviour	%	%	%	%	%	%
Currently do	54	67	63	66	71	72
Don't do but would like to	17	20	19	21	20	19
Neither	30	12	18	13	10	9
Base	1 627	323	1 324	568	440	457

Diet

One in six (17%) informants reported that they currently did something to improve or maintain their health which related to diet (e.g. 'eating a good diet', 'eating properly', 'eating healthy food') while an additional 5% said they would like to do something about their diet There was some evidence of increasing concern with a healthy diet among older age groups. Thus, only 14% of women and 6% of men aged 16–24 reported that they participated in any form of diet-related health behaviour compared with 28% of women and 19% of men aged 55–64. Although this age pattern was similar for men and women there was also a clear gender effect. In each age group a higher proportion of women reported some form of diet-related behaviour compared with men. Overall, 22% of women compared with 12% of men reported diet-related behaviour, and more women currently not doing something diet-related reported that they wanted to do something (7% and 4% respectively) (Table 2.16).

There was also some relationship with socio-economic status. Those in non-manual social classes reported far higher levels of participation in diet-related behaviour compared with those in manual social classes. Those who were unemployed and long-term sick also reported lower levels (14%) of participation in any form of diet-related behaviour (Table 2.17).

Physical activity

In response to the unprompted question about health-related behaviour, over four out of ten (41%) informants reported that they participated in some form of physical activity to improve or maintain their health, and 22% reported that they would like to do some sort of physical activity. About 1% of informants said that

Table 2.16: Proportion reporting diet-related behaviour to improve or maintain their health by age and gender

	16–24	25–34	35–44	45–54	55–64	65–74	Total
Diet-related behaviour	%	%	%	%	%	%	%
Women							
Currently do	14	21	25	30	28	20	22
Don't do/would like to	8	7	8	8	6	3	7
Neither	78	72	67	61	67	76	71
Men							
Currently do	6	10	13	15	19	15	12
Don't do/would like to	4	5	4	4	3	<0.5	4
Neither	90	85	83	81	78	84	84
Bases							
Women	428	511	436	397	332	318	2 422
Men	462	523	439	392	330	263	2 409

Table 2.17: Proportion reporting diet-related behaviour to improve or maintain health by socio-economic status of head of household

	I&II	IIINM	IIIM	IV&V	Unemployed	Sick	Home	Education
Diet-related behaviour	%	%	%	%	%	%	%	%
Currently do	21	21	17	13	14	14	15	22
Don't do but would like to	5	7	5	6	5	5	7	7
Neither	73	72	79	80	81	82	78	71
Base	1 335	537	1 238	610	304	170	173	57

they worked hard (although it is not clear whether this implies physical work) and 1% that they had 'an active lifestyle'. However, the majority of informants cited leisure time physical activity. The definition of physical activity did not include those who reported 'walking' (17% of informants). This is because no minimum distance or time was specified in the question. Walking is an important aspect of physical activity but data from, for example, the Allied Dunbar National Fitness Survey (HEA/Sports Council, 1992) or the 1990 General Household Survey (OPCS, 1992) which include a time/distance component is likely to be more reliable (Table 2.18).

Table 2.18: Proportion reporting participation in physical activity to improve or maintain health

	General physical activity (excluding walking)	Walking	Swimming
	%	%	%
Currently do	41	17	10
Don't do but would like to	22	4	12
Neither	37	79	78
Base	4 869	4 869	4 869

There was a noticeable decline in reported participation in physical activity among older age groups. Thus, for example, those aged 16–24 were almost twice as likely as those aged 55–64 to report doing some form of physical activity to maintain their health (57% and 30% respectively). This pattern is similar to that found in the *Allied Dunbar National Fitness Survey* (HEA/Sports Council, 1992), and from the 1990 General Household Survey (OPCS, 1992). The proportions of those currently doing nothing who report that they would like to adopt healthier behaviour also decreases with age. Thus the highest levels of participation and willingness to adopt were found in the younger age groups (Table 2.19).

There was also a gender effect, with 44% of men reporting participation in physical activity compared with 38% of women. By contrast, however, higher proportions of women (25%) than men (19%) reported that they would like to take up physical activity.

There was a relationship between socio-economic activity and participation in physical activity. Almost half (45%) of those in social classes I–II compared with 33% of those in social classes IV–IV reported participating in physical activity. The sick and disabled (27%) and those looking after home and family (32%) reported the lowest levels of participation in physical activity (Table 2.20).

Food buying, food labelling

Informants were asked a series of questions about food labelling in order to try and assess their knowledge about and interest in diet and nutrition.

Informants were first asked if they did most of the food shopping for the household or if someone else did it. Over eight out of ten (82%) of women said that they mostly did the food shopping compared with only three out of ten (32%) men. Among those aged 16–24 less than half (45%) of women and only 14% of men were responsible for buying the food for the household (Table 2.21).

Those informants who identified themselves as the main food buyers for their

Table 2.19: Proportion reporting participation in physical activity to improve or maintain health by age and gender

	16–24	25–34	35–44	45–54	55–64	65–74	Total
Participation in physical activity	%	%	%	%	%	%	%
Women							
Currently do	54	46	36	35	30	18	38
Don't do/would like to	27	31	30	23	23	14	25
Neither	19	24	34	42	47	68	37
Men							
Currently do	60	56	44	33	29	25	44
Don't do/would like to	18	22	22	21	12	13	19
Neither	22	22	34	46	59	62	37
Bases							
Women	438	513	437	399	339	315	2 441
Men	470	527	441	394	333	262	2 429

Table 2.20: Proportion reporting participation in physical activity to improve or maintain health by socio-economic status of head of household

	I&II	IIINM	IIIM	IV&V	Unemployed	Sick	Home	Education
Participation on in physical activity	%	%	%	%	%	%	%	%
Currently do	45	44	41	33	36	27	32	50
Don't do but would like to	24	23	22	21	19	23	22	32
Neither	30	33	37	47	45	50	46	18
Base	1 348	541	1 247	614	306	170	173	57

Table 2.21: Proportion responsible for buying food in their household by age and gender

	16–24	25–34	35–44	45–54	55–64	65–74	All ages
Proportion buying food	%	%	%	%	%	%	%
Women	45	86	91	93	92	86	82
Men	14	36	36	32	31	41	32
Bases							
Women	450	530	456	407	348	327	2 517
Men	475	539	456	406	338	269	2 483

Table 2.22: Proportion of food buyers who look at the sell by date on food packages by gender

	Women	Men	All adults
Look at sell by date	%	%	%
Always	69	54	65
Usually	18	19	18
Sometimes	8	8	8
Rarely	7	7	4
Never	12	12	6
Base	2 060	779	2 839

household were then asked a series of questions about food labelling. They were first asked if they looked at the 'sell-by' date. Overall, 65% reported that they always looked at the sell-by date while another 18% said that they usually looked at it. Only 6% of informants reported that they never looked at the sell-buy date. Women were more likely than men to look at the sell-by date (Table 2.22).

Informants were then asked if they look at the list of ingredients or nutritional information on food packages. Only 16% reported that they always looked at the nutritional information. One-quarter (25%) of informants said that they never looked at nutritional information when buying food. Men were less likely than women to look at the nutritional information; about one-third (33%) of men never looked at the nutritional information on labels compared with 23% of women.

Food buyers where the head of household was in social classes IV–V were twice as

Table 2.23: Proportion of food buyers who look at ingredients or nutritional information on food packages by socio-economic status of head of household

	I&II	IIINM	IIIM	IV&V	Unemployed	Sick	Home	Education
Look at information	%	%	%	%	%	%	%	%
Always	16	15	14	12	15	26	14	31
Usually	21	20	16	11	18	7	15	23
Sometimes	31	31	28	24	23	20	25	14
Rarely	13	12	15	15	12	16	12	21
Never	18	21	27	39	32	31	34	10
Base	775	338	656	325	199	94	122	45

Table 2.24: Proportion of food buyers who look at ingredients or nutritional information on food packages by whether reporting diet-related behaviour or not

Look at information	Reported diet-related behaviour	Did not report diet-related behaviour
	%	%
Always	24	14
Usually	24	16
Sometimes	32	27
Rarely	10	15
Never	11	28
Base	598	2 181

likely as those in social classes I–II never to look at nutritional information on food labels (39% and 18% respectively) (Table 2.23).

Informants who reported that they did something to maintain or improve their health that was diet-related were more likely to look at the nutritional information on labels than those who did not participate in any diet-related behaviour. Thus, only 11% of those who reported healthy diet-related behaviour never looked at nutritional information compared with 28% of those who reported no healthy diet-related behaviour (Table 2.24).

Informants who did look at nutritional information (even if rarely) were then asked precisely what information they looked for. The most common aspects which

Table 2.25: Ingredients/nutritional information looked for by gender

Information looked for	Women %	Men %	All adults %
Calories/kj	47	27	42
Carbohydrate	11	14	12
Energy	8	11	9
Total fat	51	47	50
Polyunsaturated	25	28	27
Saturated	25	28	26
Fibre	28	30	29
Minerals	5	6	6
Protein	15	19	16
Starch	5	4	5
Base	1 580	515	2 094

Table 2.26: Reasons for never looking at nutritional information on food labels by gender

Reason for not looking at label	Women %	Men %	All adults %
Not interested	34	45	38
Know what is in food	27	24	26
Information too complex to understand	11	6	10
Information takes too long to read	11	8	10
Base	460	251	711

informants reported looking for were total fat content (50%), number of calories (42%). Women were significantly more likely than men to look for information on calorie content (47% and 27% respectively) (Table 2.25).

Informants who never looked at ingredients were asked why not. Almost four out of ten (38%) of informants who never looked at nutritional information on labels said they were not interested, 26% reported that they already knew what was in the food they bought, while a further 10% said that the information on the labels was too difficult to understand. Men were more likely than women not be interested in the nutritional information on the food they bought (45% and 34% respectively) (Table 2.26).

References

Health Education Authority/Sports Council (1992) *Allied Dunbar National Fitness Survey*. HEA.

Office of Population Censuses and Surveys (1992) *General Household Survey 1990*. HMSO.

Office of Population Censuses and Surveys (1993) *The Health Survey for England 1991*. HMSO.

3. Primary care health services

Rhiannon Walters
Health Promotion Information Officer
Faculty of Public Health Medicine
of the Royal College of Physicians of the United Kingdom, London

The Government's health strategy for England *The Health of the Nation* (Department of Health, 1992) noted that:

> Success in key areas will depend greatly on the commitment and skills of family and community doctors, nurses ... and other professionals in the community.

Later documents produced to advise on implementation of the strategy highlight the contribution of the primary health care team. There are two ways for the team to promote health – through opportunistic health promotion when the patient is attending the surgery for some other purpose, and through designated health promotion clinics. There are constraints on the team's contribution. First, patients must find their GP and other professionals at the surgery/health centre accessible and acceptable. To be accessible the surgery must be easy to reach, there must be convenient consultation hours, waiting times should not be too long, and the consultation itself should allow sufficient time to deal with problems and to include opportunistic health promotion when it is appropriate. An acceptable health professional is one with whom patients feel able to discuss their health concerns, preferably without difficulty. Both the number of attendances for other health problems which present opportunities for health promotion, and the level of attendance at designated health promotion clinics, will be influenced by accessibility and acceptability.

Secondly, the GP and other health professionals at the surgery need to have interventions of proven effectiveness at their disposal. The primary health care team is hard pressed and must judge carefully how they allocate their time and other resources. They need to be ruthless in implementing only those interventions which have been shown to be effective in promoting health. They must also have the time, resources and adequate training to implement these interventions. Resource and training issues are important, but outside the scope of this study.

Accessible and acceptable health services

Accessible GP surgeries/health centres

Registration

The survey data were collected immediately before publication of *The Health of the Nation* in summer 1992. It showed that virtually all adults in the 16–74 age range

---

Table 3.1: Are you currently registered with a doctor or GP? (%)

Yes – NHS	97
Yes – NHS and private	3
No	1

Base: All

said they were currently registered with a doctor, and 97% were registered with a National Health Service doctor. A small proportion said they were also registered privately with a doctor (Table 3.1). Being a household survey, its sample was biased against selection of the most mobile section of the population, who are least likely to be registered. Concerns have been expressed recently that GPs have structural incentives to remove some patients from their registers (ACHCEW, 1994) and trends in registration rates should be monitored.

Travel to surgery/health centre

Almost all (95%) adults stated that it was easy to get to their doctor's surgery and two-thirds described it as 'very easy'. Women were more likely than men to find getting to the surgery difficult (7% and 4% respectively), as were those aged over 65 (10%) (Table 3.2).

Table 3.2: Ease/difficulty of getting to surgery

	Total	Women	Men	People aged					
% who found getting to the surgery				16–24	25–34	35–44	45–54	55–64	65–74
Easy	95	93	96	93	97	96	95	95	90
Difficult	5	7	4	7	3	4	5	5	10

Base: All registered with GP

Just over half (51%) of those who found it difficult to get to the surgery said that the surgery was too far away, while a quarter (25%) complained of poor public transport. Less than one in ten (9%) informants said that the surgery hours were inconvenient (Table 3.3).

Waiting time

Long waits cause irritation and inconvenience and can result in lost opportunities for health promotion. Just under half (47%) of all informants said that the last time they visited the surgery they had to wait less than 10 minutes to see the doctor.

Table 3.3: Reasons for finding it difficult to get to surgery (%)

Surgery hours are inconvenient	9
Too far away	51
Poor public transport	25
Poor access for disabled/elderly	3
Expensive to travel	2
Inconvenient location	4
Difficult with baby/children	1
Other	9

Base: All registered with GP. More than one answer allowed

Table 3.4: Length of waiting time on last visit to surgery (%)

Up to 10 minutes	47
Over 10 minutes, less than 15 minutes	14
Over 15 minutes, less than 30 minutes	24
Over 30 minutes	11

Base: All registered with GP

However, about one in ten (11%) informants reported having to wait more than 30minutes to see the doctor the last time they went to the surgery (Table 3.4).

Just under half (49%) of informants said they were registered at a surgery or health centre which operated an appointment-only system. About a third (34%) reported that their surgery or health centre operated mostly appointments but also had some time at the end of surgery for urgent cases. About one in ten (11%) informants said they attended a surgery with no appointment system (Table 3.5). When asked about their last visit to the surgery, 83% of informants said they had made an appointment, and 14% said they had just turned up (Table 3.6).

Not surprisingly, those who had made an appointment tended to have to wait less than those who just turned up at the surgery. Over half (54%) of those with an appointment were seen within 15 minutes compared with only 34% of those who just turned up (Table 3.7). In fact, those who just turned up at the surgery were twice as likely as those who had made an appointment to have to wait more than 30 minutes to see a doctor (38% and 19% respectively).

A quarter (25%) of informants said that they thought the waiting time was too long (Table 3.8). There seems to be a consensus that less than 15 minutes is about right. Of those who described their wait as 'about right' about two-thirds (67%) had waited less than 15 minutes the last time and only 8% had waited more than 30 minutes. However, of those who described their wait as 'much too long', only 5% had been seen within 15 minutes, while 84% had had to wait more than 30 minutes (Table 3.9).

Table 3.5: Which of these appointment methods comes closest to what happens at the surgery you use? (%)

Appointment only	49
Mostly appointments with some time at the end of surgery for urgent cases	34
Just turn up and wait, no appointments	11
Separate surgeries for people with and without appointments	3
Other	1
Don't know	3

Base: All registered with GP

Table 3.6: Appointment method for last visit to surgery (%)

Made appointment	83
Just turned up	14
Asked to attend	3
Other	<1

Base: All who visited surgery in last 12 months

Table 3.7: Appointment method for last visit to surgery by length of wait (%)

	Made an appointment	Just turned up	Asked to attend	Other
Under 5 minutes	9	6	15	50
5 minutes or more, less than 15	46	28	38	19
15 minutes or more, less than 30	26	28	25	13
30 minutes or more, less than an hour	15	26	18	19
An hour or more	4	12	4	–

Base: All who saw doctor when last visited surgery

Table 3.8: Did you think the wait was ... ? (%)

About right	75
A little too long	14
Much too long	11

Base: All who saw doctor when last visited surgery

Table 3.9: Did you think the wait was ... ? By length of wait (%)

	About right	A little too long	Much too long
Under 5 minutes	11	1	3
5 minutes or more, less than 15	56	6	2
15 minutes or more, less than 30	26	44	11
30 minutes or more, less than an hour	7	41	50
An hour or more	1	7	34

Base: All who saw doctor when last visited surgery

Acceptable GPs and surgery/health centre staff

Gender of GP

It has been suggested that the gender of a GP can be a barrier to their acceptability. About three-quarters (74%) of informants said they normally saw a male doctor, while 13% reported normally seeing a female doctor. Women were almost twice as likely as men to normally see a female doctor (17% and 9% respectively) (Table 3.10).

Almost two-thirds (65%) of informants said they had no preference about the gender of their doctor. Men were more likely than women to have no preference (71% and 59% respectively). About a quarter (26%) of men and women (24%) stated a preference for a doctor of the same sex. Those aged 16–24 and those aged over 55 were most likely to express a preference for seeing a doctor of the same gender. Thus, for example, 32% of men aged 16–24 and 30% of women expressed a preference for seeing a doctor of the same gender (Table 3.11).

Given that male GPs are more common, a person who wanted to see a male GP was very likely to normally see one. Thus, over 90% of those expressing a preference to see a male doctor normally did so. However, for those who expressed a preference for seeing a female doctor, fewer than half normally saw one. Women who preferred to see a female doctor were slightly more likely than men to normally see one (44% and 40% respectively). In all 15% of women and 4% of men had a preference as to the sex of their GP which was not met (Table 3.12).

Table 3.10: Is the doctor you normally see male or female? (%)

Normally sees	Total	Women	Men
Male GP	74	69	79
Female GP	13	17	9
It varies/don't know	13	14	12

Base: All who are registered with GP

Table 3.11: Which do you prefer to see, a male or female doctor? (%)

Prefers to see	Total	Women	Men	Women aged 16–24	25–34	35–44	45–54	55–64	65–74	Men aged 16–24	25–34	35–44	45–54	55–64	65–74
Male GP	21	17	26	17	13	15	19	20	21	32	20	16	25	32	34
Female GP	14	24	3	30	28	24	21	21	13	3	4	3	5	1	5
No preference/ don't know	65	59	71	54	59	60	61	59	66	65	76	81	71	67	61

Base: All registered with GP

Table 3.12: Normal by preferred sex of GP (%)

	Prefers to see			
Normally sees	Women Male GP	Female GP	Men Male GP	Female GP
Male GP	91	41	92	42
Female GP	2	44	2	40
It varies	7	16	6	18

Base: All who expressed a preference as to the gender of their GP

The primary health care team

The availability of a range of health professionals at the surgery can increase the chances of an appropriate and acceptable professional being available, although findings from studies of the effectiveness of nurse-run clinics (ICRF OXCHECK Study Group, 1994; Family Heart Study Group, 1994) are disappointing.

Of those who visited the surgery in the past year, 85% had seen a doctor on their last visit, and 20% had seen a practice nurse. Very few had dealt with any other health professionals such as health visitors, physiotherapists, or dietitians (Table 3.13).

Table 3.13: When you last visited the surgery, which of these people did you have any dealings with? (%)

Doctor/GP	85
Practice nurse	20
Physiotherapist	1
Health visitor	1
Midwife	1
Practice pharmacist	2
Receptionist	70
Social worker	<1
Counsellor	<1
Dietitian	<1
Other	<1

Base: All who visited the surgery in last 12 months. More than one answer allowed

Of those who had discussed health issues relating to Health of the Nation targets at the surgery in the past year, once again, nearly all had done so with the doctor. Mental or psychological problems and stress were most likely to be discussed with a doctor, and least likely to be discussed with a nurse (although counsellors had been involved in 4% of discussions about mental/psychological problems). Nurses were most likely to discuss diet or healthy food, weight control and exercise or fitness, but the proportion of informants discussing any topic with a nurse never exceeded a third (Table 3.14).

Table 3.14: With whom did you discuss ... ? (%)

	Total		Women		Men	
	Doctor	Nurse	Doctor	Nurse	Doctor	Nurse
Heart disease	88	13	77	24	93	8
Smoking	83	16	83	13	83	17
Diet and healthy food	67	30	60	35	75	24
Weight control	73	29	72	31	76	25
Alcohol	79	19	80	14	79	20
Exercise/fitness	75	22	68	23	80	21
Cancer	92	12	93	11	90	15
Gynaecological problems			88	17		
Mental/psychological problems	97	3	98	2	96	4
Stress	95	5	96	3	94	8
Contraception/birth control	91	11	91	10	84	16
Sexual problems	88	12				
HIV/AIDS	74	24				

Base: All who had discussed each issue at the surgery in last 12 months (women only for gynaecological problems). More than one answer allowed

31

Dissatisfaction with visits to GP and surgery/health centre staff
Informants were asked if there was anything about their last visit to the doctor which they were dissatisfied about. Overall, 15% of informants said they had been dissatisfied with something the last time they visited their doctor. There were no differences between men and women, but those aged 16–24 were slightly more likely to have been dissatisfied with their last visit to the doctor (Table 3.15).

Table 3.15: Percentage who were dissatisfied with something when they last saw the doctor

Total		15
Women		14
Men		16
People aged	16–24	18
	25–34	16
	35–44	17
	45–54	13
	55–64	13
	65–74	10

Base: All who saw the doctor when they last visited the surgery

Of those who expressed dissatisfaction, the most common complaints were the length of waiting time (27%) and dissatisfaction with the treatment or the perceived lack of treatment (26%). Other causes of complaint were not having enough time with the doctor (16%), the unsympathetic nature of the doctor (15%), the lack of information provided (9%), and the general attitude of the doctor (8%) (Table 3.16).

Table 3.16: Reasons for dissatisfaction at last visit to doctor (%)

Waiting time/waiting time for appointment	27
Short time spent with doctor/not enough contact with doctor	16
Felt as though wasting doctor's time	2
Not given enough information/lack of explanation/discussion	9
Doctor unsympathetic/patient or problem not taken seriously	15
Dissatisfied with treatment/lack of treatment	26
Poor facilities while waiting to see doctor	3
New doctor/not preferred doctor	7
Attitude of receptionist	3
Doctor's manner/general attitude	8
Doctor had no background information	1
No confidence in doctor	2
High costs	1
Others	2

Base: All who were dissatisfied when last visited the doctor. More than one answer allowed

Difficulties in discussing issues relevant to Health of the Nation targets with staff at the surgery/health centre

If the GP and other members of the surgery staff are to contribute to the implementation of Health of the Nation targets their patients must find them approachable. Some issues relevant to achievement of the targets are sensitive, and patients need to be confident that staff will not be judgemental.

When asked how easy they found it to discuss issues, informants were most likely to opt for the response 'have never needed to discuss it' on almost every issue (the exception was gynaecological problems, which was raised with women only) (Table 3.17). Of those who expressed an opinion, topics such as heart disease, diet, weight control, exercise, and smoking were considered to be easy to discuss by more than nine out of ten informants. However, about a third of informants who expressed an opinion found sexual problems (34%) and mental or psychological problems (29%) either difficult or impossible to discuss with their doctor (Table 3.18).

Visits to the surgery/health centre

Frequency of visits

Just under three out of ten (28%) informants had visited their surgery or health centre in the past month, while six out of ten (61%) had visited within the last six months (in connection with their own health). Women were more likely than men to have visited the surgery in the last month (33% and 23% respectively). This is reflected in the fact that women visited their surgery on average 5.4 times in the last year compared with 4.3 visits for men (Table 3.19).

Women aged 24–35 visited their doctor most often, with 36% having visited the

Table 3.17: Ease of discussing health issues with doctor or other health professional (%)

	Can discuss without difficulties	Can discuss with some difficulty	Don't feel can discuss it with them	Have never needed to discuss it	No opinion
Heart disease	37	8	2	53	1
Smoking	29	3	1	66	1
Diet and healthy food	48	2	1	48	1
Weight control	45	3	1	51	1
Alcohol	25	2	<1	71	1
Exercise/fitness	44	2	1	52	1
Cancer	28	5	1	65	1
Gynaecological problems	57	10	2	31	1
Mental/psychological problems	27	8	3	61	1
Stress	37	8	2	53	1
Contraception/ birth control	38	4	1	56	2
Sexual problems	18	6	3	72	1
HIV/AIDS	18	3	1	76	1

Base: All (women only for gynaecological problems)

Table 3.18: Ease of discussing health issues with doctor or other health professional (those who expressed an opinion only) (%)

	Can discuss without difficulties	Can discuss with some difficulty	Don't feel I can discuss it with them
Heart disease	91	8	2
Smoking	89	8	3
Diet and healthy food	93	5	2
Weight control	93	5	2
Alcohol	91	9	1
Exercise/fitness	94	4	2
Cancer	82	15	3
Gynaecological problems	82	15	2
Mental/psychological problems	71	22	7
Stress	79	16	5
Contraception/birth control	88	10	2
Sexual problems	66	23	11
HIV/AIDS	82	13	5

Base: All who expressed an opinion (women who expressed an opinion only for gynaecological problems)

Table 3.19: Last visit to surgery on own behalf (%)

	Total	Women	Men	Women aged						Men aged					
				16–24	25–34	35–44	45–54	55–64	65–74	16–24	25–34	35–44	45–54	55–64	65–74
In last week	10	12	8	11	13	12	12	15	9	6	6	6	9	11	15
Over 1 week, within last month	18	21	15	20	23	18	20	24	23	12	12	13	16	21	20
Over 1 month, within last 2 months	12	13	10	13	16	11	11	15	13	12	8	7	12	12	14
Over 2 months, within last 4 months	13	14	12	21	14	13	15	10	12	15	12	9	10	16	12
Over 4 months, within last 6 months	8	8	7	10	8	9	7	8	6	9	8	9	6	3	9
Over 6 months, within last year	13	13	13	12	13	14	14	10	10	13	16	15	10	11	7
Over 1 year, within last 3 years	17	13	21	9	11	17	13	11	15	18	26	25	22	16	14
Over 3 years, within last 5 years	4	3	6	3	1	3	3	3	4	8	6	6	6	4	4
Over 5 years	3	2	4	1	<1	1	2	2	5	1	4	7	6	4	3
Never/can't remember	2	1	3	1	1	1	2	1	3	2	1	3	2	2	1
Average no. of visits in last 12 months	4.9	5.4	4.3	5.6	6.0	4.6	5.1	5.6	5.7	3.8	3.4	3.2	4.7	5.3	5.8

Base: All

doctor in the last month. Only 18% of men in the same age group had visited their doctor in the last month. Among men, but not among women, there was a marked increase in the number of visits over the age of 55. Thus, for example, 35% of men aged 65–74 had visited the doctor in the last month.

Purpose of visiting the surgery/health centre
Among those who had visited a surgery or a health centre on their own behalf in the last 12 months, just under half (49%) went for the treatment of an illness or condition. Other reasons for going were to collect or order a repeat prescription, to have or get the results of a test, or to have a general medical examination. Men were more likely than women to have received treatment for an illness on their last

Table 3.20: Purpose of last visit to surgery (%)

	Total	Women	Men	People aged					
				16–24	25–34	35–44	45–54	55–64	65–74
Treatment of illness/condition	49	45	53	55	47	54	47	47	40
General check of ongoing illness/ condition	5	5	5	3	5	5	5	5	7
General medical exam/check-up	12	10	14	12	9	10	14	13	11
To collect/order repeat prescription	16	19	14	15	12	12	21	16	28
To attend a clinic	5	8	2	6	11	4	3	2	2
To have or get results of check/test	19	22	16	11	14	19	22	29	27
Vaccination	3	3	4	4	4	3	2	4	2
Family planning (including attending family planning clinic)	4	6	1	8	8	3	1	–	–
Antenatal/postnatal check	2	3	<1	2	7	1	–	–	–
To make an appointment only	<1	<1	<1	<1	<1	<1	1	1	1
Other reasons	3	3	3	3	4	4	3	3	4

Base: All who visited surgery in last 12 months. More than one answer allowed

visit (53% and 45% respectively). Those aged over 65 were less likely to go to the doctor for treatment for a specific illness but were more likely to have last been for a general check-up or to order/collect a prescription (Table 3.20).

Accessibility and acceptability to special population groups
The Health of the Nation states that at local level:

> Much could be achieved [to reduce socio-economic differentials in health] by changing the presentation, description and opening times of services to be relevant to the circumstances and perceptions of users and potential users.

The government, therefore, sees scope for reducing the effect of the 'inverse care law' (Hart, 1971) through improving accessibility and acceptability of health services to all sections of the population.

There is evidence that, like other types of health service, health promotion through primary health care is least accessible to those who need it most (Gillam, 1992; Waller *et al.*, 1990). One of these studies uses the Jarman index as a measure of deprivation, and the other is based on social class (as well as other risk factors for coronary heart disease).

Difficulty in getting to the surgery and length of wait at last visit to doctor were chosen as indicators of the accessibility of GPs, and unmet preference as to sex of GP and dissatisfaction with something at last visit as indicators of their acceptability. By these indicators, those in households headed by people of manual social class differ very little from the general population. There are only small differences in time since last visit to the surgery and no differences in average number of visits in the last year.

An indicator of more extreme deprivation than manual occupation is given by selecting those on the means-tested benefits — family credit and income support. Members of this more deprived group find their GP less accessible than the total sample, indicated by longer waits and greater likelihood of finding it difficult to get to the surgery. Indicators of lower acceptability (unmet preference as to the sex of GP and being dissatisfied with something at their last visit) differ little from the general sample. They make slightly more frequent use of their GP (Tables 3.21 and 3.22).

Table 3.21: Accessibility and acceptability by social class and means-tested benefits – selected indicators (%)

	Total	Manual social class	Receiving means-tested benefit
Find it difficult to get to surgery*	5	5	8
Waited more than 15 minutes to see doctor at last visit†	39	40	47
Unmet preference as to sex of GP*	10	11	12
Dissatisfied with something at last visit to doctor†	15	15	15

Base: * All who are registered with GP. † All who saw doctor when last visited surgery

Table 3.22: **Visits to surgery/health centre by social class and means-tested benefits**

		Total	Manual social class	Receiving means-tested benefit
Average number of visits to surgery in last year*		4.9	5.0	6.5
Last visit to surgery (%)†	Within last 6 months	61	62	62
	Over 6 months, within last year	13	12	11
	Over 1 year	24	25	24
	Never/can't remember	2	1	3

Base: * All who visited surgery in last 12 months. † All

Contributing to the Health of the Nation targets

Both clinic-based and opportunistic health promotion through general practice can contribute to the Health of the Nation targets. Historically GPs have prioritised a 'high-risk' approach. As evidence accumulates of the effectiveness of a population approach through general practice GPs are more inclined to believe that discussing risk factors for preventable diseases with those not at immediate risk is a valid use of their time. However, there are several areas, such as prevention of suicide and promotion of higher levels of physical activity, where *The Health of the Nation* acknowledges GPs' need for training. There are also areas, including diet and physical activity, where evidence of the effectiveness of interventions is sparse. The effectiveness of opportunistic health promotion is undermined by a brief consultation (Morrell *et al.*, 1986). All these factors give GPs reasonable grounds for allocating their time to other priorities.

This survey was conducted close to the publication of *The Health of the Nation*, and is therefore well placed to provide baseline data for tracking GPs' contribution towards the targets.

CHD and stroke

The government has prioritised the targets for CHD and stroke in the primary care setting. *The Health of the Nation* observed:

> All the main [CHD and stroke] risk factors can be influenced by changes in behaviour.

However, controlling for social class and marital status, it has been found that behavioural risk factors for CHD were inversely related to use of opportunistically offered health checks (Waller *et al.*, 1990).

Early in 1993 *Better Living — Better Life*, a resource for GPs on behaviour change for CHD and stroke risk factors, was published (Department of Health/General

Medical Services Committee/Royal College of General Practitioners). The 1993 GP contract was structured to provide incentives for data collection and the provision of advice and support for change for those at risk. The survey, having been conducted before these developments, can provide baseline data which can help monitor their impact.

Heart disease

Men are more likely to die (and to die young) of heart disease than women. Differences in prevalence of cardiovascular morbidity found by the 1991 Health Survey for England (OPCS, 1993) are smaller however, whether measured by self-reported illness or standard questionnaires for angina and breathlessness. Men are more likely to have had severe disease than women. For both sexes reported cardiovascular disease rises abruptly after the age of 55. The prevalence of angina and of breathlessness determined by questionnaire rose sharply for women after 45 years, and for men above 55 years.

Six per cent of adults had discussed heart disease in the last 12 months with a member of staff at the surgery. Men were more likely than women to have done so, and the proportion of 55–74 year old men who had done so rises to 15%. These sex differences, and the age distribution with sex follows the pattern of CHD mortality more closely than that of CHD morbidity found in the Health Survey (Table 3.23).

Eighty-five per cent of adults who discussed heart disease found the discussion helpful. Two out of five said had they learnt something new, especially those under 55. Half mentioned lifestyle changes: one-third had already made changes and 17% planned to make some (Table 3.24).

About two-thirds were given a recommendation or something concrete. Twenty-seven per cent were advised to reduce their weight, 25% to take (more) exercise and 20% to reduce smoking.

Forty-six per cent were asked to return or had returned for a follow-up check (57% of those over .55).

Smoking

The potential for reducing smoking prevalence through primary health care is well-known, and more smokers are likely to quit through twelve 5-minute interventions than through two more intense and effective half-hour interventions (DoH/GMSC/RCGP, 1992). A fifth of regular smokers and 8% of all adults aged 16–74 who visited the surgery or health centre in the last year discussed smoking.

Half the regular smokers found this discussion helpful. The proportion who said they learnt something new is relatively low at 15%. Fifty-two per cent of regular smokers, who discussed smoking, mention lifestyle changes made or planned.

Twenty-three per cent of smokers said they were given leaflets or booklets, and 21% that nicotine substitutes were recommended to them. Relatively little follow-up is reported. Eleven per cent said they had returned for a check up or advice (Table 3.25).

Table 3.23: Issues discussed at the surgery in the last 12 months which relate to achievement of the Health of the Nation targets on CHD and stroke (%)

	Total	Women	Men	Women aged							Men aged						
				16–19	20–24	25–34	35–44	45–54	55–64	65–74	16–19	20–24	25–34	35–44	45–54	55–64	65–74
Heart disease	6	3	8	2	1	2	2	3	7	7	4	4	6	6	11	11	15
Smoking	7	6	9	5	7	7	7	7	4	4	4	12	9	7	11	13	7
Diet/healthy food	12	12	13	6	12	10	12	13	14	13	8	7	14	12	16	18	13
Weight control	14	16	12	7	13	15	16	15	21	17	6	5	9	11	17	16	14
Exercise/fitness	8	5	11	5	4	7	5	5	6	3	14	12	12	12	11	7	8
Alcohol	2	1	4	1	1	1	1	1	<1	–	1	9	5	5	3	2	4

Base: All who have visited surgery in last 12 months

	Women: smoking behaviour			Men: smoking behaviour		
	Never smoked	Ex-smoker	Regular smoker	Never smoked	Ex-smoker	Regular smoker
Heart disease	2	4	3	7	11	5
Smoking	1	2	18	1	5	22
Diet/healthy food	12	17	10	10	16	10
Weight control	11	14	9	11	14	9
Exercise/fitness	12	12	9	12	12	9
Alcohol	2	3	7	2	3	7

Base: All who have visited surgery in last 12 months

Table 3.24: Discussion on heart disease (%)

Did you find it	Helpful	84
	Unhelpful	7
	Neither	9
	Don't know	–
Learn anything new	Yes	44
	No	55
	Don't know	1
Made any changes	Yes, have made changes	33
	Yes, plan to make changes	17
	No change made or planned	49
	Don't know	2

Base: All who have discussed heart disease

Table 3.25: Discussion on smoking (%)

		Total	Never smoked	Ex-smoker	Regular smoker
Did you find it	Helpful	52	34	58	50
	Unhelpful	25	18	11	29
	Neither	22	48	31	20
	Don't know	1	–	–	1
Learn anything new	Yes	15	22	17	15
	No	84	73	82	85
	Don't know	2	4	1	1
Made any changes	Yes, have made changes	25	22	51	19
	Yes, plan to make changes	27	–	8	33
	No change made or planned	46	73	41	46
	Don't know	2	4	1	2

Base: All who have discussed smoking

Diet and healthy food

The Health Education Authority's health education target, intended to support the Health of the Nation targets for reduction in consumption of total and saturated fat, calls for an increase in the proportion of people who discussed diet and healthy food at the GP's surgery and found it helpful. The percentage of food energy derived from fat is similarly in excess of requirements across all ages and for both sexes. Men and women of all ages consume greatly over the required proportion of saturated fat, with the old slightly worse than the young (Gregory *et al.*, 1990).

Twelve per cent of adults said they had discussed diet and healthy food in the last 12 months with a member of staff at the surgery, including similar proportions of men and women. Eighty-one per cent found the discussion helpful, and a third learnt something new. Two-thirds had made or planned changes to their lifestyle.

Forty per cent were given a diet sheet, and about one-third each mentioned leaflets/booklets and being recommended to take more exercise. Older people were more likely to mention diet sheets and less likely to mention taking more exercise. Thirty-six per cent returned for a further check-up or more advice (Table 3.26).

Table 3.26: Discussion on diet and healthy food (%)

Did you find it	Helpful	81
	Unhelpful	10
	Neither	9
	Don't know	<1
Learn anything new	Yes	33
	No	66
	Don't know	1
Made any changes	Yes, have made changes	54
	Yes, plan to make changes	13
	No change made or planned	33
	Don't know	1

Base: All who have discussed diet and healthy food

Weight control

Although the government's target is for a reduction in the prevalence of obesity (found in 16% of women and 12% of men by the 1992 Health Survey for England), work by Rose (Rose and Day, 1990) suggests that reducing the prevalence of overweight (found in 26% of women and 36% of men, excluding the obese) is likely to have an impact on the upper tail of the distribution of Body Mass Index, and so reduce obesity.

Fourteen per cent of adults had discussed weight control in the last 12 months. Women and those aged 45 or over were especially likely to have done so.

Seventy-six per cent (a smaller proportion of women and younger people) found the discussion helpful, a smaller proportion than for many other risk factors. Nevertheless about a quarter (a greater proportion of men) said they had learnt something new, and almost two-thirds had made or planned lifestyle changes. This apparent contradiction could reflect a perception of the effectiveness of the discussion.

In all about seven in ten said they were given something or recommended to do something in addition to the discussion. One-third were given a diet sheet and 30% recommended to take (more) exercise. Those under 35 were more likely to mention exercise than a diet sheet, whereas for 55–74 year olds the reverse is true. One in five also mentioned being given leaflets or booklets. Thirty-seven per cent of those who discussed weight control said they had since had a further check-up or some more advice (Table 3.27).

Table 3.27: Discussion on weight control (%)

Did you find it	Helpful	76
	Unhelpful	14
	Neither	10
	Don't know	<1
Learn anything new	Yes	27
	No	72
	Don't know	1
Made any changes	Yes, have made changes	47
	Yes, plan to make changes	18
	No change made or planned	35
	Don't know	<1

Base: All who have discussed weight control

Alcohol

Men are more likely than women to drink more than the recommended sensible maximum for their sex, and to be 'very high' alcohol consumers (over 50 units a week for men, and over 35 for women). Alcohol consumption peaks between 45 and 54 for men, and between 25 and 34 for women (OPCS, 1994).

GP interventions on alcohol have been shown to be effective, and the Health Education Authority has set a health education target for an increase in the proportion of people who had discussed sensible drinking at the GP's surgery in the previous year. The GP contract operating at the time of data collection called for a collection of data on alcohol consumption, and the current contract has reinforced this.

Two per cent of adults aged 16–74 (4% of men, 1% of women) said they had discussed alcohol in the last 12 months with a member of staff at the surgery. This proportion is considerably lower than the proportion of the population drinking over sensible limits (19% of men, 13% of women – OPCS, 1994).

Of those who had discussed alcohol, the proportion describing the discussion as helpful is low at 59%. Twenty-nine per cent said they had learnt something new, and 33% that they had made changes to their lifestyle, while another 18% planned to do so.

A third had been given something or recommended to do something. Most of these were given leaflets or booklets. Eighty-seven per cent said there had been no follow-up (Table 3.28).

Table 3.28: Discussion on alcohol (%)

Did you find it	Helpful	65
	Unhelpful	14
	Neither	21
	Don't know	–
Learn anything new	Yes	29
	No	70
	Don't know	1
Made any changes	Yes, have made changes	33
	Yes, plan to make changes	18
	No change made or planned	49
	Don't know	–

Base: All who have discussed alcohol

Exercise/fitness

While the government did not set targets for physical activity in *The Health of the Nation*, the strategy document stressed that physical activity would be important in contributing to the targets for CHD, obesity and accidents. The Allied Dunbar National Fitness Survey (HEA/Sports Council, 1992) showed that the population of England is sedentary, and as part of the Health of the Nation the government has set up a physical activity task force to prepare a national strategy.

Eleven per cent of men and 5% of women said they had discussed exercise or fitness in the last 12 months with a member of staff at the surgery.

Three-quarters of those who discussed exercise or fitness found the discussion helpful. Thirty-five per cent (54% of under 25s) learnt something new. Thirty-eight per cent said they had made changes to their lifestyle, and a further 18% planned to do so.

Twenty-nine per cent said they were advised to take (more) exercise. Eighteen per cent were given an exercise or fitness plan, and 15% given leaflets or booklets. In all about three in five said they were given something or recommended to do something.

One in five (more of those aged 35 or over) had since returned for a follow-up check (Table 3.29).

Table 3.29: Discussion on exercise and fitness (%)

Did you find it	Helpful	75
	Unhelpful	9
	Neither	13
	Don't know	4
Learn anything new	Yes	35
	No	61
	Don't know	4
Made any changes	Yes, have made changes	38
	Yes, plan to make changes	18
	No change made or planned	40
	Don't know	3

Base: All who have discussed exercise/fitness

Blood pressure and cholesterol checks

There were incentives for blood pressure checks in the GP contract operating at the time of data collection, and in the current (1993) contract. The Health of the Nation target is for a reduction in mean population blood pressure.

Nine per cent of adults 16–74 who visited the surgery or health centre did so for the purpose of obtaining a blood pressure check – 20% of over 65s. This wording did not reveal who had had a blood pressure check while attending for another purpose. The 1991 Health Survey for England (OPCS, 1993) found that 52% of 16–74s and 65% of 65–74s had had their blood pressure measured in the last year.

Government advice on cholesterol testing is that it should be offered as part of an overall CHD prevention programme only to individuals with specific named risk factors, and not 'opportunistically' to people at any degree of CHD risk. One per cent report visiting for a cholesterol check (8% reported cholesterol tests in the past year to the 1991 Health Survey for England).

Cancer

Targets in the Health of the Nation cancer key area refer to lung cancer and breast cancer mortality, cervical cancer and skin cancer incidence, and smoking. Targets for smoking are shared with the CHD and stroke key area, and the evidence from the health service section of this survey was considered above. Diet, overweight and alcohol, also considered above, are important cancer risk factors included in the 'Ten Commandments' for cancer prevention issued by Europe Against Cancer.

Evidence from the survey does not allow direct tracking of contributions to targets for particular cancers.

Cancer

Only 3% of women and 2% of men who had visited the surgery in the last year had discussed cancer. Three-quarters of these discussions were initiated by the respondent, and 92% were with a doctor rather than a nurse or other health professional (Table 3.30).

Eighty-eight per cent found the discussion helpful, although only 44% learnt anything new, and three-quarters had not made or planned to make any changes to their lifestyle as a result of the discussion. A quarter were referred to a specialist or other health professional as a result of the discussion and 12% recommended to attend a particular clinic. In all half were given something or recommended to do something. For 60% there was no follow-up to the discussion (Table 3.31).

Cervical screening

The government is concerned to increase coverage of the screening especially in 'areas of low uptake' – ethnic mix, social class mix and population mobility are believed to influence uptake rates of populations.

Seven per cent of women who had visited the surgery in the past year had done so for a cervical smear.

Table 3.30: Issues discussed at the surgery in the last 12 months which relate to achievement of the Health of the Nation targets on cancer (%)

	Total	Women	Men	Women aged							Men aged						
				16–19	20–24	25–34	35–44	45–54	55–64	65–74	16–19	20–24	25–34	35–44	45–54	55–64	65–74
Cancer	3	3	2	1	2	3	3	6	4	3	4	1	1	2	3	2	2
Gynaecological problems	16	29	1	23	32	37	39	35	16	4	–	–	1	1	1	–	1

Base: All who have visited surgery in last 12 months

	Women: smoking behaviour			Men: smoking behaviour		
	Never smoked	Ex-smoker	Regular smoker	Never smoked	Ex-smoker	Regular smoker
Cancer	3	3	4	1	2	1
Gynaecological problems	28	28	31	1	<1	2

Base: All who have visited surgery in last 12 months

Twenty-nine per cent of women who visited the surgery for any reason in the past year had discussed gynaecological problems with a doctor or health professional. Since they were asked about 'gynaecological problems (e.g. period problems, cervical smears, etc.)' it is reasonable to assume that a proportion of these discussions related to cervical smears.

Eighty-six per cent of these women found the discussion helpful, and 35% learnt something new. Lifestyle changes were made or planned by a quarter. Women were likely to be given leaflets or booklets (10%) and to be referred on to a specialist or other health professional (20%). Forty-three per cent were asked back for a further check-up or advice.

Table 3.31: Discussion on cancer (%)

Did you find it	Helpful	88
	Unhelpful	8
	Neither	3
	Don't know	–
Learn anything new	Yes	44
	No	53
	Don't know	2
Made any changes	Yes, have made changes	11
	Yes, plan to make changes	11
	No change made or planned	76
	Don't know	2

Base: All who have discussed cancer

Mental illness

There are targets in *The Health of the Nation* for reducing deaths from suicide in the general population and the mentally ill, and for improving the health and social functioning of the mentally ill. There is particular concern about deaths from suicide in men aged 25–44. The death rate from suicide is highest in this group, and rising. Although the targets relate to mortality and social functioning, the government is also concerned about the prevalence of mental illness itself, and has supported initiatives to reduce psychological morbidity such as the Defeat Depression campaign.

The survey asked whether respondents had discussed stress, mental/psychological problems or emotional problems with a health professional at the surgery in the past year. All of these issues could be expected to relate to the mental illness targets.

Mental/psychological problems

Six per cent of adults aged 16–74 (8% of women and 3% of men who have visited the surgery in the past year) said they had discussed mental or psychological problems with a member of staff at the surgery. Those aged 25–54 were more likely than those younger or older to have done so (Table 3.32).

Only 77% of those who discussed mental or psychological problems said the discussion was helpful, and respondents were more likely than with other issues to say the discussion was difficult to understand. Forty per cent learnt something new, and a similar proportion said they had made changes to their lifestyle while a further 13% said they intended to do so.

About half were given something or recommended to do something specific.

Table 3.32: Issues discussed at the surgery in the last 12 months which relate to achievement of the Health of the Nation targets on mental illness (%)

	Total	Women	Men	Women aged							Men aged						
				16–19	20–24	25–34	35–44	45–54	55–64	65–74	16–19	20–24	25–34	35–44	45–54	55–64	65-74
Mental or psychological problems	6	8	3	6	6	7	10	11	8	4	2	1	5	3	4	3	2
Stress	10	11	9	7	8	12	12	15	10	5	4	6	11	11	13	8	6

Base: All who have visited surgery in last 12 months

Eighteen per cent were recommended to see a counsellor, and 15% referred to a specialist or another health professional. Three out of ten had been back, or were asked to go back for a check-up, while 18% had been back for advice (Table 3.33).

The population group at highest risk of death from suicide, men aged 25–44, were more likely than women in the same age group to say they had not needed to discuss such problems (65% compared to 54%). They were less likely to say they could discuss them with a member of staff at the surgery without difficulties (25% compared to 30%) (Table 3.34).

Stress

One in ten adults has discussed stress in the last 12 months. Those in the 25–54 age range were more likely to have done so, as were those in single-adult households.

Three-quarters said the discussion was helpful, though 15% (a greater proportion of those under 55) said it was not. Thirty-six per cent of those discussing stress said they learnt something new, and 48% mentioned lifestyle changes as a result.

Similarly, just under half were given or recommended to do something specific. Fifteen per cent were recommended to take exercise (23% of men) and 12% were referred to a specialist or to another health professional.

Thirty-two per cent reported some follow-up since the discussion, and older people in particular said they had been back for a check-up (Table 3.35).

As with mental/psychological problems, men aged 25–44 were more likely than women in this age range to say they had never needed to discuss stress with a health professional, and less likely to say they could discuss stress with a health professional without difficulties (Table 3.36).

Table 3.33: Discussion on mental and psychological problems (%)

Did you find it	Helpful	77
	Unhelpful	14
	Neither	8
	Don't know	1
Learn anything new	Yes	40
	No	60
	Don't know	<1
Made any changes	Yes, have made changes	39
	Yes, plan to make changes	13
	No change made or planned	45
	Don't know	3

Base: All who have discussed mental/psychological problems

Table 3.34: Ease of discussing mental or psychological problems (e.g. depression, anxiety) with GP or another health professional based at the surgery or health centre (%)

	Total	Women	Men	Women aged							Men aged						
				16–19	20–24	25–34	35–44	45–54	55–64	65–74	16–19	20–24	25–34	35–44	45–54	55–64	65–74
Can discuss without difficulties	27	30	24	12	23	24	36	39	39	23	11	20	22	28	31	27	19
Can discuss with some difficulty	8	10	7	13	9	13	12	9	6	5	10	8	8	7	6	6	3
Don't feel I can discuss it with them	3	3	2	4	5	3	3	2	2	1	6	2	2	3	2	1	2
Have never needed to discuss it	61	57	66	70	62	58	49	49	52	69	73	70	68	61	59	64	75
No opinion	1	1	1	1	1	1	<1	1	1	2	–	<1	<1	2	2	2	1

Base: All

Table 3.35: Discussion on stress (%)

Did you find it	Helpful	75
	Unhelpful	15
	Neither	10
	Don't know	<1
Learn anything new	Yes	36
	No	62
	Don't know	2
Made any changes	Yes, have made changes	34
	Yes, plan to make changes	14
	No change made or planned	50
	Don't know	3

Base: All who have discussed stress

Table 3.36: Ease of discussing stress with GP or another health professional based at the surgery or health centre (%)

	Total	Women	Men	Women aged							Men aged						
				16–19	20–24	25–34	35–44	45–54	55–64	65–74	16–19	20–24	25–34	35–44	45–54	55–64	65–74
Can discuss without difficulties	37	39	35	28	30	36	45	50	42	30	24	27	31	38	45	39	32
Can discuss with some difficulty	8	9	7	7	11	10	9	7	9	4	7	11	9	7	6	3	1
Don't feel I can discuss it with them	2	3	2	3	4	4	3	2	2	1	3	4	2	2	1	1	2
Have never needed to discuss it	53	49	56	62	53	49	42	40	46	63	67	58	57	52	47	55	64
No opinion	1	1	1	–	2	1	1	1	1	2	–	<1	1	1	1	2	1

Base: All

51

Sexual health

The government has set Health of the Nation targets to reduce HIV and other sexually transmitted diseases (using gonorrhoea as a marker), to reduce conceptions in under 16s, and to reduce the sharing of needles by intravenous drug users. There are two other types of provider of primary health care which contribute to these targets, but are not covered by this survey, namely specialised family planning clinics and genito-urinary medicine clinics.

The government has supported work on HIV in the general practice setting by producing the resource pack *HIV and AIDS: Issues in primary care* (Creese and Associates, 1994). General practice makes a large contribution to work on contraception and birth control. Discussion on these subjects nowadays is likely to work on include discussion on safe sex, and so contribute to the target on sexually ansmitted diseases. While under-16s were not included in the survey, they are likely to benefit from measures to reduce unwanted conceptions in the fertile female population generally. In particular, the 16–19s included in this survey will have been exposed to health education in a school setting in the recent past, and benefit from contraceptive services aimed at 'young people'. Differences between this group and older women would be expected to be in the same direction as differences between over-20s and under-16s.

Contraception/birth control

Three per cent of women had visited the surgery within the past year for the purpose of attending a family planning clinic, and 2% for contraceptive advice. Women under 19 were less likely than all other women to know that family planning was available at the GP's surgery or health centre (47% of 16–19s compared to at least 61% of all other age groups under 55). Teenagers were the women most likely to say they would like the service to be available (14% of women aged 16–19 compared to 10% or less of women aged 20–54). Eleven per cent of those who visited the surgery/health centre in the previous year discussed contraception/birth control with a member of staff there (18% of women, 2% of men) (Table 3.37).

Eighty-seven per cent of women who had these discussions had found them helpful, and 28% had learnt something new. A quarter had made changes to their lifestyle as a result of the discussion (30% of women under 20), and 8% planned to. Apart from the discussion, 16% were given booklets or leaflets, 6% were referred to another health professional, 7% recommended to attend a clinic, and 4% given free condoms.

Twenty-six of the 28 men (94%) who had discussed contraception/birth control found the discussions helpful, and 42% had learnt something new. Thirty-nine per cent had made lifestyle changes and another 33% planned to. Nineteen per cent were given booklets/leaflets, and 10% free condoms. A quarter were referred to another health professional, and 8% recommended to attend a clinic (Table 3.38).

Forty-two per cent of women and 28% of men had been asked to return to the surgery/health centre for a check-up or advice.

Table 3.37: Issues discussed at the surgery in the last 12 months which relate to achievement of the Health of the Nation targets on sexual health

	Total	Women	Men	Women aged							Men aged						
				16–19	20–24	25–34	35–44	45–54	55–64	65–74	16–19	20–24	25–34	35–44	45–54	55–64	65–74
Sexual problems	1	1	1	3	1	1	<1	<1	–	–	–	3	<1	1	–	2	–
HIV/AIDS	1	<1	1	1	<1	1	<1	<1	–	–	3	3	1	1	–	–	–
Contraception/ birth control	11	18	2	28	44	37	13	11	<1	–	4	1	41	2	–	–	–

Base: All who have visited surgery in last 12 months

Table 3.38: Discussion on contraception/birth control (%)

		Women	Men	Women aged					
				16–19	20–24	25–34	35–44	45–54	55–64
Did you find it	Helpful	86	94	91	88	82	83	100	100
	Unhelpful	4	–	1	5	5	1	–	–
	Neither	10	6	5	6	13	11	–	–
	Don't know	<1	–	2	<1	<1	5	–	–
Learn anything new	Yes	28	42	43	31	20	28	56	–
	No	72	54	55	68	78	67	44	100
	Don't know	1	4	2	<1	2	5	–	–
Made any changes	Yes, have made changes	25	39	30	31	20	21	44	100
	Yes, plan to make changes	8	33	10	8	7	5	–	–
	No changes made or planned	66	28	58	61	71	66	56	–
	Don't know	1	–	2	<1	2	8	–	–

Base: All who have discussed contraception/birth control

Sexually transmitted diseases and HIV/AIDS

One per cent of those who visited the surgery in the past year discussed 'sexual problems (e.g. sexually transmitted diseases)' – an equal proportion of men and women. Women aged 16–19 and men aged 20–24 were slightly more likely to, although inferences must be tentative because of the small numbers involved.

The entire sample was asked whether they found it easy to discuss sexual problems (e.g. sexually transmitted diseases) with their GP or another health professional at the surgery. Seventy-two per cent had not needed to discuss these problems. Ten per cent of women and 8% of men felt they could discuss them with difficulty or not at all, with a higher proportion of women under 45 and men under 25 giving these responses (Table 3.39).

A similarly small proportion discussed HIV/AIDS – 24 individuals making up 1% of the respondents who had visited the surgery for any reason in the past year, and inferences about subgroups (set out in the tables) must be cautious.

Three-quarters of all respondents in the survey said they had never needed to discuss HIV/AIDS – a higher proportion of those aged 65–74. Four per cent said they could discuss HIV/AIDS with difficulty or not at all with those aged 16–24 most likely to say this (10% of women and 7% of men) (Table 3.40).

Conclusion

The findings of the survey suggest that more can be done through primary health care teams to contribute to the Health of the Nation targets.

There is potential to improve the acceptability of GPs. Fifteen per cent of women and 4% of men had a preference as to the gender of their GP which was not met. Ten per cent or more of respondents could discuss gynaecological problems, stress, heart disease and sexual problems only with difficulty or not at all, and 15% were dissatisfied with something when they last saw their GP. Men of working age were least likely to visit the doctor despite men's higher mortality from preventable disease.

There is also evidence that opportunities for discussing behavioural risk factors are missed. Most risk factors or diseases relating to Health of the Nation targets had been discussed by 10% or fewer of those who had visited the doctor in the last year (according to their responses – their GPs' recall might differ). The issues which had been discussed with a considerably greater proportion were the 'visible' ones of diet and weight control, and gynaecological problems which include current diseases as well as lifestyle risk factors. The missed opportunities are highlighted by the finding that most people who did report having these discussions had found them helpful.

The responsibility for improving these measures must lie, not only with GPs, but with DHAs/FHSAs and central government. These bodies determine the resources available to GPs and the structural incentives within the payment system. More experience is needed of the current health promotion banding system to determine whether this is an effective approach.

Table 3.39: Ease of discussing sexual problems (e.g. sexually transmitted diseases) with GP or another health professional based at the surgery or health centre (%)

	Total	Women	Men	Women aged							Men aged						
				16–19	20–24	25–34	35–44	45–54	55–64	65–74	16–19	20–24	25–34	35–44	45–54	55–64	65–74
Can discuss without difficulties	18	18	18	17	21	18	20	21	18	11	12	17	20	20	20	15	13
Can discuss with some difficulty	6	6	6	8	11	9	8	3	4	1	6	12	7	7	5	3	2
Don't feel I can discuss it with them	3	4	2	6	3	3	5	4	3	2	5	3	1	2	2	1	1
Have never needed to discuss it	72	71	73	68	64	68	67	71	73	83	76	67	72	70	70	77	82
No opinion	1	1	1	1	1	1	<1	1	3	2	–	2	1	1	3	2	2

Base: All

Table 3.40: Ease of discussing HIV/AIDS with GP or another health professional based at the surgery or health centre (%)

	Total	Women	Men	Women aged							Men aged						
				16–19	20–24	25–34	35–44	45–54	55–64	65–74	16–19	20–24	25–34	35–44	45–54	55–64	65–74
Can discuss without difficulties	18	17	20	11	13	18	19	19	20	10	14	23	22	24	23	16	12
Can discuss with some difficulty	3	3	3	11	6	3	4	1	2	1	4	4	3	3	3	1	1
Don't feel I can discuss it with them	1	1	1	1	3	1	1	<1	<1	1	4	3	1	<1	1	–	–
Have never needed to discuss it	76	78	75	76	78	77	76	78	75	86	77	70	73	70	71	81	85
No opinion	1	2	1	1	1	1	<1	1	4	2	1	<1	1	1	2	2	2

Base: All

There is a scarcity of evidence with which to assess the potential of members of the primary care team, other than GPs and practice nurses, to contribute to Health of the Nation targets. This survey showed that they were relatively little used, and this could be a fruitful area for evaluative research.

References

Association of Community Health Councils for England & Wales (1994). *Annual Report.* ACHCEW.

Department of Health (1992) *The Health of the Nation: a Strategy for Health in England.* Cm 1986. HMSO.

Department of Health/General Medical Services Committee/Royal College of General Practitioners (1992). *Better Living — Better Life.* Resource pack for General Practitioners. Knowledge House, Henley on Thames.

Department of Health (1994) HIV and AIDS: issues in primary care. Creese and Associates.

Family Heart Study Group (1994). 'Randomised trial evaluating cardiovascular screening and intervention in general practice. Principal results of the British Family Heart Study'. *British Medical Journal,* **308**, 313–20.

Gillam, S. (1992). 'The provision of health promotion clinics in relation to population need: another example of the inverse care law?' *British Journal of General Practice,* **42**, 54-56.

Gregory, J., Foster, K., Tyler, H. and Wiseman, M. (1990). *The Dietary and Nutritional Survey of British Adults.* HMSO.

Hart, J. T. (1971). 'The inverse care law'. *Lancet* **1**, 405–12.

Health Education Authority/Sports Council (1992) *Allied Dunbar National Fitness Survey.* HEA.

Imperial Cancer Research Fund OXCHECK Study Group (1994). 'Effectiveness of health checks conducted by nurses in primary care: results of the OXCHECK study after one year'. *British Medical Journal,* **308**, 308–12.

Morrell, D. C., Evans, M. E., Morris, R. W. and Roland, M. O. (1986). 'The "5 minute" consultation: effect of time constraint on clinical content and patient satisfaction'. *British Medical Journal* **292**, 870–3.

Office of Population Censuses and Surveys (1993). *The Health Survey for England 1991.* HMSO.

Office of Population Censuses and Surveys (1994). *The Health Survey for England 1992.* HMSO.

Rose, G. and Day, S. (1990). 'The population mean predicts the number of deviant individuals'. *British Medical Journal,* **301**, 1031–4.

Waller, D., Agass, M., Mant, D. *et al.* (1990) 'Health checks in general practice: another example of inverse care?' *British Medical Journal,* **300**, 1115–8.

4. Psychosocial health

Robert West
Reader in Psychology
St Georges Hospital Medical School
London

Incidence

'Life events' is a term that refers to a wide range of potential stressors, often of limited duration, that may have an impact on a person's life. It includes major life changes involving emotional or physical distress as well as events that need not, on the face of it, cause distress such as pregnancy and moving home. It also includes problems with relationships and financial hardship. Many different life event measures have been developed. Most contain items covered in the present survey but are more inclusive and take much longer to complete (Miller, 1993). Some researchers believe that extensive interviews are required adequately to capture life events and take account of the psychological impact they may have (Brown and Harris, 1989). The life events measure in the present survey was constrained by the fact that it formed only a small part of an already extensive interview schedule. Nevertheless, even a short life-events scale can provide useful insights into sources of stress in people's lives.

Life events have been demonstrated to be associated with both physical and mental health (Brown and Harris, 1989). In a survey carried out at approximately the same time as the present one, life events were found to be related to subsequent physical ill-health (Cox *et al.*, 1993). Research over many years has implicated life-negative events as a major factor in development of depression in women (Brown and Harris, 1989).

Table 4.1 shows that for men in the sample the most common life events, at approximately 20%, were financial difficulties and death of a close relative or friend. Problems at work and experience of theft were reported by more than 10 per cent. Structural changes in lifestyle such as moving home, losing job or retiring occurred in just under 10%, with relationships problems and injury or illness also occurring in more than 5% of cases. Racial attacks and discrimination were rare but this reflected the small number of respondents from ethnic minorities in the sample.

For women the incidence of life events followed a broadly similar pattern but problems with parents or relatives and children figured more prominently, while problems with work were less common.

Many of the life events were reported in similar numbers at all ages. Death of a close relative or friend, for example, was equally common in each age category. Many life events became less common with increasing age, including financial difficulties, problems with neighbours, problems at work, changing job, personal

Table 4.1: Incidence of each life-event by age and sex

Could you tell me which if any of these (items on the show card) have happened to you in the past 12 months? (Q45)

Males

Life event	Age						
	16–24	25–34	35–44	45–54	55–64	65–74	All
Financial difficulties	26.1	27.4	23.5	13.4	11.2	5.9	20.0
Death of a close relative or friend	17.1	16.7	20.1	20.2	19.5	17.8	18.6
Problems at work	11.0	16.5	20.9	12.9	5.8	0	13.3
Personal experience of theft	16.1	17.8	13.5	13.2	5.4	5.0	13.1
Moving home	16.5	18.8	8.1	3.0	1.7	1.8	9.7
Loss of job/retirement	12.9	11.3	8.5	8.6	12.0	2.7	9.6
Changing job	12.6	13.0	11.5	4.6	3.7	0.5	8.8
Problems with neighbours	6.8	11.3	6.6	7.0	4.2	5.5	7.5
Serious injury or illness to someone close	9.0	7.3	6.8	6.2	7.5	3.2	6.9
Problems with parents/close relative	9.7	8.6	6.8	7.8	3.7	0.5	6.9
Serious illness or injury	7.1	4.5	5.0	5.7	8.7	8.2	6.0
Divorce/separation/break up of relationship	7.1	10.7	5.2	3.5	0.4	0	5.5
Problems with children	0.7	5.6	8.5	5.7	5.4	2.7	5.3
Another member of household losing job	5.5	4.1	3.8	5.1	2.5	0.9	3.9
Problems with partner	5.2	6.6	4.4	1.6	0.4	0.9	3.8
Pregnancy (of partner)	1.6	8.6	2.6	0.8	0	0	3.1
Verbal abuse due to race or colour	2.3	1.3	0.6	1.1	0	0.5	1.0
Discrimination at work or elsewhere	1.3	1.1	0.6	0.3	0	0	0.6
Physical attack due to race or colour	1.9	0.2	0.4	0.3	0	0	0.5
Other	25.5	21.2	27.2	34.7	45.6	57.5	31.9
Base: All	310	533	497	372	241	219	2 172

experience of theft, break-up of relationships, moving and problems with close relatives. Problems at work peaked in the late 30s and of course pregnancy peaked in the 20s.

The prevalence of some types of life events were similar to those found elsewhere. For example, Goldberg and Comstock (1980) found death of an important person to be reported by approximately 20% of respondents in a US sample. They also found that the number of life events decreased with age.

Females

Life event	Age						
	16–24	25–34	35–44	45–54	55–64	65–74	All
Death of a close relative or friend	23.3	19.8	19.5	20.6	20.7	23.5	20.8
Financial difficulties	26.2	27.5	22.6	13.9	10.7	4.6	19.9
Problems with parents/close relative	18.2	11.7	11.6	11.1	6.7	2.5	11.1
Moving home	21.6	16.4	8.4	3.4	4.7	3.2	10.6
Problems with children	2.7	11.4	16.3	12.0	8.3	3.2	10.2
Personal experience of theft	11.2	11.0	11.2	10.3	8.3	3.9	10.0
Problems with neighbours	10.9	10.6	8.3	9.5	6.3	5.0	8.9
Serious injury or illness to someone close	8.5	9.0	9.2	7.4	10.7	8.5	8.8
Problems at work	9.2	9.8	11.1	10.5	4.0	0.4	8.5
Pregnancy	13.1	19.1	3.1	0.6	0	0	7.7
Another member of household losing job	7.0	8.2	9.1	8.6	7.0	2.1	7.6
Divorce/separation/break up of relationship	11.4	11.0	7.6	4.0	1.7	1.1	7.2
Changing job	13.8	9.7	7.6	4.6	1.0	0	7.1
Loss of job/retirement	6.1	5.7	4.5	5.5	7.0	0.7	5.1
Problems with partner	7.0	7.6	6.1	3.2	2.0	0.4	5.1
Serious illness or injury	4.9	3.5	4.0	5.0	4.3	9.3	4.7
Verbal abuse due to race or colour	1.5	1.4	1.2	0.6	0.3	0	1.0
Discrimination at work or elsewhere	0.2	1.0	0.2	0	0.3	0	0.4
Physical attack due to race or colour	0.2	0.1	0.2	0.2	0	0	0.1
Other	20.6	20.3	23.3	33.8	42.3	50.2	28.6
Base: All	412	734	606	476	300	281	2 809

Table 4.2 shows that, as would be expected, financial difficulties were most common among the unemployed with more than 40% of respondents whose head of household was unemployed reporting problems of this kind. Also striking is the very high proportion of financial problems among those in education. Among those in employed households there was very little difference between the proportions reporting financial difficulties despite what can be assumed to be marked differences in income.

Table 4.2: Incidence of each life-event by class and sex

Males

Life event	Class							
	I&II	IIINM	IIIM	IV&V	Unemp	Sick	Home	Educ
Problems at work	16.9	13.1	10.7	7.4	8.0	6.5	11.8	2.2
Personal experience of theft	16.8	11.6	10.6	9.9	12.0	13.9	9.3	27.4
Death of a close relative or friend	16.7	18.4	18.8	18.1	18.2	20.4	15.1	31.4
Financial difficulties	14.5	15.4	18.9	15.7	39.6	27.0	20.9	51.2
Changing job	11.6	9.2	8.1	6.0	5.1	0	6.9	1.2
Moving home	8.9	10.2	8.6	6.7	9.3	4.9	0	22.4
Problems with parents/ close relative	7.3	5.7	6.6	4.0	7.3	6.6	6.2	2.1
Serious injury or illness to someone close	6.6	5.6	6.5	4.9	8.3	10.8	9.0	14.6
Problems with neighbours	6.6	7.8	8.7	3.7	10.2	9.5	3.7	13.3
Loss of job/retirement	5.7	4.9	9.1	10.2	38.9	11.6	17.9	9.4
Serious illness or injury	5.1	6.4	6.3	6.3	8.4	20.5	8.1	0
Problems with children	5.1	4.5	6.1	2.9	7.3	5.5	2.8	0
Divorce/separation/break up of relationship	4.7	6.4	3.2	4.6	6.1	3.8	2.8	5.0
Problems with partner	4.2	3.5	3.0	2.1	3.7	8.3	3.7	1.2
Another member of household losing job	3.3	5.9	4.3	5.0	9.2	7.8	3.3	0
Pregnancy (partner)	3.1	4.0	2.8	2.3	3.5	0	1.8	0
Verbal abuse due to race or colour	1.0	1.9	0.4	0.3	1.2	1.3	3.0	15.8
Discrimination at work or elsewhere	0.6	1.1	0	0	1.0	0	1.5	2.1
Physical attack due to race or colour	0	0.9	0.3	0	1.1	4.3	1.5	2.1
Other	34.1	33.8	34.8	45.5	18.7	29.9	34.6	8.9
Base: All	715	238	669	330	170	88	51	26

Serious illness or injury were most common among males in families whose head of household was sick. With female respondents, serious illness or injury to someone else were cited most often in families whose head of household was sick. This reflects the fact that most heads of household are deemed to be the male partner.

Females

Life event	I&II	IIINM	IIIM	IV&V	Unemp	Sick	Home	Educ
				Class				
Death of a close relative or friend	21.9	19.9	20.0	19.3	17.5	22.9	25.1	17.9
Problems with parents/ close relative	13.0	10.6	10.0	7.7	13.0	4.2	16.9	30.7
Problems at work	12.0	9.6	6.5	4.7	5.8	4.5	1.1	2.6
Financial difficulties	12.0	13.5	14.9	15.4	45.2	14.0	34.5	39.3
Personal experience of theft	11.1	8.5	7.5	8.5	9.3	8.8	11.3	21.1
Serious injury or illness to someone close	10.2	8.0	7.2	8.2	9.7	15.9	8.7	6.1
Moving home	9.7	7.9	7.6	6.4	11.2	9.2	14.9	25.1
Problems with children	9.6	7.9	8.8	7.3	11.5	8.2	12.6	8.6
Changing job	8.6	8.0	6.1	6.8	4.4	2.5	4.7	2.6
Pregnancy (partner)	8.1	5.6	5.4	4.1	8.0	3.8	14.1	7.2
Problems with neighbours	7.9	7.2	6.7	9.4	8.5	13.7	12.6	6.3
Another member of household losing job	5.3	6.6	8.7	7.8	32.2	7.3	2.6	5.2
Serious illness or injury	4.3	2.6	5.9	5.1	5.0	4.0	5.0	1.8
Divorce/separation/break up of relationship	3.8	6.1	3.7	2.7	6.6	5.4	20.6	7.2
Problems with partner	3.8	5.1	4.7	3.0	9.5	2.7	6.3	5.6
Loss of job/retirement	3.3	6.3	4.6	5.8	11.6	5.5	5.5	0
Verbal abuse due to race or colour	1.1	0.5	0.4	0.7	1.7	1.1	2.5	0
Discrimination at work or elsewhere	0.6	0	0.3	0.1	0	0.7	0	0
Physical attack due to race or colour	0	0	0.1	0	0.5	0	1.3	0
Other	30.6	33.3	35.3	34.5	19.5	27.3	20.1	16.4
Base: All	670	318	609	293	142	84	124	30

As would be expected, for men loss of job or retirement in the past year was cited more often by members of unemployed households. Among those in working households, the proportion reporting loss of job or retirement was almost twice as high in social class IV–V as social class I–II. On the other hand, problems at work were cited more than twice as often by respondents in social class I–II as by those in IV–V.

Table 4.3: Incidence of each life-event by housing tenure and sex

Life event	Males		Females	
	Owns/buying	Rents	Owns/buying	Rents
Death of a close relative or friend	18.8	15.7	21.3	18.6
Financial difficulties	15.2	30.3	13.4	26.3
Personal experience of theft	12.6	13.6	9.3	10.2
Problems at work	12.2	11.1	8.3	5.7
Loss of job/retirement	9.9	11.3	4.9	5.5
Changing job	9.1	5.2	6.4	6.8
Moving home	7.6	11.1	7.5	12.3
Problems with neighbours	7.1	8.0	6.8	11.2
Serious injury or illness to someone close	6.6	6.0	8.8	8.8
Problems with parents/close relative	6.3	6.0	10.6	11.8
Serious illness or injury	5.8	7.9	4.7	4.9
Problems with children	4.9	5.3	8.7	9.7
Another member of household losing job	4.7	4.5	8.2	8.2
Divorce/separation/break up of relationship	3.9	6.2	3.8	8.3
Problems with partner	3.0	4.7	4.1	5.2
Pregnancy (partner)	2.8	2.8	5.9	7.7
Verbal abuse due to race or colour	1.1	1.3	0.8	1.1
Discrimination at work or elsewhere	0.5	0.5	0.2	0.4
Physical attack due to race or colour	0.4	0.3	0	0.4
Other	34.7	31.5	33.0	26.6
Base: All	1 858	556	1 826	634

There was a tendency for men in social class I–II to report a higher incidence of theft than those in IV–V. The trend with female respondents was less strong.

Divorce was cited as a relatively common life event by women who were looking after the home. This reflects the fact that upon separation, it is often women who find themselves as home carers.

Housing tenure is also an important marker of social circumstances. Table 4.3 shows that those living in rented accommodation more often reported financial difficulties and divorce or separation. Otherwise these was little difference between the two groups.

Table 4.4 shows the degree of stress associated with each life event. For men, serious illness or injury headed the list, closely followed by divorce and problems with their partner. Also often rated as very stressful were financial difficulties, illness or injury to someone close, physical attack due to race or colour and death of a close friend or relative. These results accord with other studies showing serious illness and marital separation to be among the most stressful life events (Holmes and Rahe, 1967).

Table 4.4: Degree of stress by life-event type by sex

Could you tell me how stressful you found (each event on the card)? (Q46)

Life event	Males				Females			
	Very	Fairly	Not very	Not at all	Very	Fairly	Not very	Not at all
Serious illness or injury	50.5	24.6	18.7	6.2	56.1	28.4	11.5	4.1
Divorce/separation/break up of relationship	47.8	28.8	19.4	4.0	59.5	28.6	8.9	3.0
Problems with partner	46.5	41.6	9.9	2.0	59.6	33.3	4.9	2.3
Financial difficulties	40.4	40.5	16.2	2.9	45.3	42.2	11.3	1.1
Serious injury or illness to someone close	39.6	41.4	17.0	2.0	59.6	32.6	7.3	0.4
Physical attack due to race or colour	37.5	25.6	15.4	21.5	100.0	0	0	0
Death of a close relative or friend	35.8	36.8	22.6	4.8	54.2	35.9	9.0	0.9
Loss of job/retirement	32.8	31.2	17.0	19.1	33.7	35.5	17.0	13.7
Problems at work	30.7	55.4	12.6	1.3	38.6	52.7	7.0	1.7
Problems with children	28.2	50.7	17.0	4.0	44.3	45.6	8.8	1.4
Discrimination at work or elsewhere	23.8	60.9	15.3	0	47.4	26.8	10.8	15.0
Problems with parents/close relative	21.2	58.3	16.9	3.6	41.3	48.2	9.3	1.3
Problems with neighbours	21.2	29.0	29.9	19.9	31.4	35.3	27.0	6.2
Moving home	20.6	33.1	26.0	20.4	28.7	31.0	23.9	16.4
Personal experience of theft	20.1	38.1	28.3	13.5	38.9	34.8	22.3	4.1
Pregnancy (self or partner)	16.4	207	35.5	27.5	21.8	19.0	27.4	31.9
Changing job	15.9	26.2	30.2	27.7	13.7	29.1	32.6	24.6
Verbal abuse due to race or colour	10.2	43.7	36.1	10.0	33.6	27.9	34.9	3.7
Another member of household losing job	10.1	42.1	29.7	18.1	41.0	41.6	13.5	4.0

Women reported their life events as being more stressful than did the men overall. They also tended to respond to the life events differently. Physical attack was rated as most stressful, followed by problems with their partner, divorce or separation and illness of someone close. Pregnancy and changing job were considered to be stressful by few women.

Table 4.5: Prevalence of stress by age and sex

Looking at this card which if these sentences best describes the amount of stress or pressure you experienced in the past 12 months? I have been/have experienced ... (Q47)

Stress level	Age						All
	16–24	25–34	35–44	45–54	55–64	65–74	
Males							
Completely free	13.6	9.8	11.0	14.3	26.3	41.9	17.2
Small amount	44.5	36.1	25.8	33.1	31.0	296	33.9
Moderate amount	30.2	36.8	44.6	33.0	26.7	17.5	32.9
Large amount	11.8	17.4	18.6	19.6	16.0	11.1	16.1
Base: All	472	535	456	403	334	269	2468
Females							
Completely free	12.2	7.5	7.1	13.6	20.2	33.5	14.3
Small amount	38.4	36.0	31.9	32.5	33.5	34.2	34.5
Moderate amount	32.7	35.3	34.2	28.6	27.3	18.1	30.2
Large amount	16.7	21.2	26.8	25.3	19.1	14.2	20.9
Base: All	452	525	454	404	345	322	2504

Stress

Prevalence

Stress has been identified as a major contributory factor in both mental and physical ill-health (Goldberger and Breznitz, 1993). Table 4.5 shows that 16% of men and 21% of women reported experiencing large amounts of stress and approximately 50% reported at least a moderate amount of stress. In all age groups, women reported more stress than men. Those aged 35–55 reported the highest levels of stress. More than 1 in 4 women in this age range reported experiencing a 'large' amount of stress. The inverted U-shaped function relating stress with age is similar to that found in the 1991 Health Survey for England (OPCS, 1993) although in that survey stress was as high in the 24–35 age range as any other. That survey also failed to show any difference in stress between men and women. In that regard its results were at variance with other surveys. This may be because the time period canvassed was only the preceding four weeks.

Table 4.6 shows that among respondents in employed households stress levels were greatest in classes I–II. As would be expected, stress levels where the head of household was unemployed and sick were considerably higher than those in employed households. An even higher level was observed in women looking after the home. Among the few women in the sample who were in full-time education, stress levels were also high, and indeed higher than among men in the same position.

Table 4.6: Prevalence of stress by class and sex

Stress level	Class							
	I&II	IIINM	IIIM	IV&V	Unemp	Sick	Home	Educ
Males								
Completely free	12.1	16.3	17.6	29.9	10.5	21.2	29.3	12.2
Small amount	29.0	31.4	37.8	33.4	34.1	24.7	29.3	53.2
Moderate amount	40.2	36.2	31.7	25.1	28.9	26.4	20.1	30.2
Large amount	18.7	16.1	12.9	11.6	26.5	27.8	21.2	4.4
Base: All	716	236	670	323	168	88	51	26
Females								
Completely free	11.4	14.3	16.3	16.3	12.0	18.8	13.2	9.1
Small amount	35.1	37.5	34.0	41.9	26.7	35.8	24.4	9.6
Moderate amount	30.9	30.1	31.3	25.3	33.8	19.6	30.2	56.7
Large amount	22.7	18.1	18.4	16.6	27.5	25.9	32.1	24.5
Base: All	668	314	610	295	143	84	125	30

Table 4.7: Prevalence of stress by housing tenure and sex

Stress level	Males		Females	
	Owns/buying	Rents	Owns/buying	Rents
Completely free	16.2	21.4	14.3	14.6
Small amount	34.4	32..0	35.5	31.6
Moderate amount	34.4	27.4	31.2	28.1
Large amount	15.0	19.2	19.0	25.8
Base: All	1 863	552	1 823	637

Respondents in rented accommodation reported higher levels of stress than owner-occupiers (Table 4.7) although the difference was not large.

There was little evidence of regional variation in stress levels (Table 4.8). Women in Northern Ireland reported less stress, but this was within the margin of error given the sample size.

Table 4.8: Prevalence of stress by region

Male

Region	Completely free	Small amount	Moderate amount	Large amount	Base (All)
Northern Ireland	19.0	44.0	20.6	16.5	64
Scotland	21.4	31.6	27.3	19.7	216
Wales	22.6	31.5	31.0	14.9	121
England	16.4	34.0	34.0	15.7	2 068
Anglia and Oxford	12.5	36.4	37.4	13.8	237
North Thames	8.3	32.2	42.4	17.2	287
North West	22.6	32.5	28.2	16.7	279
Northern and Yorkshire	24.2	35.8	26.0	14.0	283
South and West	19.7	37.5	28.1	14.8	266
South Thames	9.6	32.0	42.8	15.7	285
Trent	16.8	30.7	31.9	20.6	204
West Midlands	17.7	34.7	34.3	13.3	227

Female

Region	Completely free	Small amount	Moderate amount	Large amount	Base (All)
Scotland	16.9	32.2	28.8	22.2	227
Wales	12.6	31.7	27.7	28.0	125
Northern Ireland	27.7	39.6	28.0	4.6	61
England	13.8	34.8	30.6	20.8	2 091
Anglia and Oxford	12.2	38.2	33.6	16.0	227
North Thames	7.5	38.4	28.2	26.0	297
North West	20.1	35.0	25.3	19.6	289
Northern and Yorkshire	17.0	30.9	30.2	21.9	279
South and West	10.3	42.1	32.8	14.8	274
South Thames	10.4	31.6	31.4	26.6	292
Trent	21.1	28.1	29.9	20.9	207
West Midlands	13.6	32.8	35.1	18.5	226

Coping methods

The way that individuals cope with stress may influence their levels of stress and the extent to which stress has an impact on their lives. In general, active/approach coping methods such as discussing problems are generally thought to be more adaptive than passive/avoidance methods such as denial (Moos and Schaefer, 1993).

Table 4.9 shows that the most common coping strategies were both passive and active. In particular they were: trying not to think about the problem; and discussing it with a friend or relative. Other common methods were taking more

exercise, occupying oneself, thinking about problems, and spending time out with friends or relatives. Smoking more was quite a common strategy for both men and women. One interesting difference between men and women was that while men tended to go to the pub more often as a coping strategy, women tended to eat more.

Seeking professional advice or getting a prescription from the doctor was relatively uncommon with both sexes, but even so approximately 1 in 25 respondents sought relief from stress in a prescription and approximately 1 in 10 sought advice from their doctor.

Older respondents were more likely to report that they never had stress or pressure — which is reflected in the lower incidence of several coping strategies in the older age groups. There was a tendency for older respondents to respond to stress less by going out drinking, smoking, eating, spending time thinking about problems, and spending more time out with friends and relatives. On the other hand older respondents were more likely to get advice from their doctor and to pray or meditate in response to stress.

Table 4.9: Prevalence of coping methods by age and sex

Which if any of the things on this card do you usually do to cope with stress or pressure? (Q49)

Male

Coping method	Age						
	16–24	25–34	35–44	45–54	55–64	65–74	All
Discuss with close friend or relative	35.2	42.0	37.1	33.5	33.8	24.8	35.7
Try not to think about it	39.4	35.0	31.9	32.6	34.9	28.0	34.2
Take more exercise	20.5	28.5	23.9	19.2	16.7	18.2	22.1
Work harder to occupy self	16.7	21.1	23.7	17.9	21.3	15.1	19.7
Go to pub/have a drink	22.0	26.2	16.9	17.9	10.1	11.2	18.8
Spend more time thinking about problems	19.0	18.3	21.0	14.7	13.7	9.8	17.0
Spend more time out with friends/relatives	32.9	17.8	8.5	8.4	11.8	10.4	16.0
Smoke more	18.3	17.6	13.7	13.4	12.1	11.2	15.0
Pray/meditate	7.3	7.9	8.3	10.3	8.7	14.1	9.0
Get help/advice from doctor	1.7	4.1	8.0	9.5	16.3	16.1	8.0
Drink more	5.6	12.0	9.3	6.4	5.3	3.3	7.6
Eat more	9.0	7.3	7.8	4.9	9.1	3.4	7.2
Get help/advice from counsellor	2.1	3.7	3.5	3.9	3.6	3.9	3.4
Get prescription from doctor	1.1	1.9	2.1	2.3	9.1	7.1	3.3
Never have any stress/pressure	9.5	6.6	9.5	10.9	17.0	21.6	11.4
Base: All	475	540	455	406	340	268	2 484

Female

Coping method	16–24	25–34	35–44	45–54	55–64	65–74	All
			Age				
Discuss with close friend or relative	62.9	67.7	59.1	51.3	47.6	38.9	56.4
Try not to think about it	29.5	25.8	19.1	22.0	25	32.0	25.2
Work harder to occupy self	15.2	22.1	23.9	28.3	27.6	25.0	23.3
Eat more	25.6	24.4	23.9	20.4	17.5	11.5	21.4
Spend more time out with friends/relatives	34.2	16.3	12.5	14.3	12.3	18.9	18.3
Take more exercise	17.1	17.8	17.7	19.4	15.1	10.6	16.7
Spend more time thinking about problems	21.9	20.4	16.6	11.2	7.3	6.1	15.0
Smoke more	20.3	15.5	17.9	12.6	9.8	6.1	14.5
Pray/meditate	6.8	9.4	11.1	13.4	21.1	15.4	12.2
Get help/advice from doctor	5.0	9.0	10.2	11.9	14.5	11.7	10.0
Go to pub/have a drink	13.1	7.7	7.3	6.0	1.0	2.5	6.8
Get help/advice from counsellor	2.2	4.9	6.0	4.8	4.5	3.8	4.4
Get prescription from doctor	2.2	3.0	3.4	4.9	5.7	6.2	4.0
Drink more	3.4	5.2	5.6	3.9	3.0	0	3.8
Never have any stress/pressure	6.8	4.7	4.0	6.6	7.0	15.6	7.1
Base: All	452	527	453	404	347	325	2 508

Table 4.10 shows the incidence of coping methods broken down by social class and employment status. For most coping strategies there was little difference between the social classes. However, there was evidence that more disadvantaged groups smoked more in response to stress, while classes I–II were more likely to discuss their problems with friends or relatives and take more exercise.

Some methods of coping may be more appropriate for higher levels of stress than others. Table 4.11 shows the incidence of each coping method for each stress level reported. There was no evidence of greater use of trying not to think about stress, spending more time out, or discussing problems with increasing stress levels. However, other coping methods did become more prevalent with increasing stress. This was particularly the case for smoking, spending time thinking about problems, eating more, working harder and seeking professional advice.

Table 4.10: Prevalence of coping methods by class and sex

Male

Coping method	Class							
	I&II	IIINM	IIIM	IV&V	Unemp	Sick	Home	Educ
Discuss with close friend or relative	42.6	38.9	30.6	30.2	32.9	38.4	27.7	43.0
Try not to think about it	31.3	36.3	38.2	25.6	42.9	32.9	48.9	39.5
Take more exercise	26.2	29.0	17.6	19.2	19.2	15.0	11.3	36.6
Spend more time thinking about problems	21.7	17.1	12.9	13.9	16.5	13.6	21.7	38.6
Work harder to occupy self	18.1	22.9	19.8	23.7	19.6	19.2	10.2	27.2
Go to pub/have a drink	15.8	14.8	20.5	19.6	20.9	17.7	19.9	39.5
Spend more time out with friends/relatives	13.6	14.1	19.2	15.2	16.0	13.0	16.1	32.7
Pray/meditate	12.9	7.5	5.8	5.2	8.8	9.3	4.0	23.5
Smoke more	10.5	11.4	16.5	16.1	26.9	19.3	7.4	20.8
Drink more	8.7	8.8	6.9	5.7	7.3	9.3	0	7.6
Get help/advice from doctor	8.1	3.5	6.1	10.8	6.8	28.2	7.3	0
Eat more	7.4	6.5	6.1	7.6	10.2	6.8	8.8	3.2
Get help/advice from counsellor	3.1	2.4	4.2	1.4	4.7	4.7	9.4	0
Get prescription from doctor	2.1	0.6	3.7	6.1	2.5	9.1	4.0	2.4
Never have any stress/pressure	8.9	13.7	11.8	16.5	8.5	10.3	16.7	12.1
Base: All	654	206	593	276	156	80	43	23

Female

Coping method	Class							
	I&II	IIINM	IIIM	IV&V	Unemp	Sick	Home	Educ
Discuss with close friend or relative	61.7	57.0	56.9	43.5	50.7	50.8	58.1	79.0
Work harder to occupy self	25.8	24.8	19.0	26.3	23.3	25.8	23.4	22.5
Try not to think about it	21.9	22.2	27.1	30.7	29.6	22.5	29.1	33.4
Eat more	21.5	20.4	23.7	18.1	21.4	21.8	21.3	42.7
Take more exercise	20.2	14.1	17.5	11.8	13.5	10.7	13.9	11.3
Spend more time out with friends/relatives	17.7	16.1	19.1	16.3	18.4	9.0	21.8	29.9
Spend more time thinking about problems	17.1	14.4	15.5	12.5	20.1	10.7	15.2	15.5
Pray/meditate	16.3	15.1	8.6	9.2	9.6	14.5	9.2	23.0
Get help/advice from doctor	9.7	10.5	8.9	10.3	11.3	13.4	14.7	5.4
Smoke more	9.2	11.1	13.3	17.1	25.3	23.2	32.0	22.4
Go to pub/have a drink	7.4	3.5	6.7	6.9	8.2	1.3	6.0	30.6
Drink more	5.4	4.2	3.1	0.5	3.4	5.4	5.2	0
Get help/advice from counsellor	5.4	4.1	3.1	1.8	7.3	8.4	6.8	0
Get prescription from doctor	2.9	1.8	2.6	5.6	8.5	8.8	7.9	2.1
Never have any stress/pressure	4.5	9.7	7.9	5.9	3.5	12.9	9.1	9.1
Base: All	668	317	612	297	139	84	127	30

Table 4.11: Prevalence of coping methods by stress level

Coping method	Stress level			
	Completely free	Small amount	Moderate amount	Large amount
Discuss with close friend or relative	30.2	46.0	49.3	51.0
Try not to think about it	22.3	30.9	30.1	29.5
Work harder to occupy self	15.9	18.2	22.4	28.6
Smoke more	10.9	10.3	15.5	23.0
Spend more time thinking about problems	6.2	12.6	18.2	23.0
Take more exercise	10.1	18.8	21.1	22.0
Eat more	8.0	11.8	15.2	21.5
Spend more time out with friends/relatives	12.9	17.2	17.7	18.3
Get help/advice from doctor	10.9	4.0	8.4	18.0
Pray/meditate	8.4	8.4	11.0	15.3
Go to pub/have a drink	10.8	11.1	14.4	13.3
Get help/advice from counsellor	2.5	1.3	3.5	9.9
Drink more	3.9	3.6	6.0	9.7
Get prescription from doctor	3.0	1.7	3.5	7.6
Never have any stress/pressure	41.2	5.4	2.2	0.9
Base: All	459	1 605	1 530	909

Social support

Social support is believed to be protective against the harmful effects of stress on physical and mental health (Shumaker and Czajkowski, 1994). It includes being involved in a stable relationship and having close friends or relatives in whom one can confide and discuss problems. There are many widely-used measures of social support (Sarason and Sarason, 1994) which can be categorised as follows: 'network' measures assess primarily the number of social contacts and the nature of those contacts; 'received support' measures assess the amount and quality of support actually received from social or professional contacts; 'perceived support' measures assess the level and quality of support available as perceived by the individual in question; 'aggregate' measures focus on how far an individual feels loved and cared for; 'functional' measures assess the extent to which individuals receive support or perceive themselves as able to receive support in relation to a set of specific functions. The social support items in this survey focused primarily on networks, received support and perceived available support, but using a set of ad hoc questions rather than one of the standardised measures.

Social support structures

More than 60% of the sample had been living in the area they presently inhabited for 10 years or more (Table 4.12). As would be expected, older respondents had lived in their presently inhabited area for longer than younger respondents. There was no major difference between the men and women in the sample.

Table 4.12: Length of time living in area by age and sex

How long have you lived in this area? (Q51)

Male

| Length of time | Age | | | | | | |
	16–24	25–34	35–44	45–54	55–64	65–74	All
< 1 year	10.2	11.3	4.9	3.2	1.3	1.8	6.2
1–4 years	16.4	31.4	18.2	10.5	5.6	10.3	16.9
5–9 years	10.1	21.0	21.2	12.4	6.9	11.0	14.5
10 years +	63.3	36.3	55.7	73.9	86.1	77	62.4
Base: All	473	540	457	405	340	269	2 484

Female

| Length of time | Age | | | | | | |
	16–24	25–34	35–44	45–54	55–64	65–74	All
< 1 year	13.1	9.4	4.7	2.0	1.9	3.1	6.2
1–4 years	21.8	29.6	17.3	9.3	5.5	5.8	16.3
5–9 years	11.0	29.0	22.0	11.5	12.5	12.8	17.3
10 years +	54.1	32.0	56.1	77.3	80.0	78.3	60.3
Base: All	452	528	456	407	347	328	2517

Table 4.13 shows that there was little difference between social class and employment categories except that the small group of respondents in full time education understandably reported having lived in their present location for fewer years than other groups, the modal duration being 1–4 years.

Those living in rented accommodation had lived in their present location for slightly less time than owner-occupiers (Table 4.14). There was little difference between the regions in time spent living in present location (Table 4.15).

The very large majority of respondents of all ages reported that they had close friends and relatives with whom they could talk (Table 4.16). There was a tendency for greater numbers reporting close relatives and fewer respondents reporting close friends with increasing age. Women also tended to report slightly more close friends and relatives than men.

There was no clear evidence of differing numbers of respondents reporting close friends or relatives in different social class employment groupings (Table 4.17). However, there was a tendency for those in rented accommodation to report fewer friends and relatives than owner-occupiers (Table 4.18).

Table 4.13: Length of time living in area by class and sex

Male

Length of time	Class							
	I+II	IIINM	IIIM	IV+V	Unemp	Sick	Home	Educ
< 1 year	6.4	6.0	5.6	3.8	9.3	2.7	0	25.5
1–4 years	20.5	15.5	10.5	14.6	22.7	24.9	20.3	39.0
5–9 years	17.7	12.3	12.9	13.2	14.9	4.7	18.7	13.9
10 years +	55.4	66.2	71.0	68.4	53.1	67.7	61.0	21.6
Base (all)	718	238	673	332	169	88	51	26

Female

Length of time	Class							
	I+II	IIINM	IIIM	IV+V	Unemp	Sick	Home	Educ
< 1 year	5.5	6.4	4.5	3.0	9.4	3.3	11.1	27.8
1–4 years	18.6	12.7	13.3	13.3	22.3	14.3	17.3	63.9
5–9 years	21.1	19.8	14.5	15.2	16.2	12.8	19.0	3.0
10 years +	54.9	61.2	67.8	68.6	52.0	69.7	52.6	5.2
Base: All	669	318	614	296	143	84	126	30

Table 4.14: Length of time living in area by housing tenure

Length of time	Male		Female	
	Owns/Buying	Rents	Owns/Buying	Rents
< 1 year	4.5	9.8	4.3	10.1
1–4 years	14.3	24.9	14.3	21.5
5–9 years	15.9	11.1	18.1	15.0
10 years +	65.3	54.2	63.3	53.4
Base: All	1 874	555	1 830	641

Table 4.15: Length of time living in area by region

Male

Region	<1 year	1–4 years	5–9 years	10+ years	Base
Northern Ireland	4.6	3.1	6.4	86.0	64
Scotland	5.6	18.0	15.8	60.6	218
Wales	4.4	9.0	18.2	68.4	122
England	6.4	17.7	14.5	61.5	2 079
Anglia and Oxford	6.3	21.1	10.9	61.8	238
Northern and Yorkshire	5.3	14.4	14.7	65.7	284
Trent	4.7	16.5	13.1	65.8	205
North Thames	7.3	20.8	13.9	58.1	290
South Thames	6.9	13.6	19.6	60.0	286
South and West	8.2	20.1	14.4	57.3	269
West Midlands	6.1	17.2	10.9	65.8	227
North West	6.1	17.9	16.5	59.4	280

Female

Region	<1 year	1–4 years	5–9 years	10+ years	Base
Scotland	3.9	17.0	13.8	65.3	227
Wales	4.3	10.4	18.8	66.5	126
Northern Ireland	6.1	13.8	19.1	61.0	64
England	6.5	16.6	17.5	59.3	2 101
Anglia and Oxford	5.2	20.1	17.8	56.9	227
Northern and Yorkshire	6.2	13.8	21.5	58.5	282
Trent	6.0	17.2	15.2	61.7	207
North Thames	9.2	15.9	17.5	57.4	299
South Thames	5.7	16.0	17.0	61.2	292
South and West	9.9	21.1	16.9	52.1	276
West Midlands	4.6	13.6	12.1	69.7	225
North West	4.4	15.7	20.5	59.4	293

Table 4.16: Proportion of people with close relatives and friends by age and sex

Including people you live with, do you have any close relatives whom you speak to or see regularly? I mean people you *feel* close to. (Q52)

	Age						
	16–24	25–34	35–44	45–54	55–64	65–74	All
Male							
Close relatives	82.6	87.7	85.5	87.2	89.8	91.5	86.9
Close friends	89.7	81.4	77.5	83.4	80.2	80.5	82.3
Base (all)	472	540	457	406	340	269	2 482
Female							
Close relatives	85.6	89.9	89.1	90.8	91.0	91.0	89.4
Close friends	92.6	89.8	88.1	86.4	89.0	84.7	88.7
Base: All	452	528	455	406	345	326	2 513

Table 4.17: Proportion of people with close relatives and friends by class and sex

	Class							
	I&II	IIINM	IIIM	IV&V	Unemp	Sick	Home	Educ
Male								
Close relatives	85.7	87.7	90.2	88.7	83.9	80.7	89.2	66.3
Close friends	84.4	86.1	83.7	81.9	76.2	69.2	77.4	87.3
Base: All	717	238	673	332	169	89	51	26
Female								
Close relatives	89.0	86.6	91.7	94.4	87.4	87.1	86.8	84.6
Close friends	88.8	91.7	89.4	89.0	81.5	82.4	85.1	100
Base: All	669	318	614	296	141	84	125	30

Table 4.18: Proportion of people with close relatives and friends by housing tenure and sex

	Males		Females	
	Owns/Buying	Rents	Owns/Buying	Rents
Close relatives	87.9	84.5	90.2	88.6
Close friends	83.8	77.8	89.8	86.3
Base: All	1 857	554	1 827	640

Social support activities

The most common social support activities were speaking with neighbours and speaking with friends and relatives on the telephone (Table 4.19). Visiting with friends or relatives was slightly less common. Making use of formal social support structures such as leisure centres and health professionals was less common, as was participation in voluntary groups and adult education.

There was a tendency for women to undertake more social support activities than men. Visiting friends, having friends visit, going out with friends and speaking with friends on the telephone were more common among younger respondents. Visiting leisure centres was also more common among younger respondents. In contrast there was an increase in speaking with neighbours, and participation in voluntary groups and religious activities with increasing age. There was a tendency for men to consult health professionals more commonly with increasing age while women were most likely to consult with health professionals between 25 and 34. This no doubt reflects the fact that pregnancies generally occur in this age group.

Table 4.20 shows a general trend towards lower participation in most social activities among less advantaged social classes and unemployed respondents. This included contacts with friends, participation in voluntary groups, community and religious activities, social outings and use of leisure centres. However, there was little evidence of differences between social classes in contact with relatives and use of health professionals. The lower participation rate in more disadvantaged groups may result in part from lower income, greater pressures from other quarters or a lack of interest. Whatever the cause, a lower rate of participation in social activities may explain part of the social class gradient in physical and mental health.

Table 4.19: Participation in social activities by age and sex

Which if any of these have you done in the past fortnight? (Q54)

Male

				Age			
	16–24	25–34	35–44	45–54	55–64	65–74	All
Spoke to neighbours	54.4	71.0	70.6	75.6	75.1	77.1	69.7
Spoke to relatives on phone	56.7	73.9	74.0	67.6	67.0	70.4	68.3
Spoke to friends on the phone	75.9	69.3	62.0	62.5	57.3	55.8	65.0
Went to visit friends	81.0	67.5	49.4	51.2	50.7	40.1	58.8
Went out with friends	83.2	62.7	48.7	45.9	40.8	26.4	54.4
Had friends visit	64.3	57.3	46.8	44.3	46.4	43.3	51.6
Had relatives visit	39.6	50.6	52.0	50.7	50.4	59.4	49.7
Went to visit relatives	41.1	30.9	37.0	36.0	40.1	46.2	37.8
Went out with relatives	28.8	37.5	29.1	31.8	34.3	24.7	31.5
Went to a leisure centre	34.6	31.0	22.3	11.7	8.9	5.3	21.1
Went to another social outing	20.8	20.7	21.2	18.6	21.4	15.8	20.0
Spoke to a health professional	10.7	17.8	17.4	13.7	23.2	24.1	17.1
Participated in community or religious activity	6.0	7.3	11.5	12.1	12.8	14.6	10.2
Participated in a voluntary group	4.1	5.1	8.2	8.6	11.7	10.7	7.6
Attended adult education or night school	6.1	4.4	3.3	4.3	3.0	2.0	4.1
Base: All	474	539	457	405	340	267	2 482

Female

	16–24	25–34	35–44	45–54	55–64	65–74	All
				Age			
Spoke to relatives on phone	64.7	81.6	82.1	77.6	78.4	77.1	77.0
Spoke to neighbours	55.8	78.9	77.1	81.1	80.0	75.7	74.5
Spoke to friends on the phone	72.0	75.6	71.2	70.6	67.0	58.8	70.0
Went to visit relatives	62.5	76.0	64.7	62.4	62.3	54.4	64.6
Went to visit friends	74.1	72.6	60.7	58.5	54.8	42.2	62.0
Had relatives visit	52.7	62.9	55.2	56.4	59.8	60.5	57.9
Had friends visit	62.3	64.6	52.9	56.1	50.2	41.2	55.7
Went out with friends	70.2	51.8	46.9	42.7	43.9	31.2	49.0
Went out with relatives	30.3	42.8	32.8	34.1	38.1	31.7	35.2
Spoke to a health professional	21.3	34.3	26.4	21.4	27.9	14.7	25.0
Went to another social outing	19.3	22.0	24.6	24.5	21.8	18.3	21.9
Went to a leisure centre	34.4	29.7	22.3	16.6	10.2	6.5	21.4
Participated in community or religious activity	5.2	11.7	12.6	17.2	20.2	25.6	14.5
Participated in a voluntary group	5.9	10.1	11.5	14.3	14.9	13.0	11.3
Attended adult education or night school	4.7	7.2	8.0	6.7	7.8	3.3	6.4
Base: All	452	529	456	407	347	328	2 518

Table 4.20: Participation in social activities by class and sex

Males

	Class							
	I&II	IIINM	IIIM	IV&V	Unemp	Sick	Home	Educ
Spoke to relatives on phone	76.5	68.2	68.1	67.1	53.9	55.2	53.9	78.7
Spoke to neighbours	74.8	69.5	70.4	67.2	62.2	73.6	60.8	33.2
Spoke to friends on the phone	74.4	73.8	63.1	56.2	51.2	46.4	40.9	77.9
Went to visit friends	64.7	62.8	55.9	50.5	61.2	50.0	53.1	83.3
Went to visit relatives	59.2	61.0	68.5	60.0	65.4	64.8	51.4	76.0
Went out with friends	58.5	58.2	53.1	47.5	51.6	41.5	41.9	83.3
Had friends visit	54.3	55.0	50.6	48.7	50.6	45.8	40.6	86.9
Had relatives visit	51.2	44.0	53.0	52.6	51.9	43.9	40.0	24.8
Went out with relatives	33.2	30.0	32.0	33.8	29.8	26.1	23.5	29.3
Went to a leisure centre	25.1	26.0	21.1	16.6	10.9	12.2	15.2	37.4
Went to another social outing	23.8	23.2	19.7	15.4	12.1	17.3	14.1	18.6
Spoke to a health professional	18.8	16.5	14.9	17.6	20.3	30.7	13.8	9.0
Community or religious activity	17.4	11.9	6.1	6.5	6.5	6.7	3.4	4.5
Participated in a voluntary group	12.8	10.1	5.6	4.8	2.0	6.1	1.5	0
Attended adult education or night school	5.5	3.8	2.5	4.5	2.8	4.9	3.0	13.4
Base: All	718	238	671	332	169	89	51	27

Females

				Class				
	I&II	IIINM	IIIM	IV&V	Unemp	Sick	Home	Educ
Spoke to relatives on phone	82.7	81.6	77.7	73.6	63.1	65.9	60.2	92.9
Spoke to friends on the phone	81.3	74.9	71.6	61.7	56.7	46.4	51.8	78.8
Spoke to neighbours	79.7	75.3	73.2	74.2	66.9	67.1	73.2	38.8
Went to visit friends	68.5	62.3	62.4	54.9	55.6	51.2	59.7	82.5
Went to visit relatives	60.8	65.0	68.6	65.6	63.8	59.4	66.1	62.9
Had friends visit	60.6	59.4	54.7	46.2	51.5	41.1	54.6	74.1
Had relatives visit	53.3	54.3	63.8	61.9	49.7	64.1	63.8	39.7
Went out with friends	52.8	51.2	50.3	44.8	43.6	33.6	41.4	69.6
Went out with relatives	34.6	34.7	37.3	35.5	32.0	29.0	34.4	24.4
Spoke to a health professional	29.8	19.8	23.9	22.8	23.5	28.5	22.7	27.1
Went to another social outing	27.7	25.7	22.4	17.4	13.7	11.5	14.3	17.2
Went to a leisure centre	26.3	18.6	23.8	15.4	16.6	18.1	13.3	31.1
Community or religious activity	20.3	16.2	12.0	11.8	9.3	3.0	9.2	9.8
Participated in a voluntary group	14.9	12.6	9.7	7.9	6.6	5.5	9.3	20.7
Attended adult education or night school	8.4	8.3	4.9	5.9	3.9	3.6	3.6	9.8
Base: All	670	318	613	296	143	84	127	30

Table 4.21 shows the sources of advice and help cited by respondents. Most commonly cited by men were partners or spouses, male friends, male relatives and female relatives. Among women the most commonly cited were female relatives, partners or spouses, and female friends. There was a general tendency for women to cite more sources of help than men. Family doctors were cited as sources of help or advice by more than a quarter of respondents. Other professional groups were cited only rarely. Nurses tended not to be viewed as a source of advice or help by the large majority of respondents even though they are now becoming more involved in this kind of support in primary care settings.

Table 4.21: Sources of help or advice by age and sex

If you needed help and advice, which if any of the people on this card could you turn to easily. I mean people you *feel* close enough to discuss personal issues with? (Q55)

Male

| Sources of help or advice | Age | | | | | | |
	16–24	25–34	35–44	45–54	55–64	65–74	All
Partner or spouse	24.0	69.5	80.0	78.9	74.0	65.7	64.5
Male friend	59.3	51.7	40.4	36.1	31.6	20.0	42.3
Male relative	45.3	45.2	32.0	30.9	31.5	34.1	37.4
Female relative	48.5	40.3	26.1	28.9	25.9	32.9	34.6
Family doctor/GP	16.3	21.2	25.8	31.4	39.8	44.8	27.9
Female friend	39.0	25.1	16.3	19.3	15.4	8.2	22.0
Neighbour	5.4	6.3	6.3	10.3	11.8	19.1	8.9
Priest, clergy or religious leader	3.4	6.5	7.5	9.2	13.2	8.5	7.7
Counsellor/therapist	2.1	1.8	2.3	2.5	0.5	2.2	1.9
Someone else	2.0	1.9	1.7	1.3	2.0	1.5	1.7
Social worker	1.4	0.9	1.5	2.1	1.8	2.1	1.5
Nurse	1.2	0.6	0.8	1.3	3.2	2.3	1.4
Health visitor	0.7	1.3	1.1	0.4	1.1	0.7	0.9
Home help	1.5	0	0.4	0	0	1.1	0.5
Community leader	0.4	0.4	0.6	0.1	0.4	0	0.3
Community worker	0.9	0	0	0.2	0.3	0	0.2
Midwife	0	0.5	0	0.2	0	0	0.2
Meals on wheels	0	0	0	0	0	0	0
Base: All	474	538	457	405	339	269	2 482

Female

Sources of help or advice	Age						
	16–24	25–34	35–44	45–54	55–64	65–74	All
Female relative	67.7	69.2	57.1	53.4	60.1	62.0	62.0
Partner or spouse	42.2	71.0	70.8	67.1	57.2	46.0	60.0
Female friend	71.5	65.7	61.4	52.9	45.5	34.6	57.1
Family doctor/GP	16.3	27.0	31.8	34.4	34.2	26.0	28.0
Male relative	22.3	21.7	17.3	18.2	23.3	27.2	21.4
Male friend	29.8	15.4	13.7	11.8	8.7	6.4	15.0
Neighbour	4.6	10.7	11.6	14.1	18.9	20.8	12.8
Priest, clergy or religious leader	2.4	5.1	7.0	10.6	11.6	15.1	8.0
Health visitor	4.0	12.6	4.1	1.2	1.4	1.1	4.6
Counsellor/therapist	1.3	3.1	2.9	2.2	1.6	0.5	2.1
Community leader	1.9	2.0	1.4	1.5	1.4	3.0	1.8
Nurse	1.0	1.1	0.9	1.4	3.6	3.9	1.8
Midwife	1.6	2.8	0.6	0.2	0	0.5	1.1
Someone else	0.6	0.5	0.5	0.8	1.0	3.2	1.0
Home help	0.4	0.2	0.5	0.8	0.2	0.9	0.5
Community worker	0.1	0.4	0.5	0.2	0	0.6	0.3
Meals on wheels	0	0	0	0	0.5	0.3	0.1
Base: All	452	530	456	407	348	328	2 520

There was a trend for friends to be cited less commonly with increasing age. By contrast neighbours were cited more often by older respondents. In men, there was a decline in the number citing relatives as a source of advice or help with increasing age, but this trend was not observed in the women. Men tended to cite family doctors more commonly with increasing age. With female members of the sample the highest mention of family doctors was in the middle age groups. As would be expected, women in the sample tended to mention health visitors more often than men, the peak occurring in the 25–34 age range, the most common time for pregnancies to occur.

Table 4.22: Sources of help or advice by class and sex

Males

Sources of help or advice	Class							
	I&II	IIINM	IIIM	IV&V	Unemp	Sick	Home	Educ
Partner or spouse	70.8	64.6	68.3	65.9	58.1	53.8	28.8	33.1
Male friend	50.3	47.3	39.4	38.3	35.5	26.3	33.4	55.6
Male relative	36.9	36.2	38.7	37.8	36.6	30.5	31.1	50.7
Female relative	36.1	38.8	32.0	30.4	37.8	31.2	41.0	53.9
Female friend	29.2	23.1	17.7	17.8	15.9	15.6	15.5	56.6
Family doctor/GP	26.4	28.9	30.2	32.0	26.3	38.8	21.4	20.4
Priest, clergy or religious leader	10.4	8.7	4.8	8.6	8.1	4.4	7.4	11.1
Neighbour	8.3	8.8	10.3	13.4	3.0	8.9	3.3	0
Counsellor/therapist	2.2	2.2	1.6	1.2	1.9	2.5	4.1	8.4
Someone else	1.9	1.3	1.5	2.1	1.1	3.3	0	0
Social worker	1.5	0.6	1.6	1.8	2.1	2.0	6.8	0
Nurse	1.1	1.6	1.9	2.4	0.8	0.5	2.3	0
Health visitor	1.1	0	0.7	1.5	1.2	2.0	2.3	0
Community leader	0.4	0	0.5	0.1	0.5	1.5	0	0
Midwife	0.1	0	0.3	0.3	0	0	0	0
Community worker	0	0.2	0.3	0.9	0.4	0	0	0
Home help	0	0	0.5	0.8	0.5	0	2.3	0
Meals on wheels	0	0	0	0	0	0	0	0
Base: All	718	238	671	332	169	89	51	27

Table 4.22 shows sources of help and advice according to social class and employment category. There was a tendency for respondents in classes I–II to cite most of the sources more commonly than those in classes IV–V. It is noteworthy, however, that among men in employed households, there was only a small difference between social classes I–II and IV–V in the numbers citing partners or spouses, while among women the difference was much more marked. This suggests that women in social classes I–II feel that they get about as much support from their partners as do men; however, women in social classes IV–V feel that they receive less support from their male partners than their male partners feel they receive from the women.

Females

Sources of help or advice	Class							
	I&II	IIINM	IIIM	IV&V	Unemp	Sick	Home	Educ
Partner or spouse	71.7	59.5	65.3	48.5	54.3	52.9	21.1	44.3
Female friend	66.2	62.8	55.2	44.2	49.0	50.7	53.1	77.6
Female relative	63.1	58.7	64.1	60.7	53.0	59.3	60.3	76.1
Family doctor/GP	29.1	28.2	25.8	30.2	26.6	28.5	33.0	22.6
Male relative	24.1	24.4	17.5	19.0	15.7	26.6	21.3	27.6
Male friend	18.5	15.5	13.5	14.2	13.9	5.0	16.7	20.1
Neighbour	13.4	13.7	11.4	17.1	7.1	12.6	14.4	1.4
Priest, clergy or religious leader	10.5	8.8	7.6	7.2	5.7	7.3	3.3	4.3
Health visitor	5.6	2.4	4.0	2.8	6.6	3.4	12.3	4.4
Counsellor/therapist	2.8	2.8	1.0	0.6	3.8	1.6	1.9	1.8
Midwife	1.2	0.7	1.0	0.2	2.6	2.0	0.8	2.3
Social worker	1.1	0.9	1.2	3.4	4.3	1.8	5.5	0
Nurse	1.0	1.6	1.8	3.5	0.7	1.7	0	0
Someone else	0.8	1..2	0.4	1.4	0.5	0.7	1.6	0
Home help	0.3	0.4	0.4	0.2	0.5	1.0	1.6	0
Community worker	0.1	0.3	0.1	0.7	1.2	0.5	0	0
Community leader	0	0	0	0	0	0	0	0
Meals on wheels	0	0	0.3	0	0	0	0	0
Base: All	670	318	614	297	143	84	127	30

References

Brown, G. W. and Harris, T. O. (1989) *Life Events and Illness*. Unwin Hyman.

Cox, B. D., Huppert, F. A. and Whichelow, M. J. (1993) *The Health and Lifestyle Survey: Seven Years On*. Dartmouth Publishing, Aldershot.

Goldberg, E. L. and Comstock, G. W. (1980) 'Epidemiology of life events: frequency in general populations'. *American Journal of Epidemiology*, **111**, 736–52.

Goldberger, E. L. and Breznitz, S. (eds) (1993) *Handbook of Stress*. Free Press, New York.

Holmes, D. M. and Rahe, R. H. (1967) 'The Social Re-adjustment Rating Scale'. *Journal of Psychosomatic Research*, **11**, 213–18.

Miller, T. W. (1993) 'The assessment of stressful life events', in Goldberger, E. L. and Breznitz, S. (eds) *Handbook of Stress*. Free Press, New York, pp. 161–73.

Moos, R. H. and Schaeffer, J. A. (1993) 'Coping resources and processes: current concepts and measures', in Goldberger, E. L. and Breznitz, S. (eds) (1993) *Handbook of Stress*. Free Press, New York, pp. 234–57.

Office of Population Censuses and Surveys (1993) *Health Survey for England 1991*. HMSO.

Sarason, B. R. and Sarason, I. G. (1994) 'Assessment of social support', in Shumaker, S. A. and Czajkowski, C.M. (eds) *Social Support and Cardiovascular Disease*. Plenum, New York and London, pp. 41–64.

Shumaker, S. A. and Czajkowski, S. M. (eds) (1994) *Social Support and Cardiovascular Disease*. Plenum, New York and London.

5. Smoking behaviour

Robert West
Reader in Psychology
St Georges Hospital Medical School
London

Prevalence and cessation rates

Although cigarette smoking prevalence has been declining in the UK over the past two decades, it is still estimated to kill approximately 100 000 people each year, and remains the single largest preventable cause of early death. Smoking prevalence is tracked regularly in large national surveys, and there is evidence of a continuing slow but steady decline (OPCS, 1994).

The Health of the Nation white paper (Department of Health, 1992) set a target for reduction in cigarette smoking prevalence in England to no more than 20% by the year 2000 from a baseline of 30% among men and 28% in women in 1990. The timing of the present survey, carried out in 1992, was clearly too close to the baseline to be able to show any marked downward trend, particularly given that programmes aimed at reaching the target would not have had time to be implemented by the time this survey was carried out. Smoking prevalence in England was 32% for men and 29% for women − which was slightly higher than the Health of the Nation estimates but still within the margin of error.

The results from this survey were broadly similar to those of others carried out on large national samples in the UK. However, the overall prevalence of cigarette smoking was higher in the present survey (31%) than was found in the General Household Survey (GHS) carried out at the same time (28% − Thomas et al., 1993). Another Health and Lifestyle Survey carried out at the time found a cigarette smoking prevalence of 31% (Cox et al., 1993).

Prevalence in men was higher than in women (33% versus 30%). It must be noted, however, that the prevalence figures are for cigarette smoking only and that other surveys have shown that approximately 6 per cent of males smoke cigars or pipes (Jarvis & Jackson, 1988). Thus the difference between tobacco smoking prevalence in men and women is probably greater than present figures suggest. The cigarette smoking 'cessation rate' was slightly higher for men than women but this may reflect the fact that some men switch to pipes or cigars.

Table 5.1 also shows that, in this survey, smoking prevalence was similar across all ages up to the age of 55 after which it declined. The lower prevalence in those aged 55 and over appeared to be linked with a higher rate of quitting rather than fewer having ever smoked regularly. In fact, in men, the proportion of ex-regular smokers increased markedly with age, and the proportion of never smokers decreased with age. The 1992 General Household Survey (OPCS, 1994), with its larger sample size, was able to show a steady decline in smoking prevalence with

Table 5.1: Smoking status by age and sex

Current smoker (Q157): 'Do you smoke cigarettes nowadays?'*
Ex-regular and never regular smoker (Q158): 'Have you ever smoked regularly?'
Cessation rate: ex-regular smoker/(current smoker + ex-regular smoker)

Males

Smoking status	Age						All
	16–24	25–34	35–44	45–54	55–64	65–74	
Never regular	60.7	46.4	41.1	33.8	29.1	21.2	41.0
Current smoker	33.9	36.3	34.5	34.0	25.5	27.8	32.7
Ex-regular	5.4	17.3	24.4	32.2	45.4	51.0	26.3
Cessation rate	13.8	32.3	41.4	48.7	64.1	64.7	44.5
Base: All	471	540	455	403	339	266	2474

Females

Smoking status	Age						All
	16–24	25–34	35–44	45–54	55–64	65–74	
Never regular	57.1	56.5	47.8	48.0	56.1	53.1	53.2
Current smoker	35.6	31.2	34.7	30.8	21.1	20.9	29.8
Ex-regular	7.3	12.4	17.5	21.2	22.8	26.0	17.0
Cessation rate	17.0	28.4	33.5	40.8	51.9	55.5	36.3
Base: All	450	529	455	406	345	325	2510

* Pipe and cigar smoking were not addressed in the survey.

age after the age of 24 years, with the most marked fall occurring above the age of 60 years. As was found in the present survey, the GHS showed that the reduction in prevalence with age was due to higher cessation rates in older smokers, especially in the case of men.

In the present survey, cigarette smoking prevalence was similar for males and females up to the age of 45, after which smoking prevalence among women was lower than among men. Prevalence among females aged 16–24 was slightly higher than for males (36% versus 34%). However, the difference was within the margin of error[1] given the sample size. This slight excess of smoking among young women was not shown in the GHS.

[1] Margin of error refers to 95% confidence intervals. These are approximately ±10% for cell sizes of 100, ±6% for cell sizes of 200, ±5% for cell sizes of 300, ±4% for cell sizes of 500, ±3% for cell sizes of 1000 and ±2% for cell sizes of 2000.

Table 5.2: Smoking status by class and sex

Males

Smoking status	Class*							
	I&II	IIINM	IIIM	IV&V	Unemp	Sick	Home	Educ
Never regular	47.5	48.2	36.9	34.1	24.6	32.8	46.3	65.8
Current smoker	22.1	26.9	35.3	38.4	57.7	34.8	33.3	25.8
Ex-regular	30.3	24.9	27.7	27.5	17.7	32.4	20.4	8.4
Cessation rate	61.8	46.8	45.4	40.8	19.1	48.9	45.4	23.1
Base: All	715	237	669	331	167	89	51	27

Females

Smoking status	Class							
	I&II	IIINM	IIIM	IV&V	Unemp	Sick	Home	Educ
Never regular	59.3	58.9	53.8	49.4	36.7	40.9	35.0	54.8
Current smoker	21.2	19.9	30.8	36.3	50.7	42.6	48.9	31.9
Ex-regular	19.4	21.1	15.4	14.3	12.7	16.5	16.2	13.4
Cessation rate	47.8	51.5	33.3	28.2	20.0	27.9	24.8	29.5
Base: All	667	316	610	297	143	84	127	30

* Combined class and employment status based on head of household. Unemp: unemployed; Sick: sick or disabled; Home: looking after home or family; Educ: in full-time education.

In the younger age range similar proportions of men and women had never taken up regular smoking. In the older age groups more men had at one time smoked cigarettes regularly and more had given up or switched to pipes or cigars. This suggests a cohort effect, reflecting the fact that at one time more men took up smoking than women and now the proportions taking up smoking are similar. If the cigarette smoking cessation rates (disregarding switching to pipes or cigars) remain the same for men and women we can expect a lower overall prevalence of cigarette smoking in men than women within 10 years.

Table 5.2 shows that cigarette smoking prevalence was related to social class, with the highest prevalence in social classes IV–V and lowest prevalence in social classes I–II. Where the head of household was not currently employed the prevalence was higher than for social classes IV–V. Smokers were in a clear majority among males in unemployed households (58%). Among females in unemployed households 51% were smokers. These figures are higher than was found in the GHS (51% for men versus 38% for women) but the numbers in these cells were small in the present survey, giving a wide margin of error.

Table 5.3: Smoking status by housing tenure and sex

Smoking status	Males		Females	
	Owns/buying*	Rents	Owns/buying	Rents
Never regular	44.7	29.6	57.9	39.8
Current smoker	27.6	48.7	24.2	45.1
Ex-regular	27.8	21.8	17.9	15.2
Cessation rate	50.2	30.9	42.6	25.2
Base: All	1 865	554	1 822	641

* Owns: Owns home outright or buying with a mortgage; Rents: renting from council, housing association or private landlord.

Cessation rates were greater in social classes I–II than IV–V, but only accounted for a small proportion of the difference in smoking prevalence between the classes. Most of the difference between the classes was due to the proportion who had ever smoked regularly.

As Marsh and McKay (1994) have pointed out, the cost of smoking in disadvantaged groups is an important factor in exacerbating financial hardship, and yet these groups have reduced their smoking to a lesser extent than more prosperous sections of society. This division is illustrated in Table 5.3 which shows smoking prevalence by housing tenure. Among individuals in rented accommodation, more than 40% were smokers. The cessation rate was lower than that of owner-occupiers, but the basis for most of the difference lay in the proportions who had ever smoked regularly.

This survey found national and regional differences in smoking prevalence (Table 5.4). Scotland emerged with higher prevalence than England and Wales for both men and women. In Northern Ireland male smoking prevalence was greater than in England, whereas the female smoking rate was lower. However, the sample sizes outside England were small and the differences between countries were within the margin of error for prevalence estimates.

Within England, Northern and Northwest regions tended to have a higher smoking prevalence. This regional variation was similar to that found in other surveys (e.g. OPCS, 1994). It is worth noting, that these regional differences were largely attributable to different cessation rates. The proportions ever having smoked regularly were broadly similar.

There is concern about the extent to which children are exposed to cigarette smoke, because of the increased risk this carries of respiratory disease in childhood and possibly even lung cancer in later life. Table 5.5 shows that smoking prevalence in those with children at home was slightly higher than in those with no children at home. The cessation rate for those with no children living at home was slightly higher than for those with children. This difference is probably attributable to the lower smoking prevalence rate in older smokers whose children would have left home.

Table 5.4: Smoking status by region and sex

Males

Region	Never regular	Current smoker	Ex-regular	Cessation rate	Base
Northern Ireland	42.7	40.3	17.0	29.6	64
Scotland	43.0	38.3	18.7	32.8	217
Wales	46.3	32.2	21.5	40.0	122
England	40.4	32.0	27.6	46.3	2 072
Anglia and Oxford	38.7	27.5	33.8	55.2	235
North Thames	37.8	35.0	27.3	43.8	288
North West	41.6	34.2	24.2	41.4	276
Northern and Yorkshire	43.8	33.5	22.7	40.4	283
South and West	39.1	30.5	30.4	50.0	269
South Thames	41.8	28.8	29.4	50.5	286
Trent	41.9	34.3	23.8	41.0	207
West Midlands	38.5	31.6	29.9	48.6	228

Females

Region	Never regular	Current smoker	Ex-regular	Cessation rate	Base
Northern Ireland	72.4	27.6	–	–	64
Scotland	45.4	39.6	15.1	27.6	226
Wales	51.7	31.1	17.2	35.6	126
England	53.5	28.8	17.7	38.1	2 094
Anglia and Oxford	50.9	23.8	25.3	51.5	227
North Thames	59.6	23.1	17.3	42.8	297
North West	50.7	36.1	13.2	26.8	292
Northern and Yorkshire	47.6	34.5	17.9	34.1	279
South and West	56.2	28.2	15.7	35.8	275
South Thames	56.4	27.0	16.6	38.0	290
Trent	52.7	30.9	17.2	36.4	207
West Midlands	52.8	26.3	20.9	44.3	227

Table 5.5: Smoking status by children at home and sex

Males

	Males		Females	
Smoking status	**Children**	**None**	**Children**	**None**
Never regular	43.8	39.6	52.2	53.7
Current smoker	34.9	31.7	32.8	28.1
Ex-regular	21.3	28.7	15.0	18.2
Cessation rate	37.8	47.5	31.4	39.4
Base: All	809.7	1 664	933	1 577

Table 5.6: Average cigarette consumption by age and sex

How many cigarettes do you smoke in an average day? (Q170)

	Age						
Sex	**16–24**	**25–34**	**35–44**	**45–54**	**55–64**	**65–74**	**All**
Males	14.0	19.2	21.1	19.8	18.7	16.7	18.4
Females	13.6	16.6	18.7	17.4	15.8	12.8	16.1
All	13.8	18.0	20.0	18.6	17.4	14.8	17.3
Base: Smokers of ⩾ 1 per day	278	320	283	240	145	127	1 393

Average cigarette consumption

The average daily cigarette consumption of regular smokers[2] is shown in Table 5.6. The overall average of 17% is similar to that found in other national surveys such as the GHS. Also in line with other surveys, women smoked fewer cigarettes per day than men at all ages. In both men and women, consumption was highest among those aged 35–44 years and was lowest among those aged 16–24 and aged 65–74.

Table 5.7 shows that consumption was highest among social classes IV–V, those in unemployed households, sick and disabled respondents and those looking after the home. This was true both for men and women. Cigarette consumption was also higher among those in rented accommodation than those owning their homes (Table 5.8).

[2] Who smoked at least one cigarette per day.

Table 5.7: Average cigarette consumption by class and sex

Sex	Class							
	I&II	IIINM	IIIM	IV&V	Unemp	Sick	Home	Educ
Males	16.7	18.0	18.7	18.0	19.5	23.4	21.0	18.2
Females	15.0	14.9	15.1	17.0	16.3	17.8	17.9	13.9
All	15.9	16.4	17.1	17.6	18.0	20.4	18.6	15.7
Base: Smokers of ≥1 per day	252	108	383	215	159	63	74	16

Table 5.8: Average cigarette consumption by region and sex

Region	Males	Females	All	Base
Scotland	23.2	16.6	19.7	162
Northern Ireland	20.0	18.5	19.4	43
Wales	18.2	14.8	16.3	63
England	17.9	16.0	16.9	1 111
Anglia and Oxford	18.8	14.9	16.9	105
North Thames	16.5	15.8	16.2	158
North West	18.5	16.9	17.6	173
Northern and Yorkshire	18.7	17.9	18.3	171
South and West	18.4	15.3	16.9	140
South Thames	15.6	15.6	15.6	131
Trent	16.4	14.8	15.7	114
West Midlands	19.4	15.3	17.5	118

The pattern for average cigarette consumption of smokers across regions was broadly parallel to that for smoking prevalence (Table 5.9). Smokers in Scotland and Northern Ireland smoked at a higher rate than those in England and Wales. In England, smokers in the North and Northwest reported a higher consumption than those in other parts of the country.

The parallel between consumption and prevalence in terms of demographic trends is striking and suggests that many factors that operate at a societal level to influence prevalence, also influence consumption. On the other hand, the GHS has found little or no decline in the average daily consumption of smokers over time while there has been a steady decline in prevalence, suggesting a dissociation between factors influencing prevalence and factors influencing consumption rate among smokers.

Table 5.9: Average cigarette consumption by housing tenure and sex

	Housing tenure	
Sex	Owns/buying	Rents
Males	17.9	19.7
Females	15.1	17.5
All	16.6	18.5
Base: Smokers of ⩾1 per day	831	519

Health effects

The large majority of smokers believed that their smoking was adversely affecting their current health (Table 5.10). As would be expected, the proportion who believed that smoking was adversely affecting their health was greater for heavier smokers, with 19% of those smoking 20 or more cigarettes per day believing that their smoking was affecting their health a great deal. There was no difference between the male and female smokers in this regard.

A similar pattern was observed with responses to the question of whether smoking would damage future health (Table 5.11). Smokers who believed that smoking would damage their health at least a little were asked in what ways in might do so (Table 5.12). More than a third of these smokers believed that they would get chest infections; approximately 30% believed they would get lung cancer and 17% believed they would get heart disease. There was little evidence of consistent differences between heavier and lighter smokers concerning the kinds of diseases to which they believed they would succumb.

Of particular interest were the percentages of respondents believing that they personally would be at risk of contracting serious illnesses as a result of their smoking. About 20% thought they were likely to get heart disease, and about 30% thought they were likely to get lung cancer. At first sight these figures may seem low in comparison with other surveys showing that a large majority of smokers accept the link between smoking and serious illness (e.g. Cox *et al.*, 1993; Marsh, 1985). However, the question was phrased in terms of whether respondents thought it was *likely* that they *personally* would contract these diseases.

Table 5.13 shows that there was little difference between the proportions of smokers, ex-smokers and never smokers who reported themselves to be in poor health. This is surprising as one would expect smokers to report themselves in poorer health than non-smokers. There was a slight tendency for recent ex-smokers to report worse health than other groups. There are several possible reasons for short-term ex-smokers reporting poorer health than others. One is that they may be suffering from withdrawal discomfort associated with smoking cessation. Another is that poor health may have provoked the quit attempt.

Table 5.10: Extent of current health effects by amount smoked and sex

How much, if at all, do you think the amount you smoke affects your health now? (Q185)

Males

Health effects/now	20+ cigarettes/day	10–19 cigarettes/day	0–9 cigarettes/day
A great deal	19.7	9.2	3.5
A fair amount/A little	66.9	75.9	73.0
Not at all/Don't know	13.4	14.9	23.5
Base: Regular smokers	356	267	85

Females

Health effects/now	20+ cigarettes/day	10–19 cigarettes/day	0–9 cigarettes/day
A great deal	17.6	10.9	2.3
A fair amount/A little	66.2	71.3	72.0
Not at all/Don't know	16.2	17.8	25.8
Base: Regular smokers	282	281	107

Table 5.11: Extent of future health effects by amount smoked and sex

How much if at all do you think the amount you smoke will affect your health in the future? (Q187)

Males

Health effects/future	20+ cigarettes/day	10–19 cigarettes/day	0–9 cigarettes/day
A great deal	39.4	23.6	20.4
A fair amount/A little	46.3	56.9	58.6
Not at all/Don't know	14.3	19.4	21.0
Base: Regular smokers	356	267	85

Females

Health effects/future	20+ cigarettes/day	10–19 cigarettes/day	0–9 cigarettes/day
A great deal	37.3	28.0	14.6
A fair amount/A little	48.1	55.6	63.0
Not at all/Don't know	14.6	16.4	22.5
Base: Regular smokers	282	281	107

Table 5.12: Type of future health effects by amount smoked and sex

In what ways do you think it will affect your health in the future? What others? (Q188)

Males

Health effects/future	20+ cigarettes/day	10–19 cigarettes/day	0–9 cigarettes/day	All
Likely to get problems with breathing	30.5	32.4	40.2	32.4
Likely to get chest infections/bronchitis	34.9	25.5	35.1	31.3
Likely to get lung cancer	32.9	26.7	27.4	29.8
Likely to get breathlessness	22.7	26.4	13.7	23.0
Likely to become less fit	16.4	22.5	22.5	19.5
Likely to get heart disease	23.0	10.9	13.7	17.2
Likely to get lung problems (unspecified)	11.9	10.7	15.1	11.8
Likely to get cancer (unspecified)	8.8	9.6	10.9	9.3
Likely to get other cancer	6.8	4.1	1.9	5.2
Likely to get a serious illness (unspecified)	4.8	2.3	2.7	3.6
Other	2.9	1.6	4.7	2.6
Base: Regular smokers believing in future health effects of smoking	262	203	64	530

Females

Health effects/future	20+ cigarettes/day	10–19 cigarettes/day	0–9 cigarettes/day	All
Likely to get chest infections/bronchitis	44.7	32.8	34.7	38.2
Likely to get problems with breathing	35.3	35.5	24.4	33.9
Likely to get lung cancer	24.9	31.5	20.1	27.1
Likely to get breathlessness	23.7	17.6	22.7	20.9
Likely to get heart disease	15.4	18.1	15.7	16.6
Likely to become less fit	13.4	14.3	19.7	14.7
Likely to get cancer (unspecified)	9.7	7.6	17.6	9.9
Likely to get lung problems (unspecified)	5.3	9.0	11.2	7.7
Likely to get other cancer	4.3	7.4	6.3	5.9
Likely to get a serious illness (unspecified)	3.3	5.8	4.9	4.6
Other	1.6	4.7	2.5	3.0
Base: Regular smokers believing in future health effects of smoking	216	214	69	499

Table 5.13: Current self-rated health by smoking status and sex

How do you feel about your health? Would you say that for your age your health is ... (Q25)

Males

	20+	Cigs per day 10–19	0–0	Ex-smoker <year	Ex-smoker >year	Never regular smoker
Very good	38.1	32.7	34.6	26.0	47.3	35.8
Fairly good	50.1	59.6	55.3	54.9	42.8	54.6
Fairly poor	9.0	5.8	10.1	15.8	7.3	7.3
Very poor	2.8	1.8	0	3.3	2.6	2.3
Base: All	354	264	85	76	570	804

Females

	20+	Cigs per day 10–19	0–0	Ex-smoker <year	Ex-smoker >year	Never regular smoker
Very good	36.8	38.8	43.4	26.4	46.1	39.9
Fairly good	52.4	52.0	45.9	58.3	43.9	50.1
Fairly poor	7.5	7.5	7.6	8.9	7.7	7.3
Very poor	3.3	1.1	3.1	6.5	2.3	2.8
Base: All	278	279	107	45	381	742

Table 5.14 shows that there was little evidence of a relationship between current self-rated health and expressions of desire to give up smoking. Thus, contrary to what one might expect, smokers who considered themselves in poorer health did not appear to be more motivated to quit smoking. On the other hand, Table 5.15 shows that there was a clear relationship between attempts to give up, desire to give up and current intentions to give up and a belief that smoking was damaging current health. Therefore smokers who were motivated to stop smoking or had tried in the past believed that smoking had damaged their current health. There was a similar relationship between beliefs that smoking would damage their health in the future and desire to quit (Table 5.16). Thus desire to give up was related to a belief that smoking was damaging health even though it was not related to actual ratings of health. If one puts this together with the fact that recent ex-smokers tended to rate their health as worse than current smokers, this may be an issue that needs to be addressed in educational materials. Smokers should perhaps be prepared for the fact that in most cases their perception of their health will not improve after cessation in the short term and it might even get worse. However, the longer-term health benefits will be marked.

Table 5.14: Desire to quit by current health by sex

Do you want to continue being a smoker or do you want to give up smoking? (Q174)
Do you have any firm plans to give up smoking in the future or not? (Q175)
About how many times have you tried to give up smoking? (Q177)

Males

Desire, intention, attempts to give up	Current health			
	Very good	Fairly good	Fairly poor	Very poor
Wish to give up	63.2	66.9	64.2	37.2
Intention to give up	28.8	25.7	27.7	21.3
Tried to give up once	23.8	19.7	19.9	17.1
Tried to give up more than once	60.8	57.2	69.4	65.0
Base: Regular smokers	257	385	56	16

Females

Desire, intention, attempts to give up	Current health			
	Very good	Fairly good	Fairly poor	Very poor
Wish to give up	59.9	69.8	66.1	59.3
Intention to give up	31.1	32.9	41.1	18.0
Tried to give up once	23.3	22.4	24.7	16.7
Tried to give up more than once	57.8	59.7	54.8	62.5
Base: Regular smokers	257	341	50	17

Table 5.15: Desire to quit by how much smoking affects health now

Males

Desire, intention, attempts to give up	How much smoking affects health now		
	Not at all/ don't know	A fair amount/ just a little	A great deal
Wish to give up	42.2	67.0	76.9
Intention to give up	18.0	27.5	32.2
Tried to give up once	18.9	22.8	17.4
Tried to give up more than once	56.0	58.7	64.7
Base: Regular smokers	116	506	99

Females

Desire, intention, attempts to give up	How much smoking effects health now		
	Not at all/ don't know	A fair amount/ just a little	A great deal
Wish to give up	36.6	68.6	89.3
Intention to give up	17.6	33.4	48.4
Tried to give up once	19.2	23.7	21.3
Tried to give up more than once	49.8	60.2	66.0
Base: Regular smokers	123	465	83

Table 5.16: Desire to quit by how much smoking will affect health in the future

Males

Desire, intention, attempts to give up	How much smoking will affect health		
	Not at all/ don't know	A fair amount/ just a little	A great deal
Wish to give up	42.1	66.9	76.9
Intention to give up	18.0	27.5	32.2
Tried to give up once	18.9	22.8	17.3
Tried to give up more than once	56.0	58.7	64.7
Base: Regular smokers	114	504	99

Females

Desire, intention, attempts to give up	How much smoking will affect health		
	Not at all/ don't know	A fair amount/ just a little	A great deal
Wish to give up	33.3	65.0	83.9
Intention to give up	14.0	31.7	44.4
Tried to give up once	25.1	22.6	21.1
Tried to give up more than once	44.9	58.2	68.4
Base: Regular smokers	112	359	200

Table 5.17: Unprompted beliefs about health risk of smoking by smoking status and sex

Which diseases or conditions are smokers more likely to suffer from? *Unprompted* (Q196)

Males

Disease type	Current smoker	Ex-smoker	Never smoker
Asthma	11.1	14.2	12.9
Cancer (unspecified)	22.3	17.3	17.2
Cancer of the mouth/throat	13.5	13.3	15.4
Chest/lung diseases/infections (unspecified)	12.8	10.4	10.9
Chronic bronchitis/wheezing emphysema	51.5	58.9	49.4
Dandruff	0	0	0
Diabetes	0.3	0	0.2
Gangrene	0.9	1.0	0.3
Hardening of the arteries	7.6	8.6	6.1
Heart attack/disease	33.4	39.6	34.5
Jaundice	0.1	0	0.2
Lung cancer	63.1	72.0	80.0
Other cancer	2.2	3.8	1.6
Other chest/lung	2.7	4.5	3.9
Other heart circulation conditions	4.4	5.7	6.4
Senile dementia	0.1	0.3	0.2
Strokes	2.6	3.5	2.7
TB (tuberculosis)	0.7	0.3	1.1
Wrinkles/skin ages more quickly	0.9	0.4	0.6
Other	9.7	11.1	11.6
None	1.0	0.3	0.1
Base	771	643	993

Knowledge of smoking effects

Table 5.17 shows the proportions of respondents who mentioned specific diseases as being caused by smoking. A large majority mentioned the link between smoking and lung cancer. A smaller proportion of current smokers mentioned this link than did ex-smokers or never smokers. A majority of respondents also mentioned chronic bronchitis, and approximately one-third mentioned heart disease. There was no relationship between the proportions mentioning these latter two diseases and smoking status.

These results are very similar to those of Cox *et al.* (1993) who phrased the question in a slightly different way. They asked respondents to name risk factors for a set of specific diseases. Nevertheless, the results were very similar: approximately 85% of respondents mentioned the link between smoking and lung

Females

Disease type	Current smoker	Ex-smoker	Never smoker
Asthma	12.3	15.1	17.6
Cancer (unspecified)	21.3	20.1	17.1
Cancer of the mouth/throat	13.1	11.8	14.9
Chest/lung diseases/infections (unspecified)	14.2	15.2	14.2
Chronic bronchitis/wheezing emphysema	61.7	59.5	55.2
Dandruff	0	0	0
Diabetes	0	0.1	0.4
Gangrene	0.6	0.7	0.8
Hardening of the arteries	7.1	5.2	5.3
Heart attack/disease	34.7	34.8	30.5
Jaundice	0	0.5	0.3
Lung cancer	63.0	73.7	75.9
Other cancer	2.1	3.9	3.7
Other chest/lung	3.5	2.9	4.4
Other heart circulation conditions	4.4	7.2	3.9
Senile dementia	0.2	0	0
Strokes	3.1	4.4	2.8
TB (tuberculosis)	0.6	1.4	1.5
Wrinkles/skin ages more quickly	1.9	3.1	1.6
Other	7.7	11.8	8.5
None	0.3	0.3	0.1
Base	724	423	1 318

cancer and approximately 30% mentioned the link between smoking and heart disease. Marsh (1985) also showed a greater awareness of the link between smoking and lung cancer than between smoking and heart disease, but the difference was not so great as in the present survey. For example, Marsh found that 87% of non-smokers and 67% of smokers believed that smokers were more likely to get lung cancer, and that 67% of smokers versus 54% of non-smokers believed that smokers were more likely to suffer from heart disease.

Desire to give up in current smokers
The proportions of smokers expressing a wish to give up, an intention to give up or having tried to give up in the past, were similar for men and women (Table 5.18).

Table 5.18: Desire, firm intention and attempts to give up by age and sex

Do you want to continue being a smoker or do you want to give up smoking? (Q174)
Do you have any firm plans to give up smoking in the future or not? (Q175)
About how many times have you tried to give up smoking? (Q177)

Males

Desire, intention, attempts to give up	Age						All
	16–24	25–34	35–44	45–54	55–64	65–74	
Wish to give up	77.1	66.8	72.9	63.0	49.8	33.0	64.3
Intention to give up	32.0	27.8	32.7	23.2	21.2	12.7	26.6
Tried to give up once	20.1	23.8	16.4	24.0	28.6	14.8	21.4
Tried to give up more than once	55.4	61.5	68.0	58.3	49.7	54.6	59.1
Base: Regular smokers	135	176	139	122	81.0	64.3	721

Females

Desire, intention, attempts to give up	Age						All
	16–24	25–34	35–44	45–54	55–64	65–74	
Wish to give up	71.6	71.7	68.0	62.7	65.6	34.6	65.3
Intention to give up	38.4	34.6	32.1	27.8	35.6	19.7	32.4
Tried to give up once	28.4	15.8	22.0	21.9	28.7	20.8	22.6
Tried to give up more than once	48.7	70.7	61.9	60.8	53.7	50.8	59.0
Base: Regular smokers	143	145	142	116	64	62	671

An important part of the evidence that smoking is addictive is that a large proportion of smokers express a wish to give up smoking but clearly have not succeeded in putting that wish into effect. Table 5.18 shows that in this sample 64% of male smokers and 65% of female smokers said that they wanted to give up. Just over a quarter (27%) of male smokers and almost a third (32%) of female smokers said that they had firm intentions to give up.

There was evidence of a decline in the proportions wanting to give up with increasing age. This may be because, as smokers get older, increasing proportions of those who want to give up actually succeed, leaving a higher proportion of those who are consistent in not wanting to give up smoking. Another possibility is that as smokers get older, their desire to give up decreases. The present data does not make it clear which of these applies.

Table 5.19: Desire, firm intention and attempts to give up by class and sex

Males

Desire, intention, attempts to give up	Class							
	I&II	IIINM	IIIM	IV&V	Unemp	Sick	Home	Educ
Wish to give up	68.3	81.4	65.4	57.8	65.9	53.0	63.7	64.9
Intention to give up	30.6	37.5	20.8	28.5	30.5	16.8	27.1	49.6
Tried to give up once	19.3	23.0	23.5	23.7	18.3	21.6	14.0	0.0
Tried to give up more than once	62.7	53.2	55.2	63.1	60.8	50.0	56.8	64.9
Base: Regular smokers	135	52	215	113	89	29	15	7

Females

Desire, intention, attempts to give up	Class							
	I&II	IIINM	IIIM	IV&V	Unemp	Sick	Home	Educ
Wish to give up	67.0	54.4	70.9	58.5	68.2	59.8	67.7	100.0
Intention to give up	33.6	22.7	34.3	24.4	36.5	41.9	31.3	65.9
Tried to give up once	19.2	19.9	21.7	24.8	25.1	27.1	21.3	41.8
Tried to give up more than once	60.4	66.4	58.1	54.7	59.4	61.6	56.3	58.2
Base: Regular smokers	117	56	166	100	68	33	59	10

Further evidence that many smokers find it difficult to quit is that more than 80% of smokers reported having made one or more attempts to give up. In fact 59% of both male and female smokers reported having made two or more attempts. There was little evidence that older smokers were more likely to have made an attempt to stop smoking than younger smokers.

Table 5.19 shows that there was little difference between social class groupings in expressions of desire to give up smoking or past attempts to give up. This reinforces the view that the most important factor underlying the difference in smoking rates between social classes is the proportions taking up smoking rather than the proportions who are able or willing to give up once they have started. Table 5.20 shows desire and attempts to give up broken down by housing tenure, and the picture is consistent with that shown by the social class breakdown in that there was no clear difference between expressions of desire to give up smoking among those in rented accommodation and owner-occupiers.

Table 5.20: Desire, firm intention and attempts to give up by housing tenure and sex

Desire, intention, attempts to give up	Males		Females	
	Owns/buying	Rents	Owns/buying	Rents
Wish to give up	66.4	59.4	67.5	63.2
Intention to give up	25.5	27.1	33.8	30.9
Tried to give up once	20.4	21.9	21.1	25.2
Tried to give up more than once	58.6	59.7	60.4	56.4
Base: Regular smokers	444	247	385	269

The issue of what factors frustrate attempts to stop smoking is addressed in Table 5.21. By far the most commonly reported factors were stress and lack of willpower. In men lack of willpower was cited slightly more often while among women stress was cited more often. Peer pressure was cited as important by approximately 15% of men and 10% of women, as was the withdrawal syndrome. Missing the enjoyment of smoking and 'fancying a cigarette' were cited as reasons for relapse by only a few smokers, as was the loss of the social aspect of smoking. Weight gain was cited relatively rarely but more often by women (8%) than men (2%).

The only factor precipitating relapse that varied across the age groups was encouragement by friends, which was cited less often by older smokers.

Table 5.22 shows that were was little difference overall between the social class groupings in terms of factors precipitating relapse. For example, there was no evidence of stress playing a more important role in less advantaged groups. However, among males there was an interesting reversal of the relative importance of stress and willpower between social classes I–II and IV–V. In social classes I–II stress was cited more often than lack of willpower (38.7% versus 22.2%) whereas in social classes IV–V lack of willpower was cited more often than stress (43.9% versus 23.4%). There was no relationship between housing tenure and factors precipitating relapse (Table 5.23).

Considering the main advantages given by smokers for giving up (Table 5.24), the most striking finding is that the majority of smokers cited improvement to their *current* health (58%) and saving money (59%). Improved fitness was cited by 22% of men and 16% of women. Thus, smokers hoped to obtain an immediate improvement in health and fitness from giving up smoking. Improvement in future health, which is where epidemiological research shows the real advantages of smoking cessation lie for most smokers, was only rarely cited. This is very important because in reality most smokers would not notice an improvement in their current health. Thus any attempt to give up smoking would not produce the expected and hoped-for effects. Smokers could therefore be discouraged from

Table 5.21: Factors precipitating relapse by age and sex

What factors made you take up smoking again? (Q179)

Males

Precipitators of relapse	Age						
	16–24	25–34	35–44	45–54	55–64	65–74	All
Lack of willpower	41.1	35.4	37.9	30.8	46.0	39.3	37.6
Stress	30.9	23.5	35.3	31.2	31.0	33.1	30.2
Encouragement by friends/ colleagues	25.1	19.5	13.2	6.9	9.8	7.9	15.1
Withdrawal symptoms	8.2	8.8	8.4	11.0	4.1	9.8	8.5
Loss of enjoyment	1.9	7.7	10.6	8.1	10.1	12.5	8.0
Loss of social prop	7.2	8.0	6.5	7.4	4.4	10.9	7.3
Weight gain	0	1.9	1.0	4.5	1.5	0	1.7
Encouragement by family members	1.7	2.3	0.5	2.0	1.5	0	1.5
Just fancied one	0	2.5	0	0	2.3	0	0.2
Other	1.8	2.8	8.3	8.2	4.1	10.0	5.4
Nothing in particular	1.9	3.8	5.4	8.7	11.2	3.7	5.5
Base: Regular smokers who tried to give up	96	147	114	97	63	41	558

Females

Precipitators of relapse	Age						
	16–24	25–34	35–44	45–54	55–64	65–74	All
Stress	38.8	43.0	49.2	42.7	38.7	38.0	42.6
Lack of willpower	30.1	29.7	30.6	23.9	18.0	31.8	28.0
Withdrawal symptoms	11.3	10.8	11.2	14.6	9.1	5.3	11.1
Encouragement by friends/ colleagues	20.1	7.9	5.7	5.9	11.2	5.9	9.7
Weight gain	7.3	7.9	6.4	12.5	6.1	8.1	8.1
Loss of social prop	10.7	5.7	5.6	4.7	8.4	6.5	6.8
Loss of enjoyment	5.2	4.6	3.9	7.9	11.7	15.1	6.6
Encouragement by family members	1.4	2.9	5.2	1.7	3.7	0	2.7
Just fancied one	0	0.5	0	0	0	0	0.1
Other	2.5	1.4	3.2	5.4	1.3	6.6	3.1
Nothing in particular	3.5	4.3	3.3	7.6	10.8	4.1	5.1
Base: Regular smokers who tried to give up	109	123	116	95	51	41	535

Table 5.22: Factors precipitating relapse by class and sex

Males

Precipitators of relapse				Class				
	I&II	IIINM	IIIM	IV&V	Unemp	Sick	Home	Educ
Stress	38.7	38.9	32.6	20.4	28.9	33.8	12.7	42.2
Encouragement by friends/colleagues	23.3	3.4	12.4	17.8	16.4	2.5	9.6	23.7
Lack of willpower	22.2	39.5	43.9	43.9	39.1	35.9	60.1	65.9
Loss of enjoyment	7.8	2.5	9.7	6.8	2.7	15.6	0	0
Withdrawal symptoms	7.2	0	9.8	9.8	8.4	14.0	13.5	0
Loss of social prop	5.8	5.6	6.3	10.4	10.4	7.9	13.5	0
Weight gain	2.0	0	3.0	0.9	0.7	4.3	0	0
Encouragement by family members	1.3	0	1.0	1.3	1.4	3.8	5.9	0
Just fancied one	0	0	1.1	0	2.2	0	0	0
Other	6.5	2.0	4.5	4.2	2.4	4.3	7.9	34.1
Nothing in particular	1.6	14.1	5.6	2.9	12.0	2.3	0	0
Base: Regular smokers who tried to give up	107	37	163	96	69	21	9	4

Females

Precipitators of relapse				Class				
	I&II	IIINM	IIIM	IV&V	Unemp	Sick	Home	Educ
Stress	47.1	29.0	42.3	48.4	43.9	53.8	40.3	73.9
Lack of willpower	20.6	34.9	29.8	22.3	34.2	21.9	23.5	38.6
Withdrawal symptoms	10.5	10.6	10.7	7.5	11.3	17.8	15.2	0
Loss of social prop	8.5	3.9	3.3	10.0	3.5	0	6.7	44.6
Loss of enjoyment	8.1	9.6	3.4	9.8	6.4	7.0	8.5	0
Encouragement by friends/colleagues	7.1	11.7	14.1	9.2	5.9	5.9	6.33	1.8
Weight gain	4.0	5.8	7.5	12.2	5.5	24.1	8.9	22.5
Encouragement by family members	3.9	4.7	3.2	3.5	1.2	0	1.9	0
Just fancied one	0	1.3	0	0	0	0	0	0
Other	3.3	3.5	1.1	4.6	5.6	4.6	0.8	0
Nothing in particular	6.7	5.4	3.5	4.9	8.1	2.8	6.8	0
Base: Regular smokers who tried to give up	90	48	129	78	57	29	43	10

Table 5.23: Factors precipitating relapse by housing tenure and sex

Precipitators of relapse	Males		Females	
	Owns/buying	Rents	Owns/buying	Rents
Lack of willpower	37.3	38.7	29.4	26.3
Stress	33.5	26.7	41.1	46.8
Encouragement by friends/ colleagues	12.6	17.3	10.0	8.1
Withdrawal symptoms	8.8	8.4	9.8	12.0
Loss of enjoyment	8.1	6.9	7.2	5.8
Loss of social prop	6.6	9.4	6.5	7.4
Weight gain	2.0	1.3	8.1	7.2
Encouragement by family members	1.9	0.9	2.6	2.6
Just fancied one	0.4	1.9	0.2	0
Other	6.4	3.6	2.7	4.0
Nothing in particular	5.5	6.1	6.1	3.8
Base: Regular smokers who tried to give up	341	192	307	213

Table 5.24: Advantages to giving up by age and sex

What do you think would be the main advantages of giving up smoking, for you personally? *Unprompted* (Q184)

Males

Advantages to giving up	Age						
	16–24	25–34	35–44	45–54	55–64	65–74	All
Saves money	66.6	62.7	59.7	57.7	46.5	53.0	59.3
Current health would improve	53.2	65.5	65.6	61.7	53.4	35.1	58.5
Improve fitness	29.3	34.8	17.1	16.4	9.4	13.5	22.4
Less worry about health in future	17.3	13.1	15.0	7.7	10.1	3.4	12.2
Smell on self/hair/clothes/breath	9.8	8.9	4.8	5.3	5.4	1.3	6.6
Other people's health (e.g. family, children)	6.7	8.4	9.6	1.7	0	0	5.5
More socially acceptable	7.6	3.5	6.6	4.6	1.3	1.7	4.7
Free of pressure from other people (nagging)	5.1	2.4	5.2	2.3	2.1	1.9	3.4
Increased attractiveness to other people	1.4	0	1.5	0	0	0	0.6
Other	1.2	0.4	1.0	0.4	0.8	1.0	0.8
None	3.9	2.5	5.4	3.5	7.8	22.1	5.8
Base: Regular smokers	131	174	140	118	80	62	705

Females

Advantages to giving up	Age						
	16–24	25–34	35–44	45–54	55–64	65–74	All
Saves money	61.4	62.6	59.9	56.6	60.5	54.4	59.8
Current health would improve	61.1	57.4	65.2	55.8	58.2	37.1	57.8
Improve fitness	19.2	17.8	20.9	17.2	5.6	5.2	16.3
Smell on self/hair/clothes/breath	12.8	16.9	14.8	10.9	6.2	5.8	12.5
Less worry about health in future	8.9	9.6	9.3	8.1	8.8	3.3	8.5
Other people's health (e.g. family, children)	9.5	15.2	8.9	5.0	0.7	3.5	8.4
More socially acceptable	5.8	5.5	5.9	6.8	0	1.5	5.0
Free of pressure from other people (nagging)	0.3	1.9	1.2	4.6	0.7	0	1.6
Increased attractiveness to other people	1.3	1.0	3.3	1.5	0	0	1.4
Other	2.3	2.8	1.1	1.7	0.8	1.4	1.8
None	4.1	4.9	1.7	9.1	10.4	11.7	6.0
Base: Regular smokers	142	144	136	115	64	59	659

persisting with an attempt to stop smoking because they have not experienced immediate health benefits.

Social acceptability and relief from social pressure were also rarely cited as advantages of giving up. This suggests that, at the time of the survey, moves to make cigarette smoking socially unacceptable had not had much impact on the conscious beliefs of smokers.

There were no clear gender differences in the advantages of giving up that were cited by smokers. The older respondents were less likely to cite current health, improved fitness, other people's health, social acceptability, and worry about future health as advantages in cessation. In fact they were more likely to indicate that there were no advantages in cessation. This could be because any older smokers who saw clear advantages to cessation would have already given up.

Turning to differences in advantages of giving up across social classes (Table 5.25), respondents in social classes IV–V were less likely to cite improved fitness, social acceptability and worry about future health than classes I–II. There was no consistent evidence that saving money was more important for less advantaged social groups. This lack of difference between more and less advantaged social groups is reinforced by the results shown in Table 5.26 comparing respondents in rented accommodation with owner-occupiers.

Smokers who had never tried to give up were asked what they considered to be the main disadvantages of doing so (Table 5.27). For the women weight gain was the most commonly cited problem while for men it was withdrawal symptoms. Loss of enjoyment was cited by approximately 20% of respondents. Social factors seemed not to be important.

Table 5.28 shows that when asked what they would like to do to keep themselves healthy, 16% of smokers mentioned giving up smoking. There was no difference between the men and women in this regard. The proportion citing giving up smoking in this context was higher in the 25–54 age range than among those aged less than 25 or more than 55.

Table 5.29 shows that social classes I–II were more likely to mention desire to give up smoking to improve their health than social classes IV–V, but unemployed smokers were closer in this respect to classes I–II than IV–V.

Smoking cessation

Knowing the reasons given by ex-smokers for having stopped may be helpful in planning future health promotion campaigns. Table 5.30 gives a breakdown of these reasons by age group of ex-smokers and gender. The most commonly cited reasons were those that related to health. This included general concern about health, diagnosis of health problems, becoming more aware of the health risks of smoking, advice from a doctor and concern over the effects of passive smoking on the family. Within the health reasons, general concern over health was by far the most important single factor. The second major reason given for giving up smoking was cost, with more than 1 in 5 ex-smokers citing this as a contributory factor.

Table 5.25: Advantages to giving up by class

Males

Advantages to giving up	Class							
	I&II	IIINM	IIIM	IV&V	Unemp	Sick	Home	Educ
Current health would improve	63.0	48.9	61.4	63.4	52.8	73.7	34.9	55.8
Saves money	48.4	72.3	65.4	72.2	49.3	46.0	47.9	91.7
Improve fitness	29.0	26.4	19.4	17.1	26.6	2.2	3.5	69.5
Less worry about health in future	13.0	7.3	13.5	7.1	15.6	6.7	9.7	15.4
More socially acceptable	10.2	8.4	4.9	1.7	1.5	0	0	0
Smell on self/hair/ clothes/breath	8.6	4.9	5.5	9.3	5.6	0	0	15.4
Free of pressure from other people	5.8	3.9	1.3	3.7	4.1	2.8	0	0
Other people's health (e.g. family, children)	4.3	5.1	5.4	9.3	2.0	5.8	2.5	0
Increased attractiveness to other people	0	0	0.5	0	0	0	0	27.4
Other	0	0.8	1.7	0	1.6	0	0	0
None	4.7	4.9	5.9	3.8	1.9	7.0	23.3	8.3
Base: Regular smokers	133	52	214	109	88	28	15	7

Females

Advantages to giving up	Class							
	I&II	IIINM	IIIM	IV&V	Unemp	Sick	Home	Educ
Saves money	63.2	61.1	55.2	63.2	56.2	40.4	60.2	85.1
Current health would improve	58.3	59.5	58.8	51.9	60.2	62.1	59.9	71.5
Improve fitness	26.8	7.4	14.8	14.1	13.6	14.8	16.6	18.0
Smell on self/hair/ clothes/breath	18.7	14.2	10.8	11.7	10.8	8.4	14.9	4.9
Less worry about health in future	16.9	4.5	6.6	1.4	9.1	7.7	6.9	22.2
More socially acceptable	11.7	4.2	5.2	1.6	0	3.7	6.2	0
Other people's health (e.g. family, children)	10.4	3.4	10.1	5.1	10.6	2.5	13.4	12.4

Females (cont.)

Advantages to giving up	Class							
	I&II	IIINM	IIIM	IV&V	Unemp	Sick	Home	Educ
Free of pressure from other people	3.5	1.5	0.4	2.3	2.2	0	0	0
Increased attractiveness to other people	2.5	0	2.3	0	2.6	0	2.0	0
Other	2.4	0.8	1.5	1.5	2.9	6.2	0.9	0
None	1.9	5.6	4.3	8.8	13.4	5.3	9.0	0
Base: Regular smokers	115	54	163	100	67	32	58	10

Table 5.26: Advantages to giving up by housing tenure and sex

Advantages to giving up	Males		Females	
	Owns/buying	Rents	Owns/buying	Rents
Saves money	62.5	54.8	59.0	61.2
Current health would improve	60.7	56.1	56.9	59.3
Improve fitness	21.7	24.1	17.3	13.7
Less worry about health in future	12.4	11.4	10.0	6.5
Smell on self/hair/clothes/ breath	7.8	4.9	14.8	8.5
More socially acceptable	6.8	1.1	6.3	3.1
Other people's health (e.g. family, children)	5.5	5.1	8.6	8.7
Free of pressure from other people	3.7	2.6	2.0	1.2
Increased attractiveness to other people	0.9	0	1.7	1.1
Other	0.9	0.5	2.1	1.5
None	5.5	6.7	5.0	7.8
Base: Regular smokers	442	242	378	264

Table 5.27: Disadvantages of giving up by sex among those who had not tried

What do you think would be the main disadvantages of giving up smoking, for you personally? *Unprompted* (Q183)

Disadvantages of giving up	Males	Females	All
Weight gain	18.0	41.9	29.2
Withdrawal symptoms	27.4	17.0	22.5
Loss of enjoyment	20.8	19.6	20.2
Stress	11.2	15.5	13.2
Loss of social prop	4.0	11.8	7.6
Friends smoke/would feel left out	3.5	1.4	2.5
Other	4.7	4.0	4.4
None	28.7	15.3	22.4
Base: Regular smokers with no quit attempts	128	113	241

Table 5.28: Would like to give up smoking by age and sex

Are there any things you would like to do to keep yourself healthy but don't do at the moment? *Unprompted* (Q29)

	Age						All
	16–24	25–34	35–44	45–54	55–64	65–74	
Males	10.9	19.4	29.4	12.2	6.1	13.5	16.5
Females	11.6	20.7	18.3	20.0	14.0	4.4	16.0
Base: Regular smokers							
Males	132	174	136	118	79	64	704
Females	135	140	136	114	61	61	647

Table 5.29: Like to give up smoking by class and sex

	Class							
	I&II	IIINM	IIIM	IV&V	Unemp	Sick	Home	Educ
Males	20.4	19.7	16.4	12.8	17.5	20.3	6.0	37.5
Females	20.7	10.1	15.3	11.5	21.0	9.3	14.2	31.8
Base: Regular smokers								
Males	133	52	209	109	89	29	15	7
Females	109	56	159	100	65	31	56	10

There was no clear evidence of important differences in reasons cited by different age groups. Neither was there clear evidence of differences between the reasons given by men and women in the sample.

Table 5.31 shows reasons for stopping smoking by social class and sex. There was little evidence that the reasons were markedly different for different social class groupings. One might expect that groups with a smaller disposable income would cite cost as a factor more frequently. Although there was some evidence that this was the case, the differences between social classes were within the margins of error for the sample sizes concerned.

Table 5.32 shows that there was little difference between the reasons given for cessation by those in rented accommodation and owner-occupiers. Thus cost was, perhaps surprisingly, not considered more important by those in rented accommodation than owner-occupiers, despite that fact that the financial burden of smoking must have been higher for the former group.

Table 5.33 shows precipitators of smoking cessation by age and sex. A large proportion of smokers could not think of any particular factor that triggered the attempt to quit. Those who could, cited a health event (e.g. coughs, smoking-related illness, death or illness of friend or relative) most often. An increase in the cost of smoking was cited by 5% of ex-smokers. Advertising campaigns, TV programmes and No Smoking Day appeared to play at most a modest role as triggers to cessation. However, it should be noted that their importance may have gone unrecognised by many of those smokers who cited no particular trigger, and they may also have contributed to a climate of opinion that made smokers more receptive to the idea of giving up without actually triggering a quit attempt.

Table 5.30: Reasons for smoking cessation by age by sex

Why did you give up smoking? (Q163)

Males

Reasons for cessation	Age						
	16–24	25–34	35–44	45–54	55–64	65–74	All
General concern about health/ fitness	36.6	56.8	49.4	31.6	34.4	34.2	39.6
Cost/save money	22.6	33.4	26.1	33.0	21.9	19.5	26.0
Became more aware about health risks	4.3	18.1	19.9	17.5	15.9	18.7	17.3
Diagnosis of health problems	24.8	7.6	5.5	10.7	19.3	18.1	13.6
Pressure from family	6.9	6.1	16.5	4.5	5.2	7.2	7.6
Advice from doctor	0	2.4	1.3	5.8	8.6	11.9	6.3
Worried about effects on family	3.1	9.5	5.9	3.5	2.4	2.0	4.2
Aesthetic/cosmetic reasons	0	9.7	2.5	1.1	3.0	1.8	3.1
Pressure from friends/work colleagues	7.1	6.8	3.4	1.0	0.3	0.9	2.3
Pregnancy	0	2.3	4.8	0	0	0.7	1.3
Set example for family	4.6	2.2	0.9	2.0	0	0	1.0
Because people can't smoke at work	0	2.2	1.3	0	0	0	0.5
No specific reason	9.1	8.8	8.7	8.0	9.4	8.3	8.7
Other	0	5.1	3.3	3.5	2.1	3.2	3.2
Base: Ex-regular smokers	26	90	108	126	154	132	637

Females

Reasons for cessation	Age						
	16–24	25–34	35–44	45–54	55–64	65–74	All
General concern about health/ fitness	33.9	33.0	39.3	30.1	30.3	41.1	34.8
Cost/save money	27.9	12.3	24.0	23.9	16.2	23.8	21.0
Pregnancy	16.4	28.0	22.4	14.6	12.7	2.1	15.3
Became more aware about health risks	14.8	9.5	15.9	13.1	7.0	10.2	11.5
Diagnosis of health problems	5.4	5.7	4.8	7.5	18.6	19.0	10.9
Pressure from family	16.1	9.7	15.2	10.6	8.7	4.2	10.1
Set example for family	0	5.4	5.4	4.9	3.3	2.0	3.8
Advice from doctor	0	2.5	1.9	1.3	4.7	6.4	3.1
Aesthetic/cosmetic reasons	2.0	4.6	4.9	0.6	5.9	0	3.0
Pressure from friends/work colleagues	3.3	5.2	4.6	0.4	1.5	1.2	2.5
Worried about effects on family	0	3.4	1.8	1.1	2.7	1.9	1.9
Because people can't smoke at work	0	0	0.8	1.0	1.1	0	0.6
No specific reason	10.7	9.1	2.7	6.8	7.3	6.7	6.7
Other	0	3.6	1.3	2.9	4.3	6.4	3.5
Base: Ex-regular smokers	31	64	78	86	79	85	424

Table 5.31: Reasons for smoking cessation by class by sex

Males

Reasons for cessation	I&II	IIINM	IIIM	IV&V	Unemp	Sick	Home	Educ
				Class				
General concern about health/fitness	39.0	47.6	38.1	37.7	46.5	28.2	40.0	0
Became more aware about health risks	23.8	19.2	16.8	14.0	3.4	9.8	0	0
Cost/save money	21.6	24.3	30.5	26.3	34.1	25.8	28.0	0
Diagnosis of health problems	10.6	11.2	15.5	10.8	6.2	39.3	14.6	100.0
Pressure from family	10.3	6.4	6.6	8.1	3.2	0	20.4	0
Worried about effects on family	3.5	8.2	6.2	0.9	8.4	0	0	0
Pressure from friends/ work colleagues	3.4	4.0	1.5	1.1	4.9	0	0	0
Advice from doctor	3.1	2.8	9.8	9.1	2.9	1.5	10.9	0
Aesthetic/cosmetic reasons	2.7	0	2.5	3.8	9.4	4.5	4.6	0
Pregnancy	1.7	0	2.2	0.6	0	0	0	0
Because people can't smoke at work	1.6	0	0	0	0	0	0	0
Set example for family	1.2	0	1.4	0	0	0	4.6	0
No specific reason	8.1	10.2	6.8	10.7	18.7	8.2	8.6	0
Other	3.8	8.3	2.2	0	2.9	0	0	0
Base: Ex-regular smokers	213	58	180	89	30	28	10	2

Females

Reasons for cessation	Class							
	I&II	IIINM	IIIM	IV&V	Unemp	Sick	Home	Educ
General concern about health/fitness	33.7	34.2	34.8	36.4	49.4	29.1	37.5	10.1
Pregnancy	28.7	15.8	12.2	10.0	9.9	4.2	14.6	0
Cost/save money	16.5	24.0	24.1	27.8	21.0	15.4	12.1	10.1
Became more aware about health risks	16.0	15.2	8.6	7.3	23.7	7.6	5.7	0
Pressure from family	14.0	11.0	9.0	5.4	3.5	40.5	2.3	0
Diagnosis of health problems	8.8	11.5	7.2	10.8	9.4	21.9	19.2	0
Set example for family	5.5	5.0	3.6	1.7	6.9	3.7	0	0
Pressure from friends/ work colleagues	3.6	4.2	1.6	2.4	2.1	0	0	0
Aesthetic/cosmetic reasons	3.5	3.6	3.3	2.5	5.1	0	0	0
Advice from doctor	2.5	3.8	2.2	3.3	0	10.2	0	0
Worried about effects on family	2.4	0.5	0	3.9	0	6.7	2.2	0
Because people can't smoke at work	1.9	0	0	0	0	0	0	0
No specific reason	4.7	4.6	6.0	2.5	12.6	0	10.8	57.1
Other	2.7	0.6	4.8	8.3	0	0	3.2	0
Base: Ex-regular smokers	130	65	94	42	18	14	19	4

Table 5.32: Reasons for smoking cessation by housing tenure by sex

Reasons for cessation	Males		Females	
	Owns/buying	Rents	Owns/buying	Rents
General concern about health/fitness	40.1	37.2	36.4	30.0
Cost/save money	25.1	27.4	20.5	21.8
Became more aware about health risks	19.4	9.8	12.7	7.8
Diagnosis of health problems	12.8	17.5	8.7	18.8
Pressure from family	8.7	3.6	10.8	7.5
Advice from doctor	6.0	8.0	2.8	4.5
Worried about effects on family	3.5	7.2	1.3	4.3
Pressure from friends/work colleagues	2.4	2.2	2.9	1.1
Aesthetic/cosmetic reasons	2.0	5.4	2.8	3.0
Pregnancy	1.5	0.7	16.4	11.7
Set example for family	0.8	1.4	4.5	1.5
Because people can't smoke at work	0.7	0	0.7	0
No specific reason	8.5	8.3	5.0	13.0
Other	3.2	3.4	3.5	2.4
Base: Ex-regular smokers	505	121	324	96

Table 5.33: Precipitators of smoking cessation by age and sex

Did anything in particular happen to make you want to give up at that time? IF YES: What was this? (Q164)

Males

| Precipitators of cessation | Age | | | | | | |
	16–24	25–34	35–44	45–54	55–64	65–74	All
No, nothing	68.6	55.6	45.4	50.0	46.3	50.1	49.8
Developed cough/cold/bad throat	4.4	8.2	9.8	9.8	11.3	6.6	9.1
Smoking-related illness/death of relative/friend	0	5.4	7.0	6.4	5.8	9.8	6.6
Cost of cigarettes went up	7.5	4.2	3.4	6.7	5.6	7.2	5.6
Advertising campaign	0	0	0	2.2	5.8	4.6	2.6
TV programme	0	0	1.0	0.8	4.6	3.2	2.0
New Year's resolution	0	3.5	1.0	0	1.7	0	1.1
No smoking policy at work	0	3.3	0	0	0.9	0	0.7
Talked to smoking advice phone line	0	1.3	0	0.5	0	2.0	0.7
No smoking day	0	0	2.1	0.9	0	0	0.6
Other	19.5	4.5	12.9	9.0	5.5	6.7	8.2
Base: Ex-regular smokers giving specific reason for smoking cessation	18	80	95	102	109	92	496

Females

| Precipitators of cessation | Age | | | | | | |
	16–24	25–34	35–44	45–54	55–64	65–74	All
No, nothing	70.4	41.0	51.5	51.6	27.3	45.7	46.4
Smoking-related illness/death of relative/friend	7.8	2.7	9.5	6.1	9.8	13.1	8.4
Developed cough/cold/bad throat	0	1.7	3.7	7.8	15.5	4.2	6.1
Cost of cigarettes went up	0	1.6	4.9	4.4	5.3	8.2	4.7
Advertising campaign	0	3.8	0	2.6	4.0	0	1.8
New Year's resolution	0	0	1.0	2.2	4.1	0	1.4
TV programme	0	0	0	1.2	1.9	4.2	1.4
Talked to smoking advice phone line	3.4	6.0	1.1	0	0	0	1.3
No smoking day	0	1.7	0	0.8	0	2.0	0.8
No smoking policy at work	0	0	0	0	0	0	0
Other	0	8.3	10.9	7.6	11.5	9.3	8.7
Base: Ex-regular smokers giving specific reason for smoking cessation	24	41	56	67	49	60	296

Table 5.34: Precipitators of smoking cessation by class and sex

Males

Precipitators of cessation	I&II	IIINM	IIIM	IV&V	Unemp	Sick	Home	Educ
				Class				
No, nothing	46.4	46.1	47.5	48.0	51.2	76.8	48.0	0
Smoking-related illness/ death of relative/friend	8.3	9.6	6.7	4.7	3.3	0	0	0
Developed cough/cold/ bad throat	8.3	7.3	10.4	11.8	16.0	5.1	0	0
Cost of cigarettes went up	4.5	7.4	5.9	9.8	5.5	0	0	0
Advertising campaign	3.3	0	2.7	1.7	8.6	0	0	0
New Year's resolution	1.1	0	1.0	2.3	3.2	0	0	0
No smoking policy at work	1.1	1.9	0.5	0	0	0	0	0
TV programme	0.6	5.1	4.7	0	0	0	0	0
No smoking day	0.5	0	0.7	1.7	0	0	0	0
Talked to smoking advice phone line	0.3	0	0.8	2.7	0	0	0	0
Other	8.2	16.6	5.8	10.1	3.6	6.0	0	0
Base: Ex-regular smokers giving specific reason for smoking cessation	175	52	130	68	27	17	7	0

Tables 5.34 and 5.35 show that there was little difference in frequency of citation of different reasons by social class or housing tenure.

Table 5.36 shows how many times ex-smokers reported that they had tried to give up prior to succeeding. The surprising result is that more than 50% said that they had succeeded at the first attempt. This suggests that the majority of those who will eventually succeed in giving up will manage it at the first attempt. The evidence also shows that more than two-thirds will manage it by the second attempt. Only a small proportion of successes occurred at third or later attempts. Other research has suggested that the chances of success in giving up smoking improve with successive attempts. The present data does not appear to support this conclusion. The data also suggests that the likelihood of the success of attempts to give up smoking are better than the 1–2% found in prospective studies (Hughes *et al.*, 1990). However, it is important to bear in mind two possible sources of bias. The first is that approximately 11% of the ex-smokers had abstained for less than one year and many would be expected to return to

Females

Precipitators of cessation	Class							
	I&II	IIINM	IIIM	IV&V	Unemp	Sick	Home	Educ
No, nothing	45.6	41.1	55.0	45.9	27.6	19.6	36.7	100.0
Cost of cigarettes went up	6.2	5.7	3.1	0	10.9	0	14.2	0
Smoking-related illness/ death of relative/friend	5.8	13.7	4.1	15.6	17.2	9.6	6.5	0
Developed cough/cold/ bad throat	5.2	4.1	5.3	4.7	6.4	24.9	0	0
Talked to smoking advice phone line	2.8	0.9	1.6	0	0	0	0	0
New Year's resolution	0.7	0	2.7	1.4	0	10.7	0	0
Advertising campaign	0	1.9	3.2	0	2.0	11.0	0	0
TV programme	0	5.2	0	3.0	0	0	7.0	0
No smoking day	0	0	1.7	2.3	0	5.4	0	0
No smoking policy at work	0	0	0	0	0	0	0	0
Other	10.2	13.1	6.8	9.5	2.8	3.7	6.5	0
Base: Ex-regular smokers giving specific reason for smoking cessation	83	48	74	30	15	10	11	4

smoking. Perhaps more importantly many smokers may have failed to recall previous unsuccessful attempts to stop smoking, particularly those that lasted for less than one week.

It has been suggested that women find it harder to give up smoking than men. In population surveys, this has been based on the finding of higher cessation rates among men than women. However, when switching to pipes or cigars is taken into consideration gender differences in cessation rates disappear (Jarvis and Jackson, 1988). The present results provide further support for a lack of difference between men and women in the number of smoking cessation attempts made by male and female ex-smokers (Table 5.36).

There was no evidence for social class differences in the number of quit attempts made by ex-smokers (Table 5.36).

Ex-smokers were asked what methods they had used to help them give up smoking. The majority of both men and women said that they had not used any

Table 5.35: Precipitators of smoking cessation by housing tenure

	Males		Females	
Precipitators of cessation	Owns/buying	Rents	Owns/buying	Rents
No, nothing	50.0	50.4	44.6	53.4
Developed cough/cold/ bad throat	8.4	13.6	5.6	8.2
Smoking-related illness/death of relative/friend	7.1	4.8	9.2	6.1
Cost of cigarettes went up	5.2	7.8	5.0	3.0
Advertising campaign	3.2	0	2.2	0.5
TV programme	2.1	1.7	1.8	0
New Year's resolution	1.2	1.0	0.9	3.2
No smoking day	0.7	0	0.5	2.0
No smoking policy at work	0.7	0.7	0	0
Talked to smoking advice phone line	0.6	1.2	1.2	2.0
Other	8.6	2.6	8.5	8.3
Base: Ex-regular smokers giving specific reason for smoking cessation	399	86	231	62

particular aid (Table 5.37). Approximately 20% cited support from their family and 10% cited support from their friends. Advice from a doctor was cited by 4% of women and 9% of men. Aids from the chemist, such as nicotine gum, was cited by 6% of men and 5% of women. Telephone helplines were cited very rarely, as were alternative therapies such as acupuncture and hypnosis.

There was no clear difference between the methods used by men and women. Small cell sizes make interpretation of differences in methods used by age group problematic. However, there was some evidence of a decline in citation of support from friends with increasing age, and some suggestion of a decrease in the importance of support from family with age among the women in the sample. It should be borne in mind, however, that this does not imply that older smokers use different methods for giving up. The age breakdown refers to the current age of respondents, not the age at which they gave up smoking.

Table 5.38 shows the methods of smoking cessation by social class. There was no clear evidence of differences across the social class groupings.

Table 5.36: Number of attempts prior to achieving smoking cessation by class and sex

About how many times did you attempt to give up smoking before you succeeded? (Q166)

Males

| Number of attempts | Class | | | | | | | | |
	I&II	IIINM	IIIM	IV&V	Unemp	Sick	Home	Educ	All
Succeeded first time	50.4	58.8	53.5	52.1	38.7	56.4	40.2	100.0	51.9
Twice	22.2	22.8	19.8	19.0	20.2	33.3	16.4	0	21.5
3-4 times	11.9	1.0	13.6	11.7	20.6	7.9	43.4	0	12.1
5-9 times	8.7	3.3	3.4	7.1	9.4	2.4	0	0	5.9
10-14 times	2.3	7.4	5.2	5.6	0	0	0	0	3.9
15-19 times	1.1	0	0	0	2.2	0	0	0	0.4
20+ times	3.4	6.7	4.6	4.5	9.0	0	0	0	4.2
Base: Ex-regular smokers	202	55	178	88	30	28	10	2	592

Females

| Number of attempts | Class | | | | | | | | |
	I&II	IIINM	IIIM	IV&V	Unemp	Sick	Home	Educ	All
Succeeded first time	62.0	70.0	50.3	55.7	36.9	50.0	64.2	90.0	58.8
Twice	15.8	13.8	18.7	16.1	40.2	13.2	26.6	0	17.8
3-4 times	8.5	12.8	13.6	8.7	11.6	20.2	9.2	10.1	11.3
5-9 times	9.2	0.7	8.2	9.0	0	0	0	0	6.1
10-14 times	2.9	1.0	4.8	10.5	0	9.0	0	0	3.4
15-19 times	0.4	0	0	0	0	0	0	0	0.1
20+ times	1.2	1.8	4.4	0	11.3	7.6	0	0	2.5
Base: Ex-regular smokers	123	67	92	42	17	13	18	4	376

Table 5.37: Methods of smoking cessation by age and sex

Here is a list of things some people have used to give up smoking. Could you tell me please which, if any, you used? (Q165)

Males

| Methods of cessation | Age | | | | | | |
	16–24	25–34	35–44	45–54	55–64	65–74	All
Help and support from family	19.8	20.7	24.1	16.8	13.9	22.4	19.2
Help and support from friends	16.8	16.9	15.3	14.4	9.0	4.5	11.6
Advice from doctor	26.3	4.9	3.0	9.1	12.8	10.7	9.3
Aids bought from chemist (e.g. Nicorette)	6.3	7.1	9.2	8.9	4.2	2.6	6.1
Help and support at work	0	4.1	9.8	3.8	2.8	1.2	4.0
Booklets	1.3	1.2	6.6	1.9	3.6	1.9	3.0
Alternative treatments	0	0.7	3.2	1.6	3.4	1.6	2.1
Prescription from doctor	0	0	0.5	1.4	0	0	0.4
Individual counselling and advice	0	0	0	1.2	0	0.8	0.4
'How to quit' videos	9.3	0	0	0	0	0	0.4
Special clinics or 'stop smoking' groups	0	0	0	0	0.6	0	0.2
Quitline/telephone helpline/advice line	0	0	0	0	0	0	0
Other	0	11.4	4.6	17.7	11.5	11.1	11.0
None of these	48.1	55.5	61.4	53.3	57.3	60.4	57.3
Base: Ex-regular smokers	24	91	111	126	153	134	639

Females

Methods of cessation	Age						
	16–24	25–34	35–44	45–54	55–64	65–74	All
Help and support from family	24.5	28.1	23.8	20.7	14.3	9.6	19.3
Help and support from friends	22.0	11.2	11.5	7.0	6.2	0.8	8.2
Aids bought from chemist							
(e.g. Nicorette)	3.0	7.7	5.9	13.8	1.5	0	5.6
Advice from doctor	0	2.0	3.5	3.4	10.6	3.3	4.3
Booklets	8.3	7.4	6.1	4.0	0	1.8	4.0
Alternative treatments	0	5.4	3.3	7.7	3.4	0	3.7
Help and support at work	7.4	5.4	3.1	2.5	0	0.8	2.6
Prescription from doctor	0	1.3	1.6	4.7	0	0	1.5
Special clinics or 'stop smoking'							
groups	0	0	0	1.1	0.7	1.8	0.7
Individual counselling and advice	0	1.9	0	0	0	0	0.3
'How to quit' videos	0	0	0	0.3	0	0	0.1
Quitline/telephone helpline/advice							
line	0	0	0	0	0	0	0
Other	9.9	7.7	8.1	7.1	12.8	17.7	10.7
None of these	50.4	50.4	57.1	55.7	63.4	73.2	60.0
Base: Ex-regular smokers	31	64	79	86	79	81	420

Table 5.38: Methods of smoking cessation by class and sex

Males

Methods of cessation	Class							
	I&II	IIINM	IIIM	IV&V	Unemp	Sick	Home	Educ
Help and support from family	19.5	19.1	19.2	22.0	3.4	19.2	16.3	100.0
Help and support from friends	15.2	1.0	11.7	9.6	7.8	13.4	0	100.0
Advice from doctor	7.6	5.1	11.3	4.0	4.4	23.0	0	100.0
Aids bought from chemist (e.g. Nicorette)	7.2	3.3	7.2	4.7	3.2	0	4.1	0
Help and support at work	6.4	1.5	3.9	2.8	0	4.1	0	0
Booklets	5.8	1.5	1.5	0.8	1.0	2.9	0	0
Alternative treatments	2.8	0	1.8	4.2	0	0	0	0
Prescription from doctor	0.8	0	0	0.6	0	0	0	0
Individual counselling and advice	0.5	0	0	0	0	0	0	0
Special clinics or 'stop smoking' groups	0	0	0.5	0	0	0	0	0
Quitline/telephone helpline/advice line	0	0	0	0	0	0	0	0
'How to quit' videos	0	0	0	0	0	0	0	100.0
Other	11.0	14.2	8.4	14.8	5.3	15.4	8.8	0
None of these	54.8	62.9	58.8	55.8	79.9	41.2	70.8	0
Base: Ex-regular smokers	215	59	180	89	30	28	10	2

Females

Methods of cessation	Class							
	I&II	IIINM	IIIM	IV&V	Unemp	Sick	Home	Educ
Help and support from family	21.4	21.5	25.4	11.5	6.7	21.4	12.1	0
Help and support from friends	6.6	11.5	9.5	6.7	3.5	8.4	9.7	0
Booklets	6.3	2.2	3.2	0	3.9	2.5	3.7	0
Aids bought from chemist (e.g. Nicorette)	5.1	4.2	8.2	3.4	6.7	0	2.0	10.1
Advice from doctor	4.7	0.6	2.4	5.9	1.6	14.3	3.5	10.1
Alternative treatments	4.1	3.4	2.1	2.0	5.1	10.2	0	0
Help and support at work	2.4	3.5	1.9	2.5	0	0	3.5	0
Special clinics or 'stop smoking' groups	2.0	0.4	0	0	0	0	0	0
Prescription from doctor	0.6	1.0	4.2	2.0	0	0	0	0
Individual counselling and advice	0	0	0	0	0	0	0	0
Quitline/telephone helpline/advice line	0	0	0	0	0	0	0	0
'How to quit' videos	0	0.4	0	0	0	0	0	0
Other	7.7	15.9	11.9	11.8	5.3	0	32.5	0
None of these	58.6	57.2	53.0	62.5	79.1	69.3	56.0	90.0
Base: Ex-regular smokers	129	67	91	42	18	14	18	4

References

Cox, B. D., Huppert, F. A. and Whichelow, M. J. (1993) *The Health and Lifestyle Survey: Seven Years On.* Dartmouth Publishing, Aldershot.

Department of Health (1992) *The Health of the Nation: a Strategy for Health in England.* Cm 1986. HMSO.

Hughes, J. R., Gulliver, S. B., Fenwick, J. W. *et al.* (1992) 'Smoking cessation among self-quitters'. *Health Psychology*, **11**, 331–4.

Jarvis, M, and Jackson, P. (1988) 'Data Note 12: Cigar and pipe smoking in Britain: implications for smoking prevalence and cessation'. *British Journal of Addiction*, **83**, 323–30.

Marsh, A. and McKay, S. (1994) *Poor Smokers.* Policy Studies Institute.

Office of Population Censuses and Surveys (1994) *General Household Survey 1992.* HMSO.

6. Passive smoking and smoking policies

Lesley Owen
Researcher
Health Education Authority
London

Passive smoking

There is now considerable evidence that passive smoking can damage health. Two recent summaries of the evidence show, for example, that lung cancer in adults and serious respiratory illnesses in babies are caused by breathing in other people's tobacco smoke.

Two main sources of smoke exist: mainstream smoke – smoke drawn through the tobacco and taken in by the smoker; and sidestream smoke – smoke which arises from smouldering tobacco and passes directly into surrounding air. Smokers are exposed to both sources to a greater extent than non-smokers, but the harmful effects of both types may also be suffered by non-smokers who inhale them.

In *The Health of the Nation* (Department of Health, 1992), the government identified the need to protect non-smokers from passive smoking. Several strategies have since been introduced which seek to reduce exposure to passive smoking in public places as well as the workplace. The high profile debate that passive smoking receives together with strategies to reduce exposure to passive smoking are perceived by the tobacco industry as a major threat to its *continued* survival.

This section provides information on the proportion of adults aged 16–74 exposed to the risks of passive smoking. It identifies factors associated with increased risk of exposure, together with information on the situations in which exposure occurs and the length of time spent breathing in other people's smoke.

Table 6.1: Exposure to passive smoking (%) by gender

	Female	Male	All
16–19	77	77	77
20–24	71	76	73
25–34	48	66	57
35–49	51	63	57
50–59	44	51	47
60–74	24	33	28
All	48	59	53
Base	2520	2485	5005

Exposure to smoke

Just over half adults (53.5%) aged 16–74 claim to spend a period of time during an average day in places where they are inhaling other people's cigarette smoke. Younger people are particularly at risk – over three-quarters of 16–19 year olds are exposed to passive smoking compared with just over one-quarter of 60–74 year olds. Men are more likely than women to be exposed to other people's smoke (59% compared with 48%) as are people in manual and unskilled occupations (social class IIIM, IV & V). The only age group in which men do not have significantly more exposure than women of the same age is 16–19.

Table 6.2: Exposure to passive smoking by social class of respondent

Social class of respondent	%	Base
I & II	49	1 174
III NM	50	803
III M	60	750
IV & V	62	740
Unemployed	58	336
Sick/disabled	49	138
Looking after family/home	38	590
Full-time education	73	290

Just over half of those who have never smoked say they are exposed to other people's smoke. This figure rises to 63% among recent ex-smokers (i.e. those who have given up for less than a year) more of whom say they are exposed to passive smoking than long-term ex-smokers and current smokers. Exposure amongst recent ex-smokers is of concern in terms of sustaining non-smoking status as they may be exposing themselves to risky situations in which relapse is likely to occur, e.g. the presence of significant others, such as friends, smoking. Indeed, stress and lack of willpower, encouragement by friends and peer groups was one of the most commonly mentioned reasons given for relapse, especially amongst 16–24 year olds.

Table 6.3: Percentage of respondents exposed to passive smoking by smoking status (%)

Current	61
Ex-smoker < 1 year	63
Ex-smoker > 1 year	44
Never	52
Base: All	4 983

Base: Includes 'Don't know' responses

Interestingly, sources of exposure among recent ex-smokers are much more like those of current smokers than those who have never smoked or are ex-smokers. In contrast, comparisons of exposure among long-term ex-smokers and never smokers would seem to suggest that long-term ex-smokers are actively avoiding potential sources of exposure to passive smoking. Recent ex-smokers also claim to spend more time exposed to other people's smoke than long-term ex-smokers and never smokers. Taken together, these findings could indicate that recent ex-smokers are vulnerable to relapse as they haven't made the necessary lifestyle changes to sustain their new found non-smoking status.

Table 6.4: Source of exposure to passive smoke by smoking status

	Current smoker %	Ex-smoker <1 year %	Ex-smoker >1 year %	Never smoker %	All %
Home	35	33	15	18	24
Work	34	30	27	31	31
Pub/restaurants	45	47	29	37	38
Other social places	39	36	27	33	34
Shop	10	15	10	15	12
Travelling	24	19	11	16	18

Source of exposure to passive smoke

Generally, the settings that most frequently expose people to the risks of passive smoking are pubs and restaurants and other places that are visited socially. In each of these places, men are more likely than women to say they would be exposed to passive smoking in these places in an average day. The workplace is a source for almost one-third of adults aged 16–74, again more so for men than for women (39% compared with 23%).

Table 6.5: Source of exposure to passive smoke by sex

Exposure to one or more sources	Female %	Male %	All %	Base
Home	23	23	24	4 848
Work	23	39	31	4 836
Pub/restaurants	31	45	38	4 814
Other social places	29	39	34	4 823
Shop	10	14	12	4 805
Travelling	16	20	18	4 811

The findings in Table 6.5 are not standardised for age and other related variables such as social class.

Earlier it was seen that young people are most at risk from exposure to passive smoking. Table 6.6 shows that the situations in which this most frequently occurs are pubs and restaurants and other places that people meet socially. This suggests that smoking among young people is very much a social activity, a finding which should be taken on board in developing an effective and appropriate strategy for this group.

Table 6.6: Source of exposure to passive smoke (%) by age

	16–19	20–24	25–34	35–49	50–59	60–74
Home	37	37	25	23	19	12
Work	28	47	38	39	26	7
Pub/restaurants	62	62	44	39	28	14
Other social places	61	55	35	33	27	16
Shop	21	17	15	12	10	5
Travelling	42	27	18	15	14	8

Exposure was also related to employment status – for men and women, exposure was lowest amongst the retired (on state and occupational pensions) and men and women looking after the home and family. Surprisingly, exposure was highest for those in full-time education, although this is clearly linked to the age of respondent as was seen earlier.

Table 6.7: Exposure to passive smoking by economic status (%)

Full-time work	64
Part-time work	50
Retired	25
Unemployed	58
Full-time education	73
Sick/disabled	49
Looking after home/family	38

Duration of exposure

Those who are exposed to passive smoking estimate their average daily exposure at 3.6 hours, almost a quarter of a wakeful (16-hour) day. Young women have the highest daily exposure with an average of 4.5 hours, and the amount of daily exposure gradually declines with age. For men, exposure is highest amongst 25–34 year olds and then gradually declines with age.

Table 6.8: **Average estimated number of hours' exposure to passive smoking by age and gender**

Age	Women	Men	All
16–19	4.4	3.6	4.0
20–24	4.5	3.7	4.1
25–34	3.6	3.9	3.8
35–44	3.3	3.5	3.4
45–54	3.2	3.5	3.4
55–64	2.8	3.3	3.1
65–74	2.1	2.3	2.2
All	3.5	3.6	3.6

Of those exposed to passive smoking, nearly a third of the population are exposed in at least four settings on an average day. Importantly, a systematic increase is seen in length of time exposed with the number of settings in which a person is exposed. Thus it is important to consider the total number of possible sources of exposure and not just assume that exposure in one setting, e.g. the workplace, will be more important than exposure in other settings.

Table 6.9: **Number of settings and length of time exposed to passive smoking**

Number of settings	% Exposed	Duration (h)	Base
1	19	2.59	513
2	23	2.72	614
3	25	3.27	672
4	20	4.45	527
5	10	5.99	264
6	2	6.55	62

Although current smokers are less likely to report being exposed to other people's smoke than ex-smokers and never smokers, they estimate greater periods of exposure, with 4.3 hours for women and 4.6 hours for men. Moreover, recent ex-smokers claim to spend significantly more time exposed to other people's smoke than long-term ex-smokers and never smokers.

Table 6.10: Average estimated number of hours' exposure to passive smoking by smoking status and gender (%)

Smoking status	Women	Men	All
Current smoker	4.5	4.7	4.6
Ex-smoker < 1 year	4.1	3.0	3.4
Ex-smoker > 1 year	2.4	3.0	2.8
Never smoker	3.1	3.0	3.0

Length of exposure to other people's smoke is an important consideration, as there is a well established dose–response relationship between passive smoking and degree of risk to health – the latter related to the length of exposure and concentration of tobacco smoke in the environment.

Implications of findings

These findings have a number of implications for the way in which exposure to passive smoking might be reduced. Possible measures will inevitably touch upon sensitive and controversial issues that require further debate, e.g.

1. Firmer controls on smoking in the workplace and in public places.

2. Infringement of individual liberties, e.g. the rights of the individual versus the good of the group.

3. Social control, e.g. younger people are more at risk, therefore appropriate measures will inevitably impinge upon lifestyles associated with those particular groups.

It is clear that a number of measures will be necessary in attempting to achieve the Health of the Nation targets on reducing the prevalence of cigarette smoking and tobacco consumption. This chapter has highlighted some of the characteristics associated with an increased risk of exposure to passive smoking. It has also identified important differences between smokers and non-smokers which should be taken into consideration in the development of an effective strategy.

Workplace smoking policies

As part of a strategy towards reducing the prevalence of cigarette smoking, the Department of Health has identified the need to increase the proportion of the population whose workplace operates a smoking policy, i.e. a ban on smoking or smoking permitted in special sections only.

Only 18% of those in paid employment have a total ban on smoking in operation at their place of work. Just over a quarter of respondents (28%) claim they are allowed to smoke anywhere at work, and about half of workers (54%) have smoking allowed in specially designated areas at their place of work (Table 6.11).

Table 6.11: Smoking policy at work (%)

	All	Women	Men
Allowed anywhere	28	19	35
Special sections	54	57	51
Banned	18	24	14
Base	2 796	1 248	1 548

Men are more likely than women to work where smoking is unrestricted, whereas women are more likely than men to have a total ban at their place of work. Although the numbers are small there do appear to be differences across age bands within sex. For example, only 6% of 16–19 year old women work where a total ban is in operation compared 27% of 16–19 year old men. This pattern is reversed among 20–24 year olds.

Table 6.12: Smoking policy at work by age and gender

Age in years		16–19	20–24	25–34	35–44	45–54	55–64	65–74
Women	Allowed anywhere	17	26	17	19	19	21	–
	Special sections	77	55	60	54	55	51	45
	Banned	6	19	23	26	26	28	55
Base		72	154	306	327	268	108	12
Men	Allowed anywhere	22	32	37	36	34	39	54
	Special sections	51	60	51	50	49	48	36
	Banned	27	8	12	15	16	13	10
Base		52	182	440	383	312	163	16

Those who work in non-manual jobs (classes I, II and IIIM) are twice as likely as manual workers (IIIM and IV–V) to have a smoking ban in the workplace. (Most women work in non-manual jobs, and therefore more women have a smoking ban at their place of work.) Skilled manual workers (social class IIIM) are especially likely to say smoking is allowed anywhere at their place of work (42% – see Table 6.13).

Table 6.13: Smoking policy at work by social class of respondent (%)

	I&II	IIINM	IIIM	IV&V
Allowed anywhere	22	22	42	35
Special sections	55	57	47	51
Banned	23	21	11	14
Base	943	644	570	1 548

In workplaces where smoking is allowed in special sections only, the areas where it is allowed tend to be confined to catering/eating areas (36%) and private offices (34%). It tends not to be allowed in all open work areas (82%) and customer/visitor areas (55%). In general, restrictions are operated to a greater extent in women's places of work, for instance, smoking tends not to be allowed in open work areas in 89% of cases of women's workplaces compared to 76% of men's workplaces (Table 6.14).

Table 6.14: Workers saying smoking is not allowed in each part of their place of work (%)

	All	Women	Men
All open work areas	82	89	76
Private offices	49	53	44
Catering/eating areas	47	50	45
Conference/meeting areas	48	52	45
Customer/visitor areas	55	62	49

There are variations on restrictions by social class. For instance, among social class I and II, 46% 'are not allowed to smoke in private offices compared to 57% of workers in social IIIN. Conversely, 59% of social class I and II and not allowed to smoke in catering and eating areas compared to 43% of workers in social class IIINM (Table 6.15).

Table 6.15: Percentage of workers saying smoking is not allowed in each part of their place of work

	All	I&II	IIINM	IIIM	IV&V
All open work areas	82	83	87	75	83
Private offices	49	46	57	43	50
Catering/eating areas	47	59	43	34	43
Conference/meeting areas	48	56	55	31	43
Customer/visitor areas	55	56	65	42	55

With regards to measures taken within the workplace by employers against smoking, the most frequently used provision is the use of no-smoking signs which are used in 51% of workplaces. Just over half this number provide a smoking room. Relatively few employers take active measures to promote cessation, for example, 6% work with trade unions to promote smoking bans/control and 3% run stop smoking groups. However, 15% of employers provide leaflets on giving up smoking and put up posters. Such measures are more likely to be found by the employers, of non-manual workers. No differences in gender emerged for measures used by employers, with the exception of non-smoking signs the use of which was reported more amongst male employees (Table 6.16).

Table 6.16: Measures used by employers regarding smoking policy (%)

	All	I&II	IIIN	IIIM	IV&V
Leaflets on how to stop smoking	15	21	15	9	8
Posters on how to stop smoking	15	18	16	12	12
A complete ban on smoking at work	14	19	18	9	9
No-smoking signs	51	52	53	49	49
A smoking room	28	34	27	22	25
Advice from work's doctor/nurse	7	9	7	7	4
Base	2 466	793	621	474	523

Note: The above is not exhaustive and includes only the most frequently cited measures.

A third of the workers claim they do not want any further measures to be adopted with regards to smoking. A slightly smaller proportion (29%) support further action in the form of a complete ban on smoking at work – a measure favoured slightly more by men than women (Table 6.17). Young women in particular were least likely to support this measure (16% of 16–19 year olds compared 36% of 16–19 year old men).

Table 6.17: Desired additional smoking policy measures expressed by employees (%)

	All	Women	Men
A complete ban on smoking at work	29	27	31
A smoking room	14	13	16
Posters on how to stop smoking	9	8	9
Leaflets on how to stop smoking	9	9	9
No-smoking signs	8	7	9
Support from management to reduce work stress	8	7	9
Run stop smoking groups	7	6	7
None of these	32	34	31
Base	2 442	1 131	1 310

Lack of support for further action with the measures listed was most common among unskilled manuals workers (social classes IV and V) of whom only 20% endorsed a complete ban on smoking at work compared with 33% of professional workers (social classes I and II – Table 6.18).

Table 6.18: Desired additional smoking policy measures expressed by employees (%)

	I&II	IIIN	IIIM	IV&V
A complete ban on smoking at work	33	30	31	20
A smoking room	13	14	15	15
Posters on how to stop smoking	9	7	11	9
Leaflets on how to stop smoking	9	9	9	9
No-smoking signs	7	8	10	9
Support from management to reduce work stress	11	7	7	4
Run stop smoking groups	9	6	7	4
None of these	30	35	27	39

Smoking policies in public places

There is a widespread support for smoking restrictions in many public places. Relatively few people say they would support a policy of allowing unrestricted smoking in any of the kinds of public places asked about; the only exception is pubs, where a quarter of adults (25%) support allowing smoking everywhere.

Table 6.19: Smoking policy in public places

	Allowed everywhere	Allowed in special places only	Banned completely	Don't know
In hospitals or clinics	1	10	89	–
In shops	3	8	88	1
In banks and post offices	5	9	85	1
In cinemas	3	23	73	1
On public transport	3	26	71	1
In restaurants and cafés	3	45	52	–
In offices and workplaces	3	51	45	1
In pubs	25	51	22	2

Base: All 4 999

The majority of adults say smoking should be banned in hospitals and clinics (89%), shops (88%), banks and post offices (85%), cinemas (73%) and on public transport (71%). They are more divided in their opinions on restaurants and cafés, just slightly more likely to say they favour a total ban than restricted smoking (52% and 45% respectively). On office and workplace policy people are also divided, but slightly more are likely to favour restrictions (51%) than a total ban (45%). About half of adults (51%) think smoking should be restricted in pubs, but a further one in five (22%) say it should be banned completely.

Table 6.20: Support for a complete ban on smoking in public places by sex

	All	Women	Men
Hospitals and clinics	89	89	89
Shops	88	91	85
Bank and post offices	85	89	82
Cinemas	73	74	72
Public transport	71	73	68
Restaurants and cafes	52	52	52
Offices and workplaces	45	47	43
Pubs	22	23	21

Table 6.20 gives the proportion of men and women of each age group who say they would support a complete ban in each of the public places listed.

There are slight differences between men's and women's views on four of the public places asked about (shops, banks and post offices, public transport, and offices and workplaces). In each case, women are slightly more likely to support a complete ban.

Table 6.21: Support for a complete ban on smoking in public places by age and sex

Women

	16–19	20–24	25–34	35–44	45–54	55–64	65–74
Hospitals and clinics	94	93	86	89	86	91	91
Shops	85	90	88	92	95	93	92
Banks and post offices	90	87	87	89	90	90	89
Cinemas	72	72	70	73	77	82	73
Public transport	64	67	73	73	75	79	76
Restaurants and cafés	34	41	47	51	55	64	61
Offices and workplaces	33	32	40	46	55	62	56
Pubs	9	12	19	22	29	33	28

Table 6.22: Support for a complete ban on smoking in public places by age and sex

Men

	16–19	20–24	25–34	35–44	45–54	55–64	65–74
Hospitals and clinics	92	91	90	92	87	86	85
Shops	82	81	35	87	89	87	82
Banks and post offices	78	79	84	82	84	81	83
Cinemas	60	67	69	72	78	78	77
Public transport	53	63	69	69	73	69	70
Restaurants and cafés	37	39	48	56	57	59	62
Offices and workplaces	41	35	36	43	49	46	52
Pubs	9	11	21	24	26	23	25

Base: *n*s can't be included because they differ for each location

There is no significant variation by age in the proportions supporting a complete ban in shops, banks and post offices and hospitals and clinics. Support for a complete ban on smoking on public transport and cinemas is slightly lower among younger people than among older people, and more so among men than women. There is a more marked difference in younger and older people's views on banning smoking in restaurants and cafés, pubs and offices and workplaces; again, it is younger people who are less likely to express support for a complete ban.

Table 6.23: Support for complete smoking ban in public places by social class of respondent

	Social class of respondent				
	I&II	IIINM	IIIM	IV&V	Other
In hospitals/clinics	89	91	88	89	88
In shops	89	89	88	89	86
In banks and posts offices	88	87	83	83	84
In cinemas	80	75	72	69	68
On public transport	78	73	67	70	66
In restaurants and cafés	57	52	54	52	46
In offices and workplaces	50	47	41	43	43
In pubs	28	22	21	21	19

Base: All = 4 999

Looking at an analysis by social class for most of the public places asked about there is no significant variation by social class in the level of support for a complete ban on smoking. Where differences emerge, it is those in social classes I and II who are particularly keen to see a complete ban. The most marked differences of view by social class are over the issue of smoking in cinemas where support for a complete ban declines from 80% among those in social classes I and II (professional and managerial) to 69% of those in social classes IV and V (semi- and unskilled manual workers).

Table 6.24: Support for a complete ban on smoking in public places by smoking status

	All	Never smoker	Ex-smoker	Regular smoker	Light smoker	Heavy smoker
In hospitals and clinics	89	94	91	82	85	78
In shops	88	90	89	86	89	83
In banks and post offices	35	90	86	80	83	76
In cinemas	73	81	79	58	62	52
On public transport	71	81	76	53	59	48
In restaurants and cafés	52	68	57	31	34	27
In offices and workplaces	45	60	47	29	33	23
In pubs	22	34	24	8	9	6

Base: All

Not surprisingly regular smokers, and in particular heavy smokers, are less keen than others to support bans. Nevertheless, even among regular smokers, a substantial majority support a complete ban on smoking in shops (86%), hospitals and clinics (82%), banks and post offices (80%) and just over half support bans in cinemas (58%) and on public transport (53%). The majority of current regular smokers would not support complete bans on smoking in restaurants and cafés, offices and workplaces or pubs. However, they would support smoking restrictions in restaurants and cafés (63%) and in offices and workplaces (63%). Many more current regular smokers feel smoking in pubs should be completely unrestricted (45%); what may be more surprising is that 46% of them say they would be in favour of allowing smoking only in special smoking sections in pubs.

Government policy

Three-quarters of adults (76%) say they would support a total ban on the advertising of tobacco products, and more than half (58%) express strong support; one in eight (12%) oppose this measure.

Table 6.25: Support for a total ban on the advertising of tobacco products by sex

	All	Women	Men
Strongly support	58	63	54
Tend to support	18	18	18
Neither support nor oppose	11	9	13
Tend to oppose	7	6	9
Strongly oppose	5	3	6
Don't know	1	1	1

Base: All

A total ban on the advertising of tobacco products is supported especially by women (81% compared with 72% of men); women are also more likely than men to express strong support (63% and 54% respectively). Men and women aged 25 years and older are also more likely to express strong support for this measure.

Table 6.26: Support for a total ban on the advertising of tobacco products by smoking status

	All	Never	Ex-regular	Regular	Light	Heavy
				Smoking status		
Strongly support	58	67	63	44	44	44
Tend to support	18	17	17	20	22	18
Neither support nor oppose	11	8	10	15	15	14
Tend to oppose	7	5	7	11	10	12
Strongly oppose	5	2	3	9	8	10
Don't know	1	1	<0.5	2	1	2

The majority of current regular smokers (64%) also support a total ban on the advertising of tobacco products, though opposition rises to 18% and 22% among light and heavy smokers respectively.

Table 6.27: Support for other government initiatives

	Support	Oppose
Increasing the prices of tobacco products through higher taxes	59	29
Stricter enforcement of the rules on under-age sales	96	2
More government funds for anti-smoking education	84	7

Respondents were asked to indicate their support for several possible government initiatives. Virtually all adults aged 16–74 would support stricter enforcement of the laws on under-age sales of tobacco – only 2% opposed this. Increasing the price of tobacco products through higher taxes attracted the most opposition, and the least support, of all the measures listed.

Eighty-four per cent of adults say they support more government funds for anti-smoking education. About one in fourteen adults opposes this (7%).

Table 6.28: Support for government initiatives by smoking status

	Never smoker	Ex-smoker	Regular smoker
A total ban on advertising	84	80	64
Increasing the prices of tobacco products through higher taxes	78	68	29
Stricter enforcement of the rules on under-age sales	96	97	95
More government funds for anti-smoking education	88	85	79

Support for the initiatives varies by smoking status. Smokers' and non-smokers' views on increasing the price of tobacco products through higher taxes are directly opposed. Two-thirds of ex-regular smokers (68%) and three-quarters of those who have never smoked (78%) say they would support such price increases, whereas three in five current regular smokers (60%) oppose this.

Non-smokers, especially those who have never smoked, are more likely to express support for more funds for anti-smoking education, and a total ban on advertising, than current smokers. Current regular smokers are just as likely as non-smokers and former smokers to express support for a stricter enforcement of the laws on under-age sales of tobacco.

The only issue on which men and women appeared to differ was the policy for a total ban on advertising – which received more support from women (81%) than men (72%).

Table 6.29: Support for government initiatives by sex

	Women	Men
A total ban on advertising	81	72
Increasing the prices of tobacco products through higher taxes	60	58
Stricter enforcement of the rules on under age-sales	96	96
More government funds for anti-smoking education	85	83

Support for stricter enforcement of the rule on under-age sales of tobacco and for more government funds for anti-smoking education showed little variation by social class. Those in non-manual jobs were, however, more likely than manual workers to support an increase in the price of tobacco through higher taxes, and a total ban on advertising.

Table 6.30: Support for government initiatives by social class of respondent

	I&II	IIINM	IIIM	IV&V	Other
A total ban on advertising	78	82	73	75	74
Increasing the prices of tobacco products through higher taxes	68	63	57	54	52
Stricter enforcement of the rules on under-age sales	97	98	95	96	94
More government funds for anti-smoking education	84	84	84	83	84

The youngest respondents in the survey (16–24 year olds) were least likely to support a total ban on advertising and stricter enforcement of the rules on under-age sales compared with respondents in older age categories. They were also less likely to support increases in the price of tobacco through taxation – as were 65–74 year olds. It would be interesting at this point to establish the relative effectiveness of these different measures as a means of reducing prevalence and consumption. It would then be possible to examine the relationship, if any, between those policies that receive strongest support and those that are most effective.

Table 6.31: Support and opposition for government initiatives by age of respondent

	16–24	25–34	35–44	45–54	55–64	65–74
Total ban on advertising						
Support	69	77	80	79	81	77
Neither	17	11	10	10	7	9
Oppose	14	12	10	11	12	14
Increase in price through taxes						
Support	57	61	63	60	58	56
Neither	13	10	10	9	14	11
Oppose	30	28	27	30	28	33
Stricter enforcement of rules on under-age sales						
Support	93	97	97	97	98	98
Neither	4	2	2	2	1	1
Oppose	3	1	1	2	1	1
More government funds for anti-smoking education						
Support	85	87	87	84	83	79
Neither	9	8	6	7	8	9
Oppose	6	5	7	10	10	12

Conclusions and implications

Uptake of smoking policies in the workplace, and support for smoke-free public places, are two ways of assessing the climate of opinion on non-smoking being the norm. Evidence in this chapter suggests that, whilst members of the population hold favourable views in most cases on these matters, there is still much to be done to promote healthier workplaces and public places.

Work needs to be continued to encourage workplaces to adopt smoking policies, with a particular push towards making the workplace smoke-free. A greater emphasis is also required on introducing such policies into the workplaces of manual employees.

The most popular measure in the workplace is the use of no-smoking signs. There was little support among employees for further action using the other measures listed on the questionnaire. Further work is required to change these attitudes among employees.

Stricter enforcement of the laws on under-age tobacco sales and more government funds for anti-smoking education were the two most popular of the possible government initiatives presented. A ban on advertising of tobacco products and an increase in the price of tobacco products through taxation attracted less support but were still supported by the majority of the population. Young people, in particular, were least likely to endorse these latter strategies, and also formed the group most concerned about policies that would impact upon their social lives, such as smoking bans in pubs, cafés and restaurants. These factors must be taken into account when planning initiatives that form part of these major strategies.

References

Department of Health (1992) *The Health of the Nation: a Strategy for Health in England*. Cm 1986. HMSO.

7. Cancer

Hilary Whent
Researcher
Health Education Authority
London

There is very little quantitative data from large-scale national surveys available about people's knowledge of cancer and their perceptions of the causes of cancer. The HEA's Health and Lifestyles Survey included twenty-one questions specifically relating to cancer; these asked about knowledge of types of cancer, knowledge of ways of reducing the risks of some specific cancers and reactions to a number of attitudinal statements.

Awareness of specific types of cancer
Respondents were asked 'Which specific types of cancer, if any, have you heard of?' and the question was unprompted.

Table 7.1: Specific types of cancer which respondents had heard of (%)

	Total	Women	Men
Lung cancer	66	59	74
Breast cancer	62	74	50
Cervical cancer	33	44	21
Leukaemia	28	31	25
Bowel cancer	28	29	27
Skin cancer	26	24	28
Stomach cancer	24	24	23
Throat cancer	24	22	27
Liver cancer	16	17	14
Bone cancer	12	14	10
Brain cancer/tumour	11	11	11
Testicular cancer	9	7	11
Cancer of the uterus (womb)	8	12	4
Cancer of the lymph glands	8	9	6
Cancer of the pancreas	5	5	4
Ovary (ovarian) cancer	5	8	2
Prostate cancer	4	4	4
Base: All	4 981	2 511	2 471

Awareness of specific cancers is related to a number of factors, including incidence and mortality, people's personal experiences, health promotion campaigns related to prevention, screening services and media coverage.

Table 7.1 shows high awareness of some of the most common causes of cancer mortality, with 74% of men mentioning lung cancer, 74% of women mentioning breast cancer and 59% mentioning lung cancer. Only 4% of men in the HEA's Health and Lifestyles Survey mentioned prostate cancer, despite its relatively high incidence. The high awareness of cervical cancer (mentioned by 44% of women) probably reflects the attention received in relation to the screening programme.

Table 7.2: Ten most commonly cited types of cancer by women by age

	16–24	25–34	35–44	45–54	55–64	65–74	All
Breast cancer	74	76	80	73	77	63	74
Lung cancer	64	63	68	57	52	42	59
Cervical cancer	49	52	49	42	39	26	44
Leukaemia	20	35	44	36	24	22	31
Bowel cancer	16	30	33	40	32	24	29
Skin cancer	25	25	26	27	22	16	24
Stomach cancer	15	23	30	28	27	23	24
Throat cancer	26	20	23	19	25	16	22
Liver cancer	10	19	19	21	19	15	17
Bone cancer	8	15	17	17	18	11	14
Cancer of the uterus (womb)	7	10	13	17	15	11	12
Base: Women	452	527	456	407	344	325	2 511

Table 7.3: Ten most commonly cited cancers by men by age

	16–24	25–34	35–44	45–54	55–64	65–74	All
Lung cancer	76	77	75	75	72	61	74
Breast cancer	54	58	55	45	42	33	50
Skin cancer	30	31	33	24	22	22	28
Throat cancer	30	28	27	30	23	19	27
Bowel cancer	13	26	30	36	33	25	27
Leukaemia	17	25	30	29	29	22	25
Stomach	13	25	25	25	27	28	23
Cervical cancer	20	26	22	18	22	15	21
Liver cancer	11	12	16	19	18	11	14
Testicular cancer	9	14	15	9	9	4	11
Base: Men	474	540	457	399	337	264	2 471

Awareness of certain types of cancer is age related; for example 49% of women aged 16–24 and 52% of women aged 25–34 mentioned cervical cancer compared to 26% of women in the 65–74 year old age group. Interestingly, prostate cancer which is common in men in older age groups is not reflected in the pattern of awareness.

In general, awareness of particular types of cancer decreases with lower socio-economic status of respondent; for example 37% of respondents in social classes I and II mentioned bowel cancer compared to 23% in social classes IV and V.

Personal experience and experience of cancer in close friends and relatives

Nearly all respondents (95% of women and 98% of men) claimed to have not personally ever suffered from any type of cancer (about 1% did not answer the question).

About 69% of women and 57% of men said that they knew of a close member of their family or close friend who had suffered from cancer. Not surprisingly these proportions increased with age of respondent. For example, 46% of 16–24 year olds knew of a close friend or relative who had suffered from cancer compared with 70% of 55–74 year olds.

Respondents' knowledge about reducing the risks of some specific cancers

Knowledge about the risk factors associated with cancer has increased considerably over the last 30 years. Studies amongst women in the 1960s (Briggs and Wakefield, 1967; Hobbs, 1967) found that when asked to name some of the risk factors associated with cancer, only a small proportion could do so. By the 1980s, however, this had changed as people had become aware of, for example, smoking, diet, drinking, exposure to sun, as risk factors for particular types of cancer (Cancer Relief Macmillan Fund, 1988). The present study indicates high levels of knowledge of risk factors for some cancers.

In the next section, it is important to note that all responses were unprompted but respondents were probed.

Lung cancer

The vast majority of lung cancer cases (81% in the UK) are caused by smoking (HEA, 1991). Recent research has shown that non-smokers are put at risk by being exposed to other people's smoke. It is estimated that about a quarter of all lung cancer cases in non-smokers are due to passive smoking (ISCSH, 1988)

In the Health and Lifestyles Survey the question: 'What if anything can people do to reduce the risk of lung cancer?'was asked. Almost all (95%) respondents said 'Not smoking/give up smoking'. This high awareness of smoking as a risk factor for lung cancer is in line with evidence from other surveys. The next most

148

common suggestion was 'Avoid passive smoking' (16%). There was evidence of a social class gradient with 25% from social classes I and II mentioning passive smoking compared to 11% in social class IIIM.

Bowel cancer

At present the evidence on dietary measures to prevent colorectal cancer is inconclusive. Certain factors may act as promoters of the disease, and these include a high consumption of fat, protein, alcohol and total calorific intake, while other substances including fibre, calcium and certain micro-nutrients may act as inhibitors of the disease. Overall, the evidence suggests that a healthy, well-balanced diet, rich in fruit and vegetables, starch and fibre (especially vegetable fibre) and low in fat and alcohol consumption may offer some protection – and certainly will do no harm (Cancer Research Campaign, 1993). In the Health and Lifestyles Survey respondents were asked 'What if anything can people do to reduce the risk of bowel cancer?' Table 7.4 shows the most common responses.

Table 7.4: Factors to reduce the risk of bowel cancer

	Total	Women	Men
Eat a (more) healthy diet (generally)	27	29	25
Eat more fibre/roughage/starchy foods	31	38	23
Don't know	44	38	50
Base: All	4 977	2 508	2 469

Table 7.5: Factors to reduce the risk of bowel cancer by age and sex

	16–24	25–34	35–44	45–54	55–64	65–74
Women						
Eat a (more) healthy diet (generally)	18	28	34	34	34	25
Eat more fibre/roughage/starchy foods	15	36	49	47	46	37
Don't know	62	39	29	28	27	40
Men						
Eat a (more) healthy diet (generally)	18	26	25	29	27	22
Eat more fibre/roughage/starchy foods	11	19	30	33	31	17
Don't know	67	52	45	39	43	52
Bases: Women	451	527	455	406	344	325
Men	474	538	456	398	339	264

About half of respondents mentioned something to do with diet — either eating a healthy diet (27%) or eating more fibre/roughage (31%). Women were more aware of ways to reduce the risk of bowel cancer than men. Awareness of the role for diet seems to be highest amongst women in the middle age-groups (Table 7.5). There also appeared to be a social class gradient with respondents from higher social grades more likely to suggest dietary factors than those from lower social classes. However, half (50%) of all men and almost 4 out of 10 (38%) of women said they did not know of any ways in which they could reduce the risk of bowel cancer.

Cancer of the cervix uteri (cervical cancer)

The risk of developing cervical cancer is closely related to sexual habits, with very low rates of the disease in nuns. Early age at first intercourse and multiple partners (often these two factors go together) are high-risk factors, and the risk for a woman is raised with the number of sexual contacts her partner has had.

The causes of the disease are not known but a sexually transmitted infection (genital wart virus) is implicated. In general, women of lower socio-economic status have higher rates of the disease, and women in developing countries are at greater risk than women in the developed world. Smoking is thought to increase a woman's susceptibility to the disease, and a history of dysplasia increases a woman's risk of developing invasive carcinoma (Cancer Research Campaign, 1990).

Cervical screening can both detect cancers early, when there is a better chance of recovery, and identify and treat conditions that might otherwise develop into cancer. All women aged 20 to 64 are now offered a free cervical smear test by the NHS.

In the HEA's Health and Lifestyles Survey, respondents were asked 'What, if anything, can people do to reduce their risk of cervical cancer?'

Table 7.6: Factors to reduce the risks of cervical cancer

	Total	Women	Men
Have regular screening/cervical smears/tests	42	51	34
Avoid having a large number of sexual partners	15	20	9
Use condoms/practice safe sex	9	12	5
Don't know	39	28	50
Base: All	4973	2507	2466

The majority of women (51%) and about a third of men (34%) mentioned having a regular smear test as a way of reducing the risk of cervical cancer. Only 5% of respondents (7% of women and 3% of men) suggested 'not smoking/give up smoking'. Around half of women in the target age group for screening suggested this as a way of reducing risk of cervical cancer.

There is a marked social class gradient: 63% of women from social classes I–II compared to 43% from social classes IV–V mentioned having regular cervical smears as a way of reducing the risk of cervical cancer. There was not, however, any clear social class gradient for the response about numbers of sexual partners or condom use.

Table 7.7: Factors to reduce the risks of cervical cancer by age

	16–24	25–34	35–44	45–54	55–64	65–74
Have regular screening/ cervical smears/tests	42	56	61	52	50	38
Avoid having a large number of sexual partners	12	21	25	24	22	15
Use condoms/practise safe sex	14	17	12	10	9	4
Don't know	37	21	19	23	29	44
Base: Women only	451	527	455	405	344	325

Skin cancer

Skin cancer is the second most common cancer in the UK. Most skin cancers are completely curable if detected early. However malignant melanoma is a comparatively rare but serious form of skin cancer which develops in the pigment-producing cells of the skin. Research indicates that for the average individual three factors are important in predicting the risk of malignant melanoma: skin type, exposure to the sun and changes in an existing mole.

Table 7.8 shows responses to the question: 'What do you think are the main causes of skin cancer?'

Table 7.8: Perceived causes of skin cancer

	Total	Women	Men
Exposure to sunlight	66	68	65
Getting sunburnt	12	13	10
Using sunbeds/solaria	9	12	7
Too much sun/ being in sun too long	10	12	9
Don't know	9	8	10
Base: All	4 978	2 507	2 470

About two-thirds (66%) of respondents knew that exposure to the sun was a risk factor for skin cancer. There was little variation in these responses by age, although significantly higher proportions of younger women cite 'using sunbeds/ solaria' as a main cause: 23% in the 16–24 year age group compared with 6% in the 55–64 year olds.

About half of respondents have picked up the appropriate health education messages as shown by Table 7.9 which gives some of the common responses to the question: 'What, if anything, can people do to reduce the risk of skin cancer?'

Table 7.9: Factors to reduce the risks of skin cancer

	Total	Women	Men
Protect themselves against the sun (e.g. filter creams/ lotions, shirt, hat, etc.)	55	55	55
Avoid the sun	47	49	46
Avoid sunburn	13	15	12
Avoid using sunbeds/solaria	7	9	5
Don't know	10	9	11
Base: All	4 978	2 507	2 470

Overall, about 85% of respondents mention something to do with the sun. However, about 1 in 10 (10%) respondents said they did not know of any ways to reduce the risk of skin cancer, and lack of knowledge was higher among those aged 16–24 (12% of women and 15% of men aged 16–24).

Who people would talk to if they were worried about getting cancer

Previous studies have shown an unwillingness to talk about cancer amongst respondents (Charlton, 1979). In this study respondents who had not personally suffered from cancer, were asked who they would talk to if they were personally worried about getting cancer. A list of possibilities was provided. Three out of four (76%) respondents said they would talk to a GP or doctor. Among those aged 25–54 spouse/partner was cited as the next most common point of contact, while among 16–24 year olds parents were seen as the next most common point of contact. Friends were also a common choice, particularly amongst younger age groups. Only 2% of people said they would talk to no one.

Table 7.10: Who people would talk to if they were worried about getting cancer

	Total	Women	Men
Spouse/partner	41	40	43
Parents	20	20	20
Other relatives	14	16	11
Friends	20	23	17
GP/doctor	76	75	78
Base: All	4 788	2 374	2 414

Table 7.11: Who people would talk to if they were worried about getting cancer by age

	Age groups					
	16–24	25–34	35–44	45–54	55–64	65–74
Spouse/partner	23	50	50	46	38	35
Parents	53	31	12	5	2	1
Other relatives	13	13	12	14	15	15
Friends	37	23	18	15	11	7
GP/doctor	69	76	75	78	83	78
Base: All	915	1 035	882	771	644	541

Personal risk of cancer

Surveys carried out in the 1950s found high levels of worry about cancer amongst respondents (Paterson and Aitken-Swan, 1954 and 1958). In recent years there is some evidence to suggest that these levels of anxiety about cancer have reduced amongst the public (Briggs and Wakefield, 1967; Knopf, 1974; Davison, Cartwright and Gillis, 1984; Cancer Relief Macmillan Fund, 1988; Charlton, 1994). In this survey two-thirds of respondents who had not personally suffered from cancer said that they did not worry about getting cancer themselves. Although 10% of the women specifically mentioned breast cancer most of the respondents (22% of the women and 18% of the men) who said they did worry, said that their worry was about cancer in general rather than a specific cancer.

These respondents were also asked if they considered themselves personally at risk from cancer, or not – 62% said that they did not. Amongst regular smokers 36% perceived themselves at risk of lung cancer specifically compared with 3% amongst never smokers and 5% amongst ex-smokers.

Sources of information about cancer

About half (54%) of all respondents said they felt informed about cancer. This feeling tends to increase with age. Women, particularly in the older age groups, were more likely to indicate they felt informed than men.

Table 7.12: How well informed respondents felt about cancer

		16–24	25–34	35–44	45–54	55–64	65–74	All
Women	Informed	41	54	64	65	68	62	58
	Not informed	58	46	36	34	32	36	41
Men	Informed	41	42	55	57	53	62	50
	Not informed	58	57	45	41	45	36	49
Bases:	Women	451	525	454	406	344	325	2 505
	Men	474	540	457	399	337	264	2 470

When asked where they had got most of their information about cancer from, the most common responses were television programmes, newspaper or magazine articles and friends or relatives (Table 7.13). Over half (52%) of respondents cited television and radio as their main source of information, while 4 out of 10 mentioned contact with friends/relatives and newspapers or magazines. Fewer than 1 in 10 (8%) respondents said their knowledge about cancer came from health professionals such as GPs or practice nurses.

Table 7.13: Sources of respondents' current knowledge about cancer (%)

	Total	Women	Men
Contact with health professionals	8	11	6
Contact with others	42	45	39
TV and radio	52	47	57
Newspapers/magazines	41	42	40
Posters and leaflets	18	20	15

Respondents were also asked where they would go if they wanted more information about cancer, either generally or on any specific type of cancer. Unlike the previous question the majority (70%) spontaneously said they would consult their GP or doctor. Very few said they would get information from television/radio or from magazines, although almost 1 in 5 said they would consult library books.

Table 7.14: Main sources that respondents would consult if they wanted to know more about cancer (%)

	Total	Women	Men
Contact with health professionals	70	69	71
Contact with others	8	8	8
TV and radio	1	1	1
Newspapers/magazines	1	1	1
Posters and leaflets	16	17	14

Cancer screening

Respondents were asked if they had ever been for screening for any type of cancer. Around half of women in the appropriate age group for the National Breast Screening Programme (this provides for women aged 20 to 64 to be screened every three years) claim to have been screened for breast cancer. The majority (91%) were carried out on the NHS. Amongst the 20–64 year age group women from higher social classes are more likely to have been screened than those in lower social classes; 61% in social classes I and II and 44% in IV and V.

Table 7.15: Screening for different types of cancer (women)

	16–24	25–34	35–44	45–54	55–64	65–74	All
Breast cancer	1	9	15	37	55	20	21
Cervical cancer	36	72	74	66	66	40	60
Skin cancer	*	*	*	1	1	*	*
Other	*	1	4	5	7	5	3
No, never had screening	63	25	22	19	14	47	32
Don't know	*	*	1	*	2	1	1
Base: Women	449	521	453	400	345	327	2 494

* <0.5%

Table 7.16: Screening for different types of cancer (men)

	16–24	25–34	35–44	45–54	55–64	65–74	All
Skin cancer	*	*	*	1	1	*	*
Testicular		1	2	1	1	*	1
Other	1	4	10	14	15	18	9
No, never had screening	99	93	88	82	83	80	89
Don't know	13	12	20	19	21	10	1
Base: Men	462	528	436	388	319	258	2 392

* <0.5%

Cervical smear tests

Cervical smears tests have been provided in Britain since 1967. It is recommended that women aged 20 to 64 should be screened every three years (Report of Intercollegiate Working Party, 1987) and a computerised call/recall system was established in all District Health Authorities in 1988 (Department of Health and Social Security, 1988). Data for 1992/93 indicate that there was 83% coverage in the age group in England (Department of Health, 1990–94). In the Health and Lifestyles Survey all women were asked if they had ever had a cervical smear. Over 8 out of 10 (82%) of women said they had had a test and this proportion rose in the relevant age group. There is a social class gradient, with 92% of women from social classes I–II compared with 82% amongst those from social classes IV–V and 78% amongst those not working saying they had had a test.

Women were asked if: 'In the last 12 months has any health professional suggested you consider having a smear test or given you an appointment or a written invitation to have a cervical smear test?' High proportions (about 75%) who had not had a test in the last 3 years replied no or don't know to this question.

Attitudes towards cancer

Respondents were asked whether they agreed or disagreed with a number of statements, which aimed to assess public attitudes towards cancer. Development of cancer treatment and preventive services need to take account of public perceptions. The first was: 'If I was suffering from cancer I would rather not know about it'. Over three-quarters (78%) disagreed with this statement, although this declined with age.

Table 7.17: Attitude to statement 'If I was suffering from cancer I would rather not know about it'

	16–24	25–34	35–44	45–54	55–64	65–74	All
Women							
Agree	15	8	11	15	16	23	14
Disagree	80	84	82	76	74	65	78
Men							
Agree	13	13	12	19	15	20	15
Disagree	78	81	80	74	79	76	78
Bases: Women	452	526	454	406	344	325	2508
Men	472	536	454	397	337	264	2460

There is a social gradient with regards to disagreement and agreement with this statement, for example amongst social class I and II respondents 86% disagreed, whilst amongst IV and V 71% disagreed.

Respondents were also asked about the statement: 'One of the things that frightens me most about cancer is the side-effects of the treatments'. Over half of respondents agreed with this statement, with women more likely than men to agree (63% and 51% respectively).

Table 7.18: Attitude to statement 'One of the things that frightens me most about cancer is the side-effects of the treatments'

	16–24	25–34	35–44	45–54	55–64	65–74	All
Women							
Agree	58	61	64	65	66	67	63
Disagree	25	24	23	20	22	21	23
Men							
Agree	46	57	50	53	52	49	51
Disagree	29	27	33	31	32	32	30
Bases: Women	452	526	454	406	344	325	2508
Men	472	536	454	397	337	264	2460

The final attitudinal statement was: 'These days people can have a good chance of recovering from cancer if it's detected early enough'. The majority of respondents (90%) agreed with this statement.

Table 7.19: Attitude to statement 'These days people can have a good chance of recovering from cancer if it's detected early enough'

	16–24	25–34	35–44	45–54	55–64	65–74	All
Women							
Agree	89	89	91	92	91	92	91
Disagree	4	4	3	3	2	2	3
Men							
Agree	90	90	88	89	94	89	90
Disagree	2	4	6	4	2	3	4
Bases: Women	452	526	454	406	344	325	2 508
Men	472	536	454	397	337	264	2 460

References

Briggs, J. E. and Wakefield, J. (1967) *Public Opinion on Cancer: a Survey of Knowledge and Attitudes among Women in Lancaster.* Department of Social Research, Christie Hospital, Manchester.

Cancer Relief Macmillan Fund (1988) *Public Attitudes to and Knowledge of Cancer in the UK.* Cancer Relief Macmillan Fund.

Cancer Research Campaign (1990) *Cancer of the Cervix Uteri.* Factsheet 12.1. Cancer Research Campaign.

Cancer Research Campaign (1993) *Cancer of the Large Bowel.* Factsheet 18.1. Cancer Research Campaign.

Charlton, A. (1979) 'An evaluation study of two different approaches to teaching about cancer in secondary schools'. *International Journal of Health Education,* **22**, 42–48.

Charlton, A. (1994) *Changing Views of Cancer in Britain: a Review based on Eight Surveys.* Cancer Research Campaign.

Davison, R. L., Cartwright, R. A. and Gillis, C. (1984) *Knowledge and Opinion about Cancer in Bury, Lancashire, 1980.* Manchester Regional Committee for Cancer Education.

Department of Health and Social Security (1988) *Health Circular HC (88)1* 'Health Service management, cervical cancer screening'.

Department of Health (1990–94) *Cervical Cytology, England (1988/9–1992/3)* (Form KC53).

Health Education Authority (1991) *The Smoking Epidemic: Counting the Cost in England.* HEA.

Hobbs, P. (1967) *Public Opinion on Cancer: a Survey of Knowledge and Attitudes among Women in Merseyside*. Merseyside Cancer Education Committee, Liverpool.

Independent Scientific Committee on Smoking and Health (1988) *Fourth Report* [The Froggatt Report]. HMSO.

Knopf, A. (1974) *Cancer: Changes in Opinion after Seven Years of Public Education in Lancaster*. Department of Social Research, Christie Hospital, Manchester.

Paterson, R. and Aitken-Swan, J. (1954) 'Public opinion on cancer: a survey among women in the Manchester area'. *Lancet*, 23 October, 857–61.

Paterson, R. and Aitken-Swan, J. (1958) 'Public opinion on cancer: changes following five years of public education'. *Lancet*, 11 October, 791–3.

Report of the Intercollegiate Working Party on Cervical Cytology Screening (1987) Royal College of Obstetricians and Gynaecologists. London.

8. Sexual health

Alan Glanz
Formerly Senior Researcher
Health Education Authority
London

Introduction

The pattern of sexual behaviour and related attitudes in the population has both personal and public health significance. The national strategy for health – set out in the government's White Paper *The Health of the Nation* (Department of Health, 1992) – specifies a number of objectives and targets relating to HIV/AIDS and sexual health, including:

- to reduce the incidence of HIV infection and of other sexually transmitted diseases;

- to reduce the incidence of gonorrhoea among men and women age 15–64 by at least 20% by 1995;

- to reduce the rate of conceptions amongst the under-16s by at least 50% by the year 2000.

In its role of supporting the Health of the Nation strategy, the HEA has developed health promotion objectives and programmes in the field of sexual health. The sexual health component of the HEA's Health and Lifestyles Survey was designed to assist in assessing progress towards Health of Nation targets and monitoring indicators of effective sexual health promotion. Furthermore, the findings will hopefully contribute to a better understanding of the dynamics of beliefs and behaviour in this area and thereby improve the targeting, design and delivery of sexual health promotion initiatives.

In the light of the sensitivity of the issues covered, the sexual health module of the Health and Lifestyles Survey adopted a self-completion rather than interview format, as did the National Survey of Sexual Attitudes and Lifestyles (NSSAL) in relation to the more personal areas which that survey covered (Johnson, Wadsworth, Wellings and Field, 1994).

(Note: In all the tables included here figures may not sum to exactly 100 due to rounding of weighted numbers. Bases shown are weighted bases and vary because of item non-response. Statistical tests are conducted on unweighted data.)

Knowledge

Feeling well-informed about sexual health matters

The opening section of the questionnaire aimed to assess how well-informed people felt about certain aspects of sexual health. This was designed to be a relatively gentle introduction to the self-completion questionnaire, hopefully allaying anxieties about the personal nature of the questions to follow and familiarising respondents with the format. It was not the intention to 'test' people's knowledge on these topics. Respondents were asked to indicate how well-informed they felt about the matters listed, with response options ranging from 'very well-informed' to 'not at all well-informed'. This kind of subjective assessment clearly has limitations as an indicator of 'real' levels of knowledge in the population, since an individual's self-assessment will not necessarily coincide with objective measures. Nevertheless, the results are likely to give some indication of the pattern of information needs in the population and suggest issues for further investigation.

Contraception/birth control and abortion

Virtually all respondents felt at least fairly well-informed about contraception and birth control (Table 8.1). Women (68%) were more likely than men (53%) to feel very well-informed. Men aged 16–19 years appear to have the greatest information deficit, with 10% stating they were not very well or not at all well-informed about contraception and birth control, compared with 5% among women in this age group. This difference may to some extent be a reflection of different sex education experience at school. The HEA's *Today's Young Adults* national survey of 16–19 year olds found that 85% of young women had had lessons on contraception and birth control, compared to 77% of young men (HEA, 1992).

Both men and women were less likely to feel well-informed about abortion than about contraception and birth control. Overall, 64% of women and 61% of men felt at least fairly well-informed (Table 8.1). The difference between men and women in relation to this issue is smaller than in relation to contraception and birth control: 27% of women and 22% of men felt very well-informed. This overall difference between men and women is reflected among the youngest age group, where 34% of women aged 16–19 years and 27% of men in this age group felt very well-informed.

161

Table 8.1: How well-informed respondents feel about contraception/birth control and abortion (%)

	Contraception and birth control				Abortion			
	Very/fairly well-informed	Not very/ not at all well-informed	Don't know	Base	Very/fairly well-informed	Not very/ not at all well-informed	Don't know	Base
Women								
16–24	94	6	1	366	59	34	7	365
25–34	99	1	0	287	62	33	5	281
35–44	99	1	0	484	67	26	6	471
45–54	95	3	2	558	65	29	5	542
All	96	3	·1	1 695	64	30	6	1 659
Men								
16–24	89	7	3	511	54	39	7	503
25–34	95	5	0	577	56	39	5	562
35–44	95	3	1	488	66	30	4	480
45–54	95	3	2	436	68	26	6	414
All	94	5	2	2 012	61	34	5	1 958

HIV/AIDS and other STDs

In contrast with the previous sexual health topics, it is men who are more likely to feel well-informed about the risks of HIV and AIDS: 78% of women felt at least fairly well-informed, compared to 88% of men. Just over one-third of women (34%) and 42% of men felt very well-informed. There remains a significant proportion of the population who do not feel well-informed on this important matter: 11% of men and 20% of women reported that they were not very well-informed or not at all well-informed about HIV and AIDS. It is notable that almost one in five 16–24 year old women (19%), compared to 7% of men in this age group, felt not very or not at all well-informed about the risks of HIV and AIDS. Of particular concern is the low perceived information level of 16–19 year old women, 21% of whom stated they felt not very or not at all well-informed about HIV and AIDS. Recent qualitative research has revealed that a number of aspects of HIV transmission remain poorly understood among young people in this country (Cragg, Hainge, Taylor and Porter, 1993), and the Health and Lifestyles Survey findings indicate scope for continued education in this area.

The Health of the Nation set a specific target for sexually transmitted diseases: to reduce the incidence of gonorrhoea among both men and women aged 16–54 by at least 20% by 1995 (from 61 new cases per 1000 population in 1990 to no more than 49 per 1000). In addition, the objectives set in the area of HIV/AIDS and sexual health included: to reduce the incidence of sexually transmitted diseases. In

Table 8.2: How well-informed respondents feel about the risks of HIV/AIDS and the risks of other sexually transmitted diseases, by gender and age group (%)

	HIV and AIDS				Other sexually transmitted diseases			
	Very/fairly well-informed	Not very/ not at all well-informed	Don't know	Base	Very/fairly well-informed	Not very/ not at all well-informed	Don't know	Base
Women								
16–24	78	19	3	364	70	27	3	366
25–34	79	19	1	285	72	26	2	285
35–44	80	17	2	482	76	22	2	478
45–54	75	22	3	560	68	30	3	552
All	78	20	3	1 690	71	26	3	1 682
Men								
16–24	91	7	2	511	76	22	2	511
25–34	86	13	1	577	77	22	1	576
35–44	87	11	2	488	79	19	2	487
45–54	86	13	1	436	79	21	1	424
All	88	11	1	2 012	78	21	1	1 998

the Health and Lifestyles Survey three-quarters of respondents felt well-informed and 23% not well-informed about the risks of other (i.e. apart from HIV/AIDS) sexually transmitted diseases. There is a gender difference in relation to feeling well-informed about other sexually transmitted diseases: 78% of men felt at least fairly well-informed, compared to 71% of women. Department of Health figures show that in 1992, 1370 cases of gonorrhoea, 4209 cases of chlamydia, and 6269 cases of wart virus were seen among 16–19 year old women at NHS GUM clinics, which represent the highest rates for any age-sex group.[1] Thus it is of concern that, 16–19 year-old women have the lowest rate of self-assessed knowledge, with 30% feeling not very or not at all well-informed about STDs.

Menstruation, pre-menstrual tension, and the menopause
Not surprisingly, women were far more likely than men to feel well-informed about menstruation (periods) (Table 8.3). Around two-thirds of women in each age group felt very well-informed. Among men, those in older age groups were more likely to feel very well-informed.

Nearly three-quarters of women (74%) felt at least fairly well-informed about PMT, with younger women being less well infomred (around one third of 16–24

---

[1] New cases seen at NHS GUM clinics in England: 1992 annual figures (DH Statistics Division, 1993).

Table 8.3: How well-informed respondents feel about menstruation, pre-menstrual tension, and the menopause, by gender and age group (%)

	Menstruation				Pre-menstrual tension				The menopause (the change)			
	Very/fairly well-informed	Not very/not at all well-informed	Don't know	Base	Very/fairly well-informed	Not very/not at all well-informed	Don't know	Base	Very/fairly well-informed	Not very/not at all well-informed	Don't know	Base
Women												
16–24	92	8	1	365	61	34	4	361	33	57	10	357
25–34	96	4	0	285	73	25	2	280	35	61	4	281
35–44	96	4	1	473	79	20	1	470	52	47	1	473
45–54	96	4	1	551	79	19	2	546	71	26	1	549
All	95	4	1	1673	74	24	2	1657	52	45	4	1660
Men												
16–24	49	39	12	495	27	55	17	491	24	60	16	596
25–34	64	31	5	560	42	49	8	557	24	67	9	553
35–44	76	19	5	478	51	41	7	470	33	58	7	474
45–54	74	18	9	415	56	33	10	396	55	37	8	409
All	65	27	8	1949	44	46	11	1915	33	57	10	1933

year olds reported they were not very/not at all well informed). Just over four out of ten men (44%) felt at least fairly well-informed about PMT, with this being indicated by only 27% of 16–24 year old men.

While 52% of women overall felt at least fairly well-informed about the menopause (the change), more than a quarter (26%) of women in the age group 45–54 years stated that they felt not very or not at all well-informed about the menopause. Only one-third of men overall felt at least fairly well-informed about this matter, and among men aged 45–54 years 37% felt not very or not at all well-informed about the menopause.

Emotional side of sexual relationships

Overall a quarter of women and one-third of men felt not very or not at all well-informed about the emotional side of sexual relationships (Table 8.4). Among 16–19 year olds these were rated notably higher: 38% of women and 43% of men in this age group felt not very or not at all well-informed about the emotional side.

The emotional aspects of sexual relationships receives less attention in sexual health education than biological or medical aspects. In the HEA's national survey of young adults 59% of 16–19 year olds reported that sexual relationships had been covered as a topic in sex education in school, and only 32% reported that sexual feelings and emotions had been covered (HEA, 1992). The deficit in confidence among young people, suggested by the results of the Health and Lifestyles Survey, regarding their awareness of the emotional side of sexual relationships could be addressed through more comprehensive school-based approaches.

Table 8.4: How well-informed respondents felt about the emotional side of sexual relationships, by gender and age group (%)

	Emotional side of sexual relationships			
	Very/fairly well-informed	Not very/ not at all well-informed	Don't know	Base
Women				
16–24	62	34	4	365
25–34	72	24	3	284
35–44	74	22	5	479
45–54	74	23	4	557
All	71	25	4	1 686
Men				
16–24	56	42	2	510
25–34	64	34	2	578
35–44	67	30	4	489
45–54	74	23	3	427
All	65	32	3	2 003

Attitudes

Risk perception

Risk perception plays an important conceptual role in certain models of health behaviour, for example the health belief model (Rosenstock, 1974). A number of items in the questionnaire aimed to elicit aspects of perceived risk of HIV and AIDS. Table 8.5 shows the results for perceived risk at the societal level, with response categories 'very high' and 'quite high' collapsed to 'high' and similarly for 'low'.

Table 8.5: **Perceived risk of HIV/AIDS, by gender and age group(1): 'What do you think are the chances on average these days of people in this country getting HIV from sexual intercourse without a condom between men and women?'**

	Age group				
	16–24 %	25–34 %	35–44 %	45–54 %	All %
Men					
High	47	44	45	50	46
Moderate	41	35	34	29	35
Low	11	21	22	22	18
Base	496	551	455	399	1 902
Women					
High	67	66	65	69	66
Moderate	28	27	27	22	26
Low	6	7	8	8	7
Base	363	284	472	528	1 647

For both men and women there is very little variation between age groups in the degree of perceived risk of HIV infection for people in this country through heterosexual intercourse without using a condom. However, women are more likely than men to perceive a higher societal risk of HIV ($\chi^2 = 174.4$, 2df, p .001). More than one half of respondents (56%) perceived the heterosexual risk to be at least quite high, with one-quarter (24%) believing it was very high. This level of perceived risk is remarkably high given the prevalence of AIDS and HIV infection in the population around the time of the survey.

Responses to a further item in the questionnaire tapping perceived risk of HIV also indicate a belief in a relatively high level of risk for heterosexuals. This item focused on the credibility of official versions of the risk to heterosexuals. Table 8.6 shows the results.

Around the time of the Health and Lifestyles Survey high profile mass media campaigns produced by the HEA were under way, emphasising the threat of HIV infection to sections of the population beyond traditionally defined 'high-risk' groups. There was little difference between men and women in response to this question, and when those responding 'don't know' are eliminated from the base we find that overall seven out of ten respondents (70%) disagreed with the view that government and health officials had exaggerated the risk of HIV 'for people like me'. The formulation of this question introduces a more personal assessment of risk, and this may have lead to the considerably greater perception among the oldest age group of respondents (45–54 year olds) of both men and women that the HIV risk has been exaggerated by officials.

Table 8.6: **Perceived risk of HIV/AIDS, by gender and age group(2): 'The risk for people like me of getting HIV has been exaggerated by government and health officials'**

	Age group				
	16–24 %	25–34 %	35–44 %	45–54 %	All %
Men					
Agree	23	24	29	38	28
Disagree	67	65	60	51	61
Don't know	11	11	11	12	11
Base	490	548	447	385	1 870
Women					
Agree	19	20	25	35	26
Disagree	68	68	63	53	62
Don't know	13	12	11	12	12
Base	358	277	460	503	1 598

Investigations in social psychology have demonstrated the tendency for people to have an 'optimistic bias' when assessing their own risk of negative health events relative to that of others, and that this is particularly likely when the events are outside of personal experience and particularly undesirable (Weinstein, 1980). The Health and Lifestyles Survey suggests that this process applies in the case of HIV. Nearly two-thirds (64%) of respondents rated their chances of getting HIV as less than average and just over a quarter (26%) as about average *compared to others of the same sex and age as themselves*. Although research on perceptions of HIV risk among young people has revealed a high degree of perceived 'invulnerability' (Abrams, 1993), the Health and Lifestyles data show that the 'optimistic bias' is relatively less evident in young people among both men and women. Table 8.7 shows the distribution of responses to this question by gender and age group.

Table 8.7: Perceived risk of HIV/AIDS, by gender and age group(3): 'Compared to other men (women) of your age living in this country, do you feel that your chances of getting HIV from vaginal sexual intercourse without a condom are ...'

	Age group				
	16–24 %	25–34 %	35–44 %	45–54 %	All %
Men					
Less than average	53	66	75	70	65
About average	38	21	20	20	25
Greater than average	9	13	5	10	9
Base	477	546	445	398	1 866
Women					
Less than average	43	66	66	69	62
About average	43	25	23	22	27
Greater than average	14	10	11	9	11
Base	363	284	472	528	1 647

Finally in relation to perceived personal risk of HIV, about two-thirds of respondents (67%) agreed with the statement 'I don't think I'll ever get HIV'. No gender difference emerged. However, an age gradient in perceived personal risk is clear, with 16–24 year olds very much more likely than other age groups to *disagree* with the prediction that they will never get HIV (Table 8.8).

Table 8.8:   Perceived risk of HIV/AIDS, by gender and age group:(4) 'I don't think I'll ever get HIV'

	Age group				
	16–24 %	25–34 %	35–44 %	45–54 %	All %
Men					
Agree	55	69	74	77	68
Disagree	26	14	11	7	15
Don't know	19	17	15	16	17
Base	486	549	447	384	1 867
Women					
Agree	48	63	72	71	65
Disagree	31	17	10	7	15
Don't know	20	20	18	22	20
Base	360	280	462	523	1 626

Do those with more sexual partners have a higher level of perceived personal risk? Applying a trend test shows that a linear relationship exists between level of perceived personal risk and increasing numbers of sexual partners: 16% of respondents with one or no partners in the last 12 months *disagreed* with the statement 'I don't think I'll ever get HIV'; 26% of those with two partners disagreed; and 37% of those with three or more partners disagreed ($\chi^2_{(t)} = 61.1$, 1df, $p < .001$).

The relationship between number of partners and perceived relative personal risk is a little less clear-cut. In respect of rating their own chances of HIV infection compared to others of the same sex and age as themselves, respondents with one or no partners in the last 12 months had a similar level of perceived risk to those with two partners – 10% of the former and 9% of the latter rated their chances as greater than average. However, 15% of respondents with at least three partners rated their chances as greater than average ($\chi^2_{(t)} = 44.1$, 1df, $p < .001$).

Since a large majority (85%) of those with three or more partners – who comprise only 7% of respondents – still regard their personal risk as about or below average compared with other people of the same age and sex as themselves, the question arises whether perception of the behavioural norm or average adjusts itself to preserve the 'optimistic bias' regarding the relative risks to one's own health. This would have implications regarding approaches to health education based on raising perceived personal risk.

The relationship between perceived risk and aspects of sexual health behaviour will be explored in a subsequent section.

Attitudes towards condoms

The health education message regarding HIV and other STD prevention has centred heavily on using condoms for protection. While the general public are well-informed about this protective role, the use of condoms on appropriate occasions may be inhibited by certain attitudinal barriers (HEA, 1994). In the Health and Lifestyles Survey, therefore, attitudes were explored to a few such potential barriers.

One possible obstacle to condom use is a perception of the unreliability of this method in relation to prevention of unwanted pregnancy. The failure rate of condoms is higher than that of oral contraceptives and IUDs. The nature of this failure may, of course, involve user 'failure' and/or product failure. Whatever the reason, the Health and Lifestyles reveals that there is a widespread perception that condoms are too unreliable as a method of contraception (Table 8.9).

Table 8.9:   Attitudes to condoms (1): 'Condoms are too unreliable as a method of contraception'

	Age group				
	16–24 %	25–34 %	35–44 %	45–54 %	All %
Men					
Agree	26	34	34	38	33
Disagree	65	58	60	54	59
Don't know	9	8	6	9	8
Base	495	546	452	384	1 877
Women					
Agree	36	38	45	47	42
Disagree	58	55	47	44	50
Don't know	6	7	8	9	8
Base	364	280	459	501	1604

Overall, just under four out of ten respondents (38%) agreed that 'Condoms are too unreliable as a method of contraception', and women (42%) were more likely than men (33%) to hold this view ($\chi^2 = 22.7$, 2df, $p < .001$). Among both men and women 16–19 year olds were the least negative in this respect, with 27% of women and 18% of men in this age group in agreement. Among all respondents those with sexual experience – i.e. had 'ever' had sexual intercourse – were more likely (38%) than those with no sexual experience (29%) to agree that condoms were unreliable for contraception ($\chi^2 = 33.6$, 2df, $p < .001$).

A further potential barrier to condom use is the belief that this suggestion may carry connotations of implied lack of fidelity or disease risk and thus provoke a negative reaction by a sexual partner (Cragg, Hainge, Taylor and Porter, 1994). For women in particular there is a problem in negotiating condom use in a context of unequal gender power relations (Holland *et al.*, 1991). The existence of a problem of this kind is supported by the data in the Health and Lifestyles Survey, which show that almost one half (47%) of 16–24 year old women agreed that 'Women often do not suggest using a condom with a new partner because they are afraid of being rejected by that partner' (Table 8.10). Among 16–19 year old women the rate was 50%. This is close to twice the rate of agreement found among the same age group of men (26%) and considerably higher than among 20-24 year old men (38%). There would appear to be some failure of perception on the part of young men that fear of being rejected might commonly inhibit their female sexual partners from suggesting they use a condom.

Table 8.10: Attitudes to condoms (2): 'Women often do not suggest using a condom with a new partner because they are afraid of being rejected by that partner'

	Age group				
	16–24 %	25–34 %	35–44 %	45–54 %	All %
Men					
Agree	34	40	35	39	37
Disagree	43	40	33	22	35
Don't know	23	20	32	39	28
Base	486	548	450	385	1 869
Women					
Agree	47	47	43	41	44
Disagree	42	36	32	22	32
Don't know	11	18	25	37	24
Base	364	280	466	505	1 615

A number of studies have found that for many people a safer sex strategy consists in the belief that they can and do choose 'safe' partners and therefore do not need additional means of protection (Dockrell, Joffe and Blud, 1994; Wight, 1993a). However, the Health and Lifestyles Survey suggests that, at least at the level of generality, it is the predominant view that careful choice of sexual partners *does not* obviate the need for using condoms (Table 8.11).

Overall, roughly one in five (21%) respondents agreed that 'You don't need to use condoms for protection against HIV if you are careful about the sexual partners you choose'. However there is a clear gender difference on this issue: 17% of women agreed, compared with 25% of men ($\chi^2 = 37.0$, 2df, $p < .001$). Men in the older age groups tend to have the highest levels of agreement. The gender difference is smallest amongst the youngest age group: 15% of 16–19 year old women agreed, compared to 18% of 16–19 year old men.

The relationship between attitudes to condoms and sexual behaviour, including condom use, will be explored in a subsequent section.

Table 8.11: Attitudes to condoms (3): 'You don't need to use a condom for protection against HIV if you are careful about the sexual partners you choose'

	Age group				
	16–24 %	25–34 %	35–44 %	45–54 %	All %
Men					
Agree	20	23	26	31	25
Disagree	72	73	68	61	69
Don't know	7	4	5	8	6
Base	488	550	448	385	1 872
Women					
Agree	17	16	16	18	17
Disagree	80	80	77	73	77
Don't know	3	4	7	9	6
Base	364	281	461	509	1 616

Sexual health education

Sex education in schools remains a highly controversial issue. New arrangements have recently been introduced by the government. As an indicator of opinions about the kind of sex education which should be taught in schools, respondents were asked whether they agreed or disagreed that 'Sex education in schools should include information on how to use a condom'. The response was overwhelmingly positive: almost nine out of ten (87%) of respondents agreed. No gender differences emerged, and only the 45–54 years age group among both men and women had higher levels of disagreement. Among 16–19 year olds, 89% of men and 91% of women agreed, and this age group had the highest proportion stating they strongly agreed – 56% among both men and women.

Qualitative research has suggested that young people commonly find it difficult to communicate with their parents on sexual matters (Cragg, Hainge, Taylor and Porter, 1994). In the Health and Lifestyles Survey more than eight out of ten respondents (82%) agreed with statement that 'Most parents don't talk openly to their children about sexual health matters'. There is remarkably little difference between age groups in levels of agreement with this view. However, the youngest age groups of men and women had the highest level of disagreement: 17% of 16–19 year old men and 14% of 16–19 year old women.

Substantial support was expressed for the proposition that 'AIDS educational advertising on the TV should show how condoms should be used'. Overall, just under two-thirds of respondents (64%) agreed. Women were less likely to agree (59%) than men (68%), and the highest level of agreement was among 20–24 year old men (72%).

Sexual behaviour

Sexual experience
Over nine out of ten respondents (91%) reported that they had 'ever' had sexual intercourse, and women (93%) were somewhat more likely than men (90%) to be sexually experienced. Table 8.12 shows the rates of sexual experience for men and women in different age groups.

Table 8.12: Ever had sexual intercourse with a person of the opposite sex by gender and age group (%)

Men

	16–24	25–34	35–44	45–54	All
Yes	74	94	96	97	90
No	26	6	4	3	10
Base	506	570	480	417	1 973

Women

	16–24	25–34	35–44	45–54	All
Yes	81	97	97	96	93
No	19	3	3	4	7
Base	362	285	483	553	1 683

Sexually experienced young people
In addition the survey found that 61% of 16–19 year olds had had sexual intercourse. Men (59%) were somewhat less likely then women (63%) in this age group to be sexually experienced. This finding that women are likely to gain sexual experience at an earlier age is consistent with evidence from the NSSAL of a tendency for women to have older sexual partners (Johnson, Wadsworth, Wellings and Field, 1994).

The likelihood of having had sexual intercourse among 16–19 year olds and 16–24 year olds was not associated with social class (indicated by occupation of the head of household). However, an interesting indication of the covariance of health behaviours among young people is that the relative risk of being a current smoker is 3.2 (95% CI, 2.2 to 4.9) for 16–19 year olds who had had sexual intercourse compared to those who were not yet sexually experienced.

Number of partners in the last 12 months

Table 8.13 shows the distribution by gender and age group of reported numbers of sexual partners over the last 12 months for all respondents. The general pattern for men and women is very similar to that found in the NSSAL (Johnson *et al.*, 1994), which increases confidence in the reliability of the results of the HEA's considerably smaller-scale Health and Lifestyles Survey.

Table 8.13: Distribution of numbers of sexual partners in the last 12 months by gender and age group. (Comparable figures in brackets for gender-based totals from NSSAL: Johnson, Wadsworth, Wellings and Field, 1994) (%)

Men

	16–24	25–34	35–44	45–54	All	(NSSAL)
0	29	9	8	7	14	(13)
1	43	70	78	84	68	(73)
2	13	8	7	4	8	(8)
3–4	11	7	3	3	6	(4)
5+	4	6	3	2	4	(2)
Base	496	555	472	395	1 917	

Women

	16–24	25–34	35–44	45–54	All	(NSSAL)
0	23	6	6	5	13	(14)
1	61	86	87	80	79	(79)
2	9	5	4	4	6	(5)
3–4	4	2	2	1	2	(2)
5+	2	1	1	1	1	(0.4)
Base	354	279	469	521	1 623	

The Health and Lifestyles Survey, however, suggests a somewhat higher rate than found by the NSSAL of people having two or more sexual partners in a 12-month period. There are methodological differences between the two national surveys which make direct comparisons problematic. For example, the NSSAL covered the age rage 16–59 years, whereas the Health and Lifestyles Survey respondents were 16–54 for the sexual health questionnaire. In addition, while both surveys used self-completion methods, the question format for eliciting the number of partners differed: writing a number in a box in the case of the NSSAL, ticking a numerically pre-labelled box in the Health and Lifestyles Survey. Apart from the effects of sampling variation, a possible factor which might have led to the Health and Lifestyles Survey finding a greater proportion of respondents reporting higher numbers of sexual partners is that the box-ticking method may have reduced the self-consciousness which could inhibit – even in a self-completion questionnaire – those with more partners from reporting this behaviour. However, no research evidence is available on this methodological issue.

A finding in common between the NSSAL and the Health and Lifestyles Survey is the higher numbers of partners claimed by men. This is a widespread finding in surveys of this nature (eg Smith, 1991; Leigh, Temple, and Trocki, 1993). The gender difference may be an artefact of survey sampling, in that men may have partners among under-represented sections of the population – specifically, prostitutes and women under 16 years of age. Johnson and colleagues suggest that 'social factors may influence reporting in contemporary Britain', whereby the existence of 'double standards' leads to negative labelling for women with many partners but a relatively positive perception of men in these circumstances (Johnson, Wadsworth, Wellings and Field, 1994). In a methodological analysis of sexual behaviour surveys Smith concludes on this issue that 'intentional mis-reports are most likely the main source of the discrepancies', with gender differences in sexual values leading to 'a combination of male overreporting and female underreporting' (Smith, 1992).

People with multiple partners

In the US national survey of HIV-related risk factors among the general population, respondents who reported two or more sexual partners in the last 12 months were categorised as having multiple sexual partners (Catania et al., 1992). Table 8.14 shows the rates of multiple partners in relation to age group and marital status.

Table 8.14: Proportion of respondents reporting two or more sexual partners in the last 12 months, by gender and marital status

	Age group			
	16–34		35–54	
	%	Base	%	Base
Men				
Married	10	367	7	692
Cohabiting	21	57	23	26
Single	32	577	21	65
Div/sep/widowed	46	28	38	70
Women				
Married	6	232	5	751
Cohabiting	10	59	13	26
Single	17	297	10	52
Div/sep/widowed	20	29	12	140

The pattern in these findings is again very similar to that in the NSSAL, where 'those showing the highest prevalence of multiple partnerships are separated, divorced and widowed people' (Johnson, Wadsworth, Wellings and Field, 1994). It is striking to find that for men the rate of multiple partners in a 1-month period is higher among 35–54 year olds who are divorced, separated or widowed than among 16–34 year olds who are single. As the authors of the NSSAL report suggest, a period of relatively rapid partner change may follow the loss of a stable partnership before a new longer-term stable pattern is established (Johnson, Wadsworth, Wellings and Field, 1994). One implication of this finding is that more attention may need to be given in the targeting of sexual health education to an older age group which has experienced a breakdown of a stable relationship.

Last sexual occasion
A key focus in the questionnaire was on aspects of the last occasion of heterosexual intercourse for respondents who had 'ever' had sexual intercourse. This snapshot is assumed to be representative of patterns of sexual encounter for this population. For most respondents the last sexual occasion occurred within the last week (55%) or within the last four weeks (77%), with 91% referring to an encounter which occurred within the last 12 months.

Status of last sexual partner
Table 8.15 shows the relationship status of the person with whom the respondent last had vaginal sexual intercourse, by gender and age group. There are very clear age trends in relation to status of the last heterosexual partner, with likelihood of

this being a spouse or cohabitee increasing with age. While among older age groups it is certainly uncommon for the most recent sexual partner to have been

**Table 8.15: 'Is/was the person you last had vaginal sexual intercourse with your ...'
(Only respondents who had 'ever' had vaginal sexual intercourse were
asked this question) (%)**

	Age group				
	16–24	25–34	35–44	45–54	All
Men					
Wife/woman living with	20	73	87	90	69
Regular girlfriend	57	13	7	7	19
Occasional girlfriend	14	9	3	2	7
Someone just met/casual partner	9	4	1	1	4
Base	361	514	444	391	1 710
Women					
Husband/man living with	37	78	87	89	76
Regular boyfriend	56	18	10	8	19
Occasional boyfriend	5	3	1	1	2
Someone just met/casual encounter	1	< 0.5	< 0.5	< 0.5	1
Base	287	272	458	511	1 529

an occasional girl/boyfriend or casual partner, nevertheless for 11% of 35–44 year old women and 9% of 45–54 year old women this was the status of their last partner. This tendency was less for men of the same age groups (4% and 3% respectively).

In relation to younger respondents, there is a gender difference regarding relationship status of the last sexual partner. Young men (aged 16–24 years) were far more likely to describe their last sexual partner as an occasional girlfriend or casual partner. Conversely, for young women (aged 16–24 years) the last sexual partner was far more likely to have been their husband or cohabiting partner. This reflects the fact that in this age group women are more likely than men to be married or living with a partner. However, whereas for 97% of married/cohabiting women aged 16–24 the last sexual partner was their husband or cohabiting partner (with 3% being a regular boyfriend), this applied to only 88% of married/ cohabiting men (with 8% being a regular girlfriend and 4% an occasional girlfriend). In other age groups this gender difference does not occur.

How long known last partner
Among all respondents, 10% had known their last sexual partner for less than six months, including 4% who had known their last partner for less than one month

and 2% who had known their last partner for less than a week at the time of last heterosexual intercourse.

Table 8.16: Distribution of how long respondents had known their partner at the time of last occasion of sexual intercourse with that partner. (Only those who had 'ever' had vaginal sexual intercourse were asked this question) (%)

	Age group				
	16–24	25–34	35–44	45–54	All
Men					
Less than one month	10	7	4	2	6
More than one month, less than six months	26	6	4	1	9
More than six months, less than two years	26	9	4	3	10
At least two years	38	77	89	94	76
Base	368	517	448	387	1 720
Women					
Less than one month	3	2	2	1	2
More than one month, less than six months	12	5	2	1	4
More than six months, less than two years	30	8	7	4	11
At least two years	54	85	90	93	83
Base	288	275	460	507	1 529

In addition to the expected age difference, a gender difference emerges in relation to how long respondents had known their last sexual partner (Table 8.16). In particular, young women (16–24 years) were much more likely to have known their last partner for a longer period than male respondents in the same age group. As with reporting numbers of partners, there may be some element of reporting bias here reflecting cultural beliefs which assign a negative value to 'easy' women and a more positive value to 'fast' men.

Methods of contraception/prophylaxis
A list of methods of contraception/prophylaxis was provided in the questionnaire for respondents to indicate which method/s – more than one if applicable – was/ were used on the last occasion of sexual intercourse. The most common methods were condoms (24%) and the pill (23%). No other method was used by more than 5% of respondents, with coil/IUD and withdrawal each used by 4%. Use of multiple methods was quite common: for example, 9% of respondents (10% of women and 8% of men) reported use of both the pill and condom on the last

occasion.

Nearly four out of ten (39%) of respondents stated they had used no methods of contraception/prophylaxis on the last occasion of sexual intercourse. There is a clear age trend in relation to using no method, ranging from 7% of 16–19 year olds to 65% of 50–54 year olds. It is notable that 22% of respondents who had known their sexual partner for less than six months had used no method on the last occasion of intercourse.

Use of condoms on last occasion of sexual intercourse

Those who used a condom on the last occasion of sexual intercourse were asked to indicate the 'most important reason' for doing so. The responses confirm other findings that concern about unwanted pregnancy is generally a far more salient risk than the threat of HIV or other sexually transmitted diseases (Wight, 1993b). Overall, for 85% of those who had used a condom the most important was contraception, for 12% it was prevention of HIV, and for 3% it was prevention of other infections. However, there was some variation in the frequency with which HIV prevention was mentioned as the most important reason. Men (16%) were more likely than women (6%), and younger respondents – particularly younger men – were more likely to identify HIV prevention: 21% of 16–24 year old men and 9% of 16–24 year old women, 20% of 25–34 men and 7% of 25–34 year old women.

Awareness of the protective role of condoms in circumstances of perceived risk is indicated in the finding that 34% of respondents who had known their last partner less than six months, compared with 15% who had known their partner for up to two years and 3% among those who had known their partner for at least two years indicated that the most important reason they had used a condom on the last occasion was prevention of HIV.

In general, use of condoms on the last occasion of intercourse was far more common among younger respondents (Table 8.17). More than half of 16–19 year olds (56%) and nearly one-third of 20–24 year olds used a condom on the last occasion. A considerable gender difference is evident in relation to reported condom use among younger people: 69% of 16–19 year old men compared to 39% of 16–19 year old women, and 35% of 20–24 year old men compared to 27% of 20–24 year old women reported using a condom on the last occasion of sexual intercourse. The gender difference disappears among older age groups (Table 8.17). It is difficult to explain a very high discrepancy in condom use reported by young men and young women. This is most likely to reflect the tendency of young men to have younger female partners who may be less likely to be using other methods. In addition some young women may have been unaware that a condom was being used, and a number of young men may have offered a response that reflected a perception of 'responsible' behaviour. The NSSAL found a similar difference in reported condom use on the last occasion of heterosexual sex: 39% of 16–24 year old men compared to 24% of 16–24 year old women (Johnson, Wadsworth, Wellings and Field, 1994).

Table 8.17: Condom use on the last occasion of vaginal sexual intercourse, by gender and age group

	Men		Women		All	
	%	Base	%	Base	%	Base
Age group						
16–24	45	351	31	282	39	633
25–34	26	515	23	269	25	784
35–44	20	447	17	449	19	896
45–54	18	378	19	492	18	870

An important factor in relation to the prevalence of safer sexual behaviour is the relationship between numbers of sexual partners and condom use. Although the Health and Lifestyles Survey cannot address this directly, a clear relationship emerges between condom use on the last occasion of intercourse and number of sexual partners in the last 12 months: 22% of those who had only one or no sexual partners, 32% of those with two partners, and 41% of those with three or more partners in the last 12 months reported using a condom on the last occasion (χ^2(trend) $= 28.3$, 1df, $p < .001$). Focusing on those with two or more sexual partners in the last 12 months, it is only among the younger age groups that condom use is more common than among respondents as a whole: 53% of 16–24 year olds, 34% of 25–34 year olds, 18% of 35–44 year olds and 22% of 45–54 year olds with two partners in the last 12 months used a condom on the last occasion of sexual intercourse.

A pattern also emerges for the relationship between condom use on the last occasion and characteristics of the sexual partner concerned. The NSSAL found that single people were more likely and cohabiting people less likely to have used a condom on the last occasion (Johnson, Wadsworth, Wellings and Field, 1994). However, unlike the Health and Lifestyles Survey, the NSSAL cannot directly match up likelihood of condom use with the characteristics of the partner concerned. In the Health and Lifestyles Survey, condom use was less likely where the partnership was more 'steady': 18% of respondents whose last partner was a spouse/cohabitee and 37% of those whose last partner was a regular boy/girlfriend used a condom on the last occasion, compared with 54% where the last partner was an occasional boy/girlfriend and 44% where the last partner was someone they had just men or a casual encounter. Similarly, condom use was less likely on the last occasion of sexual intercourse where the respondent had known their last partner for a longer period of time: 18% of those who had known their partner for at least two years and 39% of those who had known their partner for between six months and two years used a condom on the last occasion, compared to 50% who had known their partner for less than six months.

The identification of factors associated with risk behaviour is a crucial requirement for the development of effective prevention initiatives. Any definition of risk behaviour is inevitably somewhat arbitrary, and no definition is likely to be comprehensive. In the context of the Health and Lifestyles data, one subgroup suitable for further investigation regarding risk behaviour comprises respondents who had known their last sexual partner for less than six months and did not use a condom on the last occasion of sexual intercourse with that partner. Condom use, and condom use specifically in order to prevent HIV, were more likely among respondents who had known their last sexual partner for less than six months, implying a greater perceived risk in these circumstances. However, this subgroup of respondents divides equally between those who did and those who did not use a condom on the last occasion. Are there particular factors which distinguish the half who appear to have been practising safer sex from the half who appear to have been taking greater risks?

Certain health behaviour models predict that those who perceive a greater risk of infection will be more likely to engage in safer sex. HIV/AIDS education campaigns have sometimes attempted to influence the level of perceived risk as a lever for increasing safer sex behaviour. However, analysis of Health and Lifestyles data suggests that perceived risk may not be a significant factor in relation to likelihood of condom use. A series of bivariate analyses of the four risk perception variables – 'I don't think I'll ever get HIV', 'The risk for people like me of getting HIV has been exaggerated by government and health officials', 'What do you think are the chances on average these days of people in this country getting HIV from sexual intercourse without a condom between men and women', and ' Compared to other men/women of your age living in this country, do you feel your chances of getting HIV from vaginal sexual intercourse without a condom are ... much less than average, etc.' – against condom use on the last occasion among respondents who had known their last partner for less than six months found no association between perceived risk and condom use. Those who had a greater perceived risk in terms of these variables had exactly the same probability of using a condom on the last occasion as those with a lower perceived risk.

Beliefs about condoms appear to have a stronger association with likelihood of condom use among the subgroup of respondents who had known their last partner for less than six months. For example, 40% of those who agreed that 'Condoms are too unreliable as a method of contraception' compared with 58% of those who disagreed used a condom on the last occasion – although this was not a statistically significant difference at the 5% level. Also, 45% of those who agreed that 'Women often do not suggest using a condom with a new partner because they are afraid of being rejected by that partner' compared with 63% who disagreed used a condom on the last occasion – again, not statistically significant at the 5% level. The small sample size for this analysis – around 300 cases – makes it difficult to achieve statistical significance, but the differences observed perhaps suggest lines for further enquiry with larger samples. However, one belief variable did show a statistically significant association with condom use: 31% of those who agreed that 'You don't need to use a condom for protection against HIV if you are careful about the sexual partners you choose' compared with 55% who disagreed, used a condom on the last occasion ($\chi^2 = 12.1$, 1df, $p < .001$). This finding is in line with other research which has found that young people believe they are adopting a safer sex strategy by choosing partners they perceive to be 'safe' (Dockrell, Joffe, and Blud, 1994; Wight, 1993b).

Condom use with new partners

In response to a question one-fifth of respondents (21%) stated that they 'always' used a condom with a new partner these days, 4% that they did so 'most times', 1% 'about half the time', 3% occasionally', 8% 'never', and 63% stated that this question did not apply to them. A high proportion of young men claimed that they always used a condom with a new partner: 51% of 16–24 year olds, including 68% of 16–19 year olds. Among young women 34% of 16–24 year olds stated they always used a condom with a new partner, including 45% of 16–19 year olds. Those with more sexual partners were more likely to state that they always used condoms with new partners: 18% of respondents who had had only one or no sexual partners in the last 12 months, compared to 41% of those who had had two or more, stated they always used condoms with a new partner. On the other hand, 13% of those with two or more sexual partners in the last 12 months stated that they never used condoms with a new partner, and this rate is likely to be an underestimate on non-condom use with new partners among this group as 20% claimed that the question did not apply to them.

References

Catania, J. A., Coates, T. J., Stall, R., *et al.* (1992). 'Prevalence of AIDS-related risk factors and condom use in the United States'. *Science,* **258**, 1101-6.

Cragg, A., Hainge, M., Taylor, C. and Porter, T. (1993) Safer sex and sexual health: Understanding young people.

Department of Health (1992) *The Health of the Nation: a Strategy for Health in England* Cm 1986. HMSO.

Dockrell, J., Joffe, H. and Blud, L. (1994) 'Sex, HIV and AIDS', in: Glanz, A., McVey, D. and Glass, R. (eds) *Talking About It. Young People, Sexual Behaviour and HIV*. Health Education Authority.

Health Education Authority (1992) *Today's Young Adult: an In-depth Study into the Lifestyles of 16–10 Year Olds*. HEA.

Health Education Authority (1994) *AIDS Strategic Monitor 1990–91*. Health Education Authority.

Holland, J. *et al.* (1991) *Pressured pleasure: Young women and the negotiation of sexual boundaries*. Tutnell Press, London.

Johnson, A., Wadsworth, J., Wellings, K. and Field, J. (1994) *Sexual Attitudes and Lifestyles*. Blackwell Scientific Publications, Oxford.

Leigh, B. C., Temple, M.T. and Trocki, K.F. (1993) 'The sexual behaviour of US adults: results from a national survey'. *American Journal of Public Health,* **83** (10) 1400-8.

Rosenstock, I.M. (1974) 'The health belief model and preventative health behaviour'. *Health Education Monographs*, **2**, 354–86.

Smith, T. W. (1991) 'Adult sexual behaviour in 1989: number of partners, frequency of intercourse and risk of AIDS'. *Family Planning Perspectives*, **23** (3), 102–7.

Smith, T. W. (1992) 'A methodological analysis of the sexual behaviour questions on the General Social Surveys'. *Journal of Official Statistics* **8** (3), 309–25.

Weinstein, N. D. (1980) 'Unrealistic optimism about susceptibility to health problems', *Journal of Behavioural Medicine*, **5**, 441–60.

Wight, D. (1993a). 'A re-assessment of health education on HIV/AIDS for young heterosexuals'. *Health Education Research*, **8**, 473–83.

Wight, D. (1993b). 'Constraints or cognition? Factors affecting young men's contraceptive and prophylactic behaviour', in Aggleton, P., Davies, P. and Hart, G. (eds) *AIDS: the Second Decade*. Falmer Press.

Appendices

MORI/6638/4
(1–5)

Serial No. . . . . . .
(6–9)

Health & Lifestyle Survey 1992

TRANSFER FROM CONTACT SHEET

CARD ① 10

Sample point number ☐☐☐☐
(11)(12)(13)(14)

Address number ☐☐☐☐
(15)(16)(17)(18)

(11-18)

INTERVIEWER: START HERE WITH INTRODUCTION AND DEMOGRAPHICS

MORI is carrying out this survey for the Health Education Authority and it is a major study on the nation's health. But before I ask any questions about health issues, I need to check some more details about yourself and your household, to make sure we interview people from all backgrounds. All the information you give me is confidential.

<u>Gender</u>   (19)
Female 1
Male 2   19

Exact Age WRITE IN   ☐☐   20-21

Q1   How many people are there usually living here — that includes yourself, any other adults and children?

1 2 3 4 5 6 7 8 <u>9 or more</u>   22

Q2   Are there any children aged 15 or under in this household?

Yes 1   ASK Q3
No 2   GO TO Q4   23

Q3   CODE NUMBERS OF CHILDREN IN EACH AGE GROUP

0–1	0	1	2	3	4+	24
2–3	0	1	2	3	4+	25
4–5	0	1	2	3	4+	26
6–10	0	1	2	3	4+	27
11–12	0	1	2	3	4+	28
13–15	0	1	2	3	4+	29

Q4   Does this household own this accommodation or do you rent it?
(30)
Owned outright 1
Owned/being bought on
 mortgage 2
Rented from council 3
Rented from housing
 association 4
Rented from private
 landlord 5
Other (WRITE IN & CODE '6')

.... 6   30

Q4b   Phone in Household
Yes......................... 7
No 8   (30)

Q5   How many rooms does this accommodation have, in total? Please exclude kitchens, bathrooms and toilets.

ENTER NUMBER   ☐☐   (31–32)

Q6   And how many bedrooms does this accommodation have?

ENTER NUMBER   ☐   (33)

Q7   And how many living rooms?

ENTER NUMBER   ☐   (34)

Q8   Does this accommodation have a kitchen which is for your household's use only?
(35)
Yes......................... 1
No 2   (35)

Q9a   Does this accommodation have a bathroom which is for your household's use only?
(36)
Yes......................... 1
No 2   (36)

Q9b   How many bathrooms does this accommodation have?

ENTER NUMBER ......   ☐   (37)

I confirm that I have conducted this interview face–to–face with the person named on the contact sheet for the address number given above and that I asked all the relevant questions and recorded the answers in conformance with the survey specifications and within the MRS Code of Conduct.

Date of interview   _____

Interviewer Name: _____

Interviewer Number: ☐☐☐☐/☐

Interviewer Signature: _____
(38–42)

THIS FORM IS THE PROPERTY OF MARKET & OPINION RESEARCH INTERNATIONAL
95 Southwark Street, London SE1 OHX

Q10 SHOWCARD A   What forms of heating do you use regularly in cold weather? MULTICODE OK

Central heating: (43)

    Mains gas 1
    Bottled gas 2
    Fuel oil 3
    Electricity – normal tariff 4
             – off peak........ 5
    Solid fuel – smokeless 6
            – non–smokeless .. 7

Non–central heating:

    Mains gas fire/
      convector 8
    Fan heaters 9
    Electric bar fires 0
    Storage heaters X
    Calor/Butane gas heaters..... Y
                  (44)
    Paraffin heaters 1
    Oil filled electric
      radiator.................. 2
    Solid fuel open grate 3
    Solid fuel stove/
      enclosed grate............ 4
Other (WRITE IN & CODE 5)

    5

Don't know 6   43–44

INTERVIEWER OBSERVATION
(CODE BY OBSERVATION)

    Address is:

    House/bungalow
                  (45)
    – detached 1
    – semi–detached/
       end of terrace........ 2
    – mid–terrace 3

    Maisonette 4
    Flat 5
    Rooms/bedsitter 6
    Other (WRITE IN &
      CODE '7')

    7   45
                  (46)
    Ground floor/street–level 1
    Low–rise (1st or 2nd floor) ... 2
    Mid–rise (3 to 6th floor)....... 3
    High–rise (7 floors or
      higher) 4   46

Q11   Do you own a car or have use of a car?
                  (47)
    Own car 1
    Use of car (eg company car) .. 2
    No car...................... 3   47

Q12   And do you personally have a full driver's licence, or not?

                  (48)
    Yes 1
    No 2   48

Ethnic Origin
Q13 SHOWCARD B   From this card, which of these best describes you?
White   (49)
    English 1
    Scottish 2
    Welsh 3
    Irish 4
    Turkish 5
    Greek 6
    Italian 7
    Other White (WRITE IN & CODE '8')

    8
Caribbean/West Indian 9
Black African
    Nigerian 0
    Ghanaian X
    Sierra Leonean .... Y
                  (50)
    Kenyan 1
    Ugandan 2
    Somali 3
    Ethiopian 4
    Other African (WRITE IN & CODE '5')

    5
Asian
    Indian 6
    Pakistani 7
    Bangladeshi.................. 8
    East African Asian 9
    Vietnamese 0
    Chinese..................... X
    Other Asian (WRITE IN & CODE 'Y')

    .... Y
                  (51)
    Arab........................ 1
    Other (WRITE IN & CODE '2')

    .... 2 (49–51)

ASK ALL EXCEPT WHITE ENGLISH
Q14   Is English your first or main language?   (52)
    Yes 1
    No 2   52

Q15   Do you speak any other languages at home?   (53)
    Yes 1
    No 2   53

    IF YES, PROBE WHICH ONE/S (54)
    Arabic..................... 1
    Bengali 2
    Cantonese 3
    Greek 4
    Gujerati.................... 5
    Hakka 6
    Hindu 7
    Italian 8
    Kutchi 9
    Mandarin 0
    Panjabi X
    Polish .... Y
                  (55)
    Portuguese................. 1
    Spanish 2
    Sylheti 3
    Turkish 4
    Urdu 5   54–
    Vietnamese 6   55
    Other (WRITE IN & CODE '7')

7

ASK ALL
Q16   **In what country were you born?**

                                                (56)

West Indies/Guyana 1
India 2
Pakistan 3
Bangladesh 4
Kenya 5
Uganda 6
Tanzania 7
Zambia 8
Malawi 9
Other Africa (WRITE IN & CODE '0')

.... 0

Northern Ireland X
England, Wales .... Y

                                                (57)

Scotland 1
Other country (WRITE IN & CODE '2')

.... 2   (56–57)

Q17   **What is your religion or church?**

                                                (58)

Islam/Muslim 1
Sikhism 2
Hinduism 3
Church of England/Wales/
  Scotland 4
Roman Catholic 5
Jewish 6
Other (WRITE IN & CODE '7') 7

....

None 8
Don't know 9   (58)

ASK ALL EXCEPT THOSE IN SINGLE PERSON HOUSEHOLDS (CODE 1 AT Q1) WHO
GO TO Q19

Q18   **I would now like to ask a few questions about you and your household and the jobs
that you do. First of all, including yourself, how many adults aged 16+ are there in
this household?**

           1   2   3   4   5   6   7   8   9   or more   (60)

ASK FOR EACH ADULT AGED 16+ IN HOUSEHOLD, STARTING WITH RESPONDENT.
(IF MORE THAN 6, USE CONTINUATION SHEET)

Q19 SHOWCARD C Which statement on this card applies to each person aged 16+ in the household, starting with you?

(IF SINGLE ADULT HOUSEHOLD, SAY: Which statement on this card applies to you?)

	Respondent (Person 1) (61)	Person 2 (63)	Person 3 (65)	Person 4 (67)	Person 5 (69)	Person 6 (71)
Paid employee working full-time(30+ hrs/week)	1	1	1	1	1	1
Paid employee working part-time(up to 29 hrs/week)	2	2	2	2	2	2
Self-employed working full-time	3	3	3	3	3	3
Self-employed working part-time	4	4	4	4	4	4
Retired with occupational pension	5	5	5	5	5	5
Retired on state benefits only	6	6	6	6	6	6
Unemployed for less than 6 months	7	7	7	7	7	7
Unemployed for more than 6 months	8	8	8	8	8	8
At school	9	9	9	9	9	9
Other full-time education	0	0	0	0	0	0
On government training scheme	X	X	X	X	X	X
Temporarily sick/disabled less than 6 months	Y	Y	Y	Y	Y	Y
	(62)	(64)	(66)	(68)	(70)	(72)
Long term sickness/disabled (6 months or longer)	1	1	1	1	1	1
Looking after home or family	2	2	2	2	2	2

(61–72)

ASK ABOUT CURRENT JOB FOR EACH PERSON WORKING (CODES 1–4 AT Q19)
FOR EACH PERSON RETIRED (CODES 5–6 AT Q19), ASK ABOUT PREVIOUS JOB
FOR EACH PERSON UNEMPLOYED LESS THAN 6 MONTHS (CODE 7 AT Q19), ASK ABOUT PREVIOUS JOB
IF NOBODY IN HOUSEHOLD CODED 1–7 AT Q19, GO TO Q22

Q20 What is/was the name or title of your/his/her job?
PROBE FOR TITLE/GRADE

Person 1 ....

Person 2 ....

Person 3 ....

Person 4 ....

Person 5 ....

Person 6 ....

Q21 What kind of work do/did you (etc) do most of the time? PROBE: Do/did you (etc) use any machinery or special skills? IF YES: What?
CHECK SPECIAL SKILLS/TRAINING

Person 1 ....

Person 2 ....

Person 3 ....

Person 4 ....

Person 5 ....

Person 6 ....

ASK ALL

Q22 Can I check which person is the head of the household? This means the person who owns or rents the household's accommodation (INTERVIEWER: PROBE AS NECESSARY. REFER TO INSTRUCTIONS FOR COMPLETE DEFINITION OF HOH IN CASE OF DOUBT).

CIRCLE HEAD OF HOUSEHOLD PERSON NUMBER 1 2 3 4 5 6 7 8 9_____(73)

Q23 SHOWCARD D   Do you receive any of these benefits?

```
                                                 (74)
Child benefit ............................1
State retirement pension .................2
Income Support/social security ..........3
Unemployment benefit ....................4
Family Credit ...........................5
Housing Benefit .........................6
Attendance Allowance ....................7
Invalid Care Allowance...................8
Mobility Allowance ......................9
Sickness Benefit ........................0
Disablement living allowance ............X
Other (WRITE IN & CODE 'Y')

...................................Y
                                                 (75)
None of these........................1_____(74-75)
```

Q24 SHOWCARD E   Household Income
Could you please give me the letter from this card for the group in which you would place your total household income from all sources, before tax and other deductions?

Please include all benefits, such as child benefit, Income Support, retirement pensions, unemployment benefit. Please also remember to include income from all members of the household.

```
                                                 (76)
A............................................1
B............................................2
C............................................3
D............................................4
E............................................5
F............................................6
G............................................7
H............................................8
I............................................9
J............................................0
K............................................X
L............................................Y
                                                 (77)
M ...........................................1
Don't know ..................................2
Refused .....................................3_____(76-77)
```

Q24b SHOWCARD EDUCATION   Please look at this card and tell me which, if any, is the highest educational qualification you have obtained?

WRITE IN CODE   ☐☐

IF CODE 20 WRITE IN QUALIFICATIONS

....

....

Q24c SHOWCARD E2 MARITAL STATUS WRITE IN CODE   ☐

HEALTH CONCERNS

Q25 First, I would like to ask you some questions about your health in general. How do you feel about your health? Would you say that for your age your health is ...

READ OUT. ALTERNATE ORDER. TICK START

	(78)	
Very good	1	
Fairly good	2	
Fairly poor	3	
Very poor	4	
Don't know	5	78

Q26 Do you have any long—standing illness, disability or infirmity? By longstanding I mean anything that has troubled you over a period of time or that is likely to affect you over a period of time?

	(79)	
Yes	1 ASK Q27a AND b	
No	2 GO TO Q28	79

SKIP TO CARD ② 10

Q27 (a) What is the matter with you? PROBE IN DETAIL What else? IF UNCLEAR ASK: What do you mean by that? WRITE IN

(11)
1234
5678
90XY

....

....

(12)
1234
5678
90XY

....

....

....

(b) Does this illness or disability (Do any of these illnesses or disabilities) limit your activities in any way?

	(13)	
Yes	1	
No	2	13

ASK ALL
Q28a Do you do anything in particular to keep or improve your health?

	(14)	
Yes	1	ASK Q28b
No/don't know	2	GO TO Q29

ASK IF YES
Q28b What are the most important things you do? PROBE FOR 3. WRITE IN ON SEPARATE LINES

1 – ....

(14)
34
5678
90XY

2 – ....

3 – ....

(15)
1234
5678
90XY
(16)
1234
5678
90XY

Q29   **Are there any things you would like to do to keep yourself healthy but don't do at the moment?** PROBE FOR UP TO THREE ACTIVITIES AND WRITE IN BELOW

(18)

Yes 1   CODE & WRITE IN BELOW

No 2   GO TO Q31   18

FOR EACH DESIRED ACTIVITY PROBE REASON

Q30   **And what stops you from doing . .?**   (19)

Q29 Desired Activity	Q30 Reason for not doing	
		(20)
1) _____	_____	(21)
	_____	(22)
2) _____	_____	(23)
	_____	(24)
3) _____	_____	(25)
	_____	(26)

ASK ALL

Q31   SHOWCARD F (R)   **Here is a list of health issues which can affect people's health. Can you tell me please which, if any, of these you feel have a bad effect on your health at the moment? Just read out the numbers of those you worry about.** MULTICODE OK

Q32   SHOWCARD F (R) AGAIN   **And which, if any, of these do you worry that they might have a bad effect on your health in the future? Just read out the numbers of the ones you worry about.** MULTICODE OK

		Q31 Current risk (27)	Q32 Future risk (29)
1.	The amount I smoke	1	1
2.	The kind of food I eat	2	2
3.	The quality of my housing	3	3
4.	Stress at home	4	4
5.	Living on my own	5	5
6.	The amount of alcohol I drink	6	6
7.	My weight	7	7
8.	Environmental pollution where I live	8	8
9.	Environmental pollution where I work	9	9
10.	Environmental pollution in general	0	0
11.	Stress at work	X	X
12.	My sexual behaviour	Y	Y
		(28)	(30)
13.	Road traffic in this area	1	1
14.	Being unemployed	2	2
15.	The amount of violent crime in this area	3	3
16.	The amount of racism in this area	4	4
	Other (WRITE IN & CODE 5)		
	....	5	5
	None of these	6	6
	Don't know	7	7 (27-30)

Q33 SHOWCARD G (R)   Here is a list of illnesses and health problems. Can you tell me please, which, if any, of these you worry that they _might_ affect your personal health and well being? Just read out the numbers of those you worry about.
MULTICODE OK

Q34 SHOWCARD G (R) AGAIN   And which, if any, of these illnesses and health problems have you personally ever suffered from? Again, just call out the numbers.
MULTICODE OK

		Q33 (31)	Q34 (33)
1.	Severe arthritis/rheumatism	1	1
2.	Breathing difficulties eg bronchitis	2	2
3.	Cancer	3	3
4.	Depression	4	4
5.	Alcoholism	5	5
6.	Stroke	6	6
7.	Degenerative diseases such as multiple sclerosis (ms), Parkinson's, osteoporosis	7	7
8.	HIV/AIDS	8	8
9.	Heart disease	9	9
10.	Back pain	0	0
11.	Diabetes	X	X
12.	STDs (sexually transmitted diseases)	Y	Y
		(32)	(34)
13.	Depression/anxiety/nerves	1	1
14.	Anorexia nervosa	2	2
	Other (WRITE IN & CODE 3)		
	....	3	3
	None of these	4	4
	Don't know	5	5

(31–34)

FOOD LABELLING

Q35 I would now like to ask you some questions about buying food. Do you do most of the food shopping for this household or does somebody else? PROBE WHO
MULTICODE OK IF RESPONSIBILITY SHARED

Main food shopping done by: (35)

Respondent 1   ASK Q36

Other household member

- wife 2
- girlfriend/partner 3
- mother/mother-in-law 4
- other female household member 5   GO TO Q41
- husband 6
- boyfriend/partner 7
- father/father-in-law 8
- other male household member 9

Other (WRITE IN & CODE '0')

.... 0

Don't know X

(35)

Q36 ASK ALL FOOD BUYERS (CODE 1 AT Q35). OTHERS GO TO Q41
SHOWCARD H (R)   When you go shopping for foods that come in packages, how frequently do you look at the following information on food labels? Please take your answer from this card.

READ OUT	Always	Usually	Sometimes	Rarely	Never	Don't know	
a) The date by which the food has to be sold or used	1	2	3	4	5	6	(36)
b) The list of ingredients or nutrition information	1	2	3	4	5	6	(37)

IF LOOKS AT LIST OF INGREDIENTS/NUTRITION INFORMATION (CODES 1-4 AT Q36b) ASK QQ37 AND 38 OTHERS SEE Q39/40

Q37 SHOWCARD I (R)   Now, from this card, what nutrition information do you look for on food packaging? Just read out the number.

(38)
```
 1   Calories/Kilocalories/Kilojoules ...................  1
 2   Carbohydrate ....................................  2
 3   Energy...........................................  3
 4   Total fat .......................................  4
 5   – Polyunsaturated fat ...........................  5
 6   – Saturated fat..................................  6
 7   Fibre ...........................................  7
 8   Minerals ........................................  8
 9   Protein .........................................  9
10   Starch ..........................................  0
11   Sugar ...........................................  X
12   Salt ............................................  Y
```
(39)
```
13   Sodium...........................................  1
14   Vitamins ........................................  2
     Other (WRITE IN AND CODE "3")

     ................................................  3
     Nothing specific ................................  4
     Don't know......................................  5
```
(38–39)

Q38 SHOWCARD J   Looking at this card, which of the following ingredients, if any, do you look for on a list of ingredients on food labels because you would like to avoid them in your diet? Just read out the number.

(40)
```
 1   Additives (in general) .......................  1
 2   (Artificial) Colours .........................  2
 3   E numbers ....................................  3
 4   Fat (in general) .............................  4
 5   – Animal fat .................................  5
 6   – Vegetable fat...............................  6
 7   (Artificial) flavourings .....................  7
 8   Preservatives ................................  8
 9   Salt .........................................  9
10   Sugar ........................................  0
11   Starch .......................................  X
11   Artificial sweeteners (aspartame,
     saccharin) ..................................  Y
```
(41)
```
     Other (WRITE IN AND CODE '1')

     ................................................  1
     Nothing specific .........................  2
     Don't know................................  3
```
(40–41)

Q39 ASK IF NEVER LOOKS AT SELL BY DATE (CODE 5 AT Q 36a)
Why do you never look at the date by which the food has to be sold or used?

(42)
I only buy things to use/eat right away 1
I trust the shop not to put out food
   that's past the date 2
I don't think there's any real risk if
   if you eat the food past the date 3
The information is too difficult to
   understand/confusing 4
The information is difficult to read/
   small print 5
Takes too long to look for all the
   dates 6
Can never find the date 7
Other (WRITE IN & CODE '8') 8

....
Don't know 9   42

Q40 ASK IF NEVER LOOKS AT LIST OF INGREDIENTS/NUTRITION INFORMATION (CODE 5 AT Q36b).
Why do you never look at the list of ingredients or nutrition information on food labels?

(43)
Not interested.............................1
I know what's in the foods I buy/
   I don't need to look 2
The information is too difficult
   to understand/confusing.....................3
The information is difficult to
   read/small print.............................4
Takes too long to read labels 5
Other (WRITE IN & CODE '6') 6

....
Don't know 7   43

ENVIRONMENT

Q41 ASK ALL
I would like to ask you a few questions about your neighbourhood. Would you say this neighbourhood ... READ OUT. ROTATE ORDER. TICK START

(44)
☐   is a place you enjoy living in.....................1
    or not? 2
    Neither/don't know 3

    is a place where you personally feel safe 4
    or not? 5
    Neither/don't know 6

☐   is a place where neighbours look after each other ..7
    or not? 8
    Neither/don't know 9

    has good facilities for young children 0
    or not? X
    Neither/don't know ....Y

(45)
    has good local transport.....................1
    or not? 2
    Neither/don't know 3

☐   has good leisure facilities for people like yourself ...4
    or not? 5
    Neither/don't know 6   (44/45)

Q42   SHOWCARD K (R)   Thinking about this neighbourhood, which if any of the items on this list do you think are a risk to your own physical health or mental well—being? Just call out the numbers of the ones you think apply.

(46)

1   The amount of road traffic.............. 1
2   Car exhaust fumes 2
3   Industrial fumes and emissions 3
4   Litter and rubbish 4
5   The level of crime and vandalism......... 5
6   The level of noise..................... 6
7   The amount of racial abuse or violence ... 7

Other (WRITE IN & CODE 8)

.... 8

None of these 9
Don't know 0   46

Q43   SHOWCARD L (R)   Thinking about your own home now, which if any of the items on this do you think are a risk to your physical health or mental well—being? Just call out the numbers of the ones you think apply.

(47)

1   Lack of heating 1
2   Dampness........................... 2
3   Condensation........................ 3
4   Mould 4
5   The general maintenance of your home ... 5
6   Lack of personal space 6
7   The quality of the drinking water 7
8   Lack of soundproofing or level of noise ... 8

Other (WRITE IN & CODE 9)

.... 9

None of these 0
Don't know X   (47)

CHECK IF RESPONDENT IS WORKING (F/T OR P/T) AT Q19

WORKING.....................1   ASK Q44
NOT WORKING 2   GO TO Q45

IF WORKING, ASK
Q44   SHOWCARD M (R)   Thinking now about the work you do, which if any of the things on this list do you think are a risk to your own physical health or mental well—being? Just call out the numbers of the ones you think apply.

(48)

1   The materials you have to handle 1
2   The equipment you have to use 2
3   Industrial fumes and emissions 3
4   The level of noise..................... 4
5   Work stress 5
6   The number of hours you work.......... 6

Other (WRITE IN AND CODE 7)

.... 7

None of these 8
Don't know 9   (48)

PSYCHO-SOCIAL HEALTH

ASK ALL
Q45 SHOWCARD N (R)   This card lists a number of things which may have happened to you. Could you tell me please which, if any, of these have happened to you in the past 12 months? You can just call out the number.

ASK FOR EACH ONE MENTIONED
Q46 SHOWCARD O (R)   And could you tell me please, from this card, how stressful you found . . . (EVENT). REPEAT FOR EACH EVENT MENTIONED

	Q45	Q46 Degree of Stress (49-50)				
	Events (49)	Very stressful	Fairly stressful	Not very stressful	Not at all stressful	Don't know
1 – Serious illness or injury	1	1	2	3	4	5 (51)
2 – Serious illness or injury of someone close to you	2	1	2	3	4	5 (52)
3 – Death of a close relative or friend	3	1	2	3	4	5 (53)
4 – Problems at work	4	1	2	3	4	5 (54)
5 – Losing your job/retirement	5	1	2	3	4	5 (55)
6 – Another member of this household losing their job	6	1	2	3	4	5 (56)
7 – Changing your job	7	1	2	3	4	5 (57)
8 – Personal experience of theft, mugging, break–in or another crime	8	1	2	3	4	5 (58)
9 – Verbal abuse due to your race or colour	9	1	2	3	4	5 (59)
10 –Physical attack due to your race or colour	0	1	2	3	4	5 (60)
11 –Discrimination at work or anywhere else due to your race or colour	X	1	2	3	4	5 (61)
12 –Divorce, separation or break–up of an intimate relationship	Y (50)	1	2	3	4	5 (62)
13 –Problems with your existing partner	1	1	2	3	4	5 (63)
14 –Pregnancy	2	1	2	3	4	5 (64)
15 –Problems with children	3	1	2	3	4	5 (65)
16 Problems with parents or close relatives	4	1	2	3	4	5 (66)
17 –Moving home	5	1	2	3	4	5 (67)
18 –Financial difficulties	6	1	2	3	4	5 (68)
19 –Problems with neighbours	7	1	2	3	4	5 (69)

None of these ....81 GO TO
Don't know 9 Q47

ASK ALL
Q47   SHOWCARD P (R)   **Looking at this card, which of these sentences best describes the amount of stress or pressure you experienced in the past 12 months?**

In the last 12 months, . . .

(70)
. . . I have been completely free of stress or pressure ....1 GO TO Q49
. . . I have experienced a small amount of stress or pressure 2
. . . I have experienced a moderate amount of stress or pressure ....3 ASK
. . . I have experienced a large amount of stress or pressure 4 Q48
Don't know 5   (70)

ASK IF CODES 2-5 AT Q47. OTHERS GO TO Q49
Q48   **How harmful would you say the amount of stress and pressure you have experienced in the last 12 months has been to your physical or mental health?**

Would you say it has been . . .

READ OUT. ROTATE ORDER. TICK START

(71)
Very harmful 1
Fairly harmful 2
Not very harmful 3
Not at all harmful...................................4
Don't know 5   (71)

ASK ALL
Q49   SHOWCARD Q (R)   **Which, if any, of the things on this card do you usually do to cope with stress or pressure? Just call out the numbers of the ones which apply.**
PROBE: **Which others?**

(72)
1   Try not to think about it 1
2   Discuss it with a close friend or relative 2
3   Work harder to occupy myself 3
4   Take more exercise/more physical activity 4
5   Go to pub/have a drink 5
6   Smoke more 6
7   Drink more 7
8   Eat more 8
9   Pray/meditate...9
10   Get help and advice from a doctor 0
11   Get prescription from doctor...........................X
12   Get help and advice from counsellor or
     advice organisation ....Y
(73)
13   Spend more time thinking about my problems 1
14   Spend more time going out with friends or relatives 2
15   Never have any stress/pressure 3   GO TO Q51
     None of these..3
     Don't know 4   (72-73)

Q50   **Apart from the things on this card, are there any <u>other</u> things you do to cope with stress or pressure?** PROBE FULLY
                                                                                 (74)
....   1 2 3 4
                                                                                 5 6 7 8
                                                                                 9 0 X Y
....   (75)
                                                                                 1 2 3 4
                                                                                 5 6 7 8
....   9 0 X Y
                                                                                 (76)
                                                                                 1 2 3 4
                                                                                 5 6 7 8
                                                                                 9 0 X Y

SOCIAL SUPPORT

Q51   ASK ALL
How long have you lived in this area?

	(77)
Less than 12 months	1
1 year	2
2 years	3
3 years	4
4 years	5
5-9 years	6
10-14 years........................	7
15-19 years........................	8
20 years or more	9
Don't know	0

(77)

Q52   Including people you live with, do you have any close relatives whom you speak to or see regularly? I mean people you <u>feel</u> close to.

	(78)
Yes	1
No	2

(78)

Q53   And do you have any close friends whom you speak to or see regularly? Again, I mean people you <u>feel</u> close to.

	(79)
Yes	1
No	2

(79)

SKIP TO CARD 3 10

Q54   SHOWCARD R   From this card, could you tell me please which, if any, of these you have done in the past fortnight? MULTICODE OK

		(11)
1	Went to visit relatives.................	1
2	Had relatives visit me.................	2
3	Went out with relatives	3
4	Spoke to relatives on the phone	4
5	Went to visit friends	5
6	Had friends visit me..................	6
7	Went out with friends.................	7
8	Spoke to friends on the 'phone	8
9	Spoke to neighbours	9
10	Spoke to a health professional (eg doctor, nurse, midwife, health visitor)	0
11	Attended an adult education or night school class	X
12	Participated in a voluntary group or local community group	Y

(12)

13	Participated in community or religious activities	1
14	Went to a leisure centre	2
15	Went to another social outing (PLEASE SPECIFY & CODE 3)	

.... 3

None of these 4

(11-12)

Q55   SHOWCARD S (R)   **If you needed help and advice, which, if any, of the people on this card could you turn to easily, I mean people you feel close enough to discuss personal issues with.**

                                                              (13)
        1   Partner or spouse................... 1
        2   Female relatives 2
        3   Male relatives 3
        4   Female friends 4
        5   Male friends....................... 5
        6   Neighbours 6
        7   Community worker 7
        8   Community leader 8
        9   Social worker 9
        10   Counsellor/therapist 0
        11   Priest or clergy or religious leader X
        12   Home help .... Y
                                                              (14)
        13   Meals-on-wheels.................. 1
        14   Family doctor/GP 2
        15   Nurse 3
        16   Midwife.......................... 4
        17   Health visitor 5
             Someone else
             (PLEASE SPECIFY & CODE 6)

             6

             None of these 7   (13–14)

HEALTH SERVICES

Q56   **Are you currently registered with a doctor or GP?**

                                              (15)
        Yes............................. 1   ASK Q57
        No 2
        Don't know...................... 3   GO TO Q65(p17)   (15)

        IF REGISTERED WITH DOCTOR/GP ASK
Q57   **Are you registered with this doctor on the National Health Service or privately?**

                                              (16)
        NHS 1
        Private......................... 2
        Both........................... 3
        Don't know 4   (16)

Q58   **Is the doctor or GP you normally see male or female?**

                                              (17)
        Male........................... 1
        Female 2
        It varies 3
        Don't know..................... 4   (17)

Q59   **Which do you prefer to see, a male or female doctor or GP?**

                                              (18)
        Male........................... 1
        Female 2
        No preference 3
        Don't know..................... 4   (18)

Q60   SHOWCARD T (R)   **Which of these best describes your doctor?**

                                                    (19)
                White 1
                Asian 2
                Chinese 3
                African 4
                West Indian 5
                Other (WRITE IN & CODE 6)

                6

                It varies 7
                Don't know 8   (19)

Q61   SHOWCARD U (R)   **Which of these appointment methods comes closest to what
       happens at the surgery/health centre you use?**   SINGLE CODE ONLY

                                                    (20)
          1   Appointment only 1
          2   Mostly appointments with
              some time at the end of
              surgery for urgent cases 2
          3   Just turn up and wait, no
              appointments 3
          4   Separate surgeries for people
              with and without appointments 4
              Other (PLEASE SPECIFY & CODE 5)

                5

                Don't know 6   (20)

Q62   **How do you normally travel to your doctor's/GP's surgery?**

                                                    (21)
                Walk 1
                Bus 2
                Taxi 3
                Drive yourself 4
                Get a lift from family/friend 5
                Train/Underground 6
                Other (WRITE IN & CODE 7)

                7

                Never visit 8   (21)

Q63   **How easy or difficult is it for you to get to your doctor's/GP's surgery?**
       READ OUT   *ALTERNATE ORDER. TICK START.*

                                                    (22)
       ☐   Very easy 1   GO TO Q65
           Fairly easy 2
           Fairly difficult 3   ASK Q64
       ☐   Very difficult 4
           Don't know 5   GO TO Q65   (22)

Q64   **Why do you find it difficult to visit your doctor's/GP's surgery?** MULTICODE OK

                                                    (23)
                Surgery hours are inconvenient 1
                Too far away 2
                Poor public transport 3
                Difficult to park the car 4
                Situated in high crime area 5
                Poor access for disabled/elderly etc. . . 6
                Difficulty in walking 7
                Other (WRITE IN & CODE 8)

                8

                Don't know 9   (23)

ASK ALL
Q65 **When did you last visit a doctor's/GP's surgery or health centre on your own behalf, not just to accompany another person?**

I am interested in any visit you may have made for yourself, not necessarily involving seeing the GP.

(24)

In last week 1	
Over 1 week, within last month 2	ASK
Over 1 month, within last 2 months....3	Q66
Over 2 months, within last 4 months...4	
Over 4 months, within last 6 months...5	
Over 6 months, within last 12 months..6	
Over 1 year, within last 3 years 7	GO
Over 3 years, within last 5 years 8	
Over 5 years, within last 10 years 9	TO
Over 10 years.......................0	
Can't remember.....................X	Q
Never ....Y	67

(24)

ASK IF CODES 1–6 AT Q65 (OTHERS GO TO Q67)
Q66 **How many times have you visited a surgery on your own behalf over the last 12 months? Again I'm interested in any visit you may have made for yourself, not necessarily involving seeing the GP.**

WRITE IN ☐☐
(25) (26)

(25–26)

ASK ALL
Q67 **When did you last visit a doctor's/GP's surgery or health centre to accompany another person such as a friend or relative or a child?**

I am interested in any visit you may have made with someone else, not necessarily involving seeing the GP.

(27)

In last week 1	
Over 1 week, within last month 2	ASK
Over 1 month, within last 2 months....3	Q68
Over 2 months, within last 4 months...4	
Over 4 months, within last 6 months...5	
Over 6 months, within last 12 months..6	
Over 1 year, within last 3 years 7	
Over 3 years, within last 5 years 8	
Over 5 years, within last 10 years 9	SEE
Over 10 years.......................0	
Can't remember.....................X	Q69
Never ....Y	

(27)

ASK IF CODES 1–6 AT Q67 (OTHERS SEE NEXT FILTER)
Q68 **How many times have you visited a surgery to accompany another person over the last 12 months? Again I'm interested in any visit you may have made with someone else.**

WRITE IN ☐☐
(28) (29)

(28–29)

ASK THOSE WHO HAVE VISITED THE SURGERY OR HEALTH CENTRE ON THEIR OWN BEHALF IN THE LAST 12 MONTHS (CODES 1–6 AT Q65). OTHERS GO TO Q79(P21).

I would now like to ask you some questions about the last occasion that you visited the surgery or health centre on your own behalf, (not the last time you accompanied someone else)

Q69   SHOWCARD V (R)   **When you last visited the surgery or health centre, which of these people did you have any dealings with? Who else? MULTICODE OK**

                                                                (30)
             Doctor/GP 1
             Practice Nurse 2
             Physiotherapist 3
             Health visitor 4
             Midwife 5
             Practice pharmacist 6
             Receptionist 7
             Social worker 8
             Counsellor 9
             Dietician 0
             Other (WRITE IN AND CODE X)

            X

             None of these ....Y   (30)

Q70   **Did you make an appointment in advance to see any one of the staff or health professionals there, or did you just turn up, or were you asked to attend?**

                                                                (31)
             Made an appointment 1
             Just turned up 2
             Asked to attend................... 3
             Other (WRITE IN & CODE 4)

             4

             Can't remember.................... 5   (31)

Q71   SHOWCARD W   **What was the purpose of your last visit to the surgery or health centre? MULTICODE OK**
                                                                (32)
     1   To make an appointment 1
     2   To collect/order a repeat prescription 2
     3   For treatment of an illness/condition 3
     4   For a general medical examination/check-up 4
          To attend a clinic:
     5   ante–natal 5
     6   diabetic...................................... 6
     7   asthma 7
     8   family planning 8
     9   other clinic (WRITE IN & CODE 9)

          9

     10   Blood pressure check............................. 0
     11   Cholesterol check X
     12   Cervical smear .... Y
                                                                (33)
     13   Vaccination ('flu jab/foreign travel etc) 1
     14   To get information/advice on health issues 2
     15   Family planning/contraceptive advice 3
     16   Blood test 4
     17   Other tests 5
     18   To hear results of a test 6
     19   Letter/sick note or certificate..................... 7
     20   General check of ongoing illness/condition 8
     21   Letter/referral to a specialist 9
     22   Other (WRITE IN & CODE 0)

          0

          None of these...................................X
          Don't know ....Y   (32–33)

Q72 ASK ALL WHO SAW DOCTOR/GP (CODE 1 AT Q69). OTHERS GO TO Q77 (P20)
How long did you have to wait at the health centre or surgery before you saw the doctor? WRITE IN

[ ][ ] minutes
(34) (35)

(34-35)

Q73 Would you say the amount of time you had to wait was . . .
READ OUT

(36)
About right.........................1
A little too long....................2
Much too long......................3
Don't know.........................4

(36)

Q74 Was there anything you were dissatisfied with when you last saw the doctor/GP?

(37)
Yes................................1   ASK Q75
No 2   GO TO Q76

(37)

ASK IF YES
Q75 What was that? PROBE What else?

(38)
1 2 3 4
5 6 7 8
9 0 X Y
....
(39)
1 2 3 4
5 6 7 8
9 0 X Y
....
(40)
1 2 3 4
5 6 7 8
9 0 X Y
....

....

Q76 ASK ALL WHO SAW DOCTOR (CODE 1 AT Q69). OTHERS SEE Q77
Thinking about when you last saw your doctor/GP . . .

a) Did the doctor give you an explanation about your condition and/or the treatment you received or not?

(41)
Yes, explained 1   ASK b
No, explanation.....................2   GO TO c
Don't know.........................3

(41)

b) Was the explanation:
READ OUT

(42)
Easy to understand 1
or Difficult to understand 2
Neither 3
Don't know........................4

(42)

c) Was the time the doctor spent with you ....
READ OUT

(43)
Long enough 1
or Too short 2
Neither 3
Don't know........................4

(43)

d) Was the doctor ....
READ OUT

(44)
Sympathetic to your
condition/problem 1
or Unsympathetic to your
condition/problem 2
Neither 3
Don't know........................4

(44)

e) Were you able to raise all the issues or problems you wanted to or not?

```
                               (45)
        Yes............................1
        No .............................2
        Don't know .....................3
```
(45)

f) Overall were you satisfied or dissatisfied with the outcome of your visit to the doctor?

```
                               (46)
        Satisfied ......................1
        Dissatisfied....................2
        Neither ........................3
        Don't know .....................4
```
(46)

ASK ALL WHO SAW A PRACTICE NURSE (CODE 2 AT Q69). OTHERS GO TO Q78.

Q77 Thinking about the last time you saw the practice nurse at the surgery or health centre ...

a) Did the practice nurse give you an explanation about your condition and/or the treatment you received or not?

```
                               (47)
        Yes, explained .................1    ASK b
        No, explanation ................2    GO TO c
        Don't know .....................3
```
(47)

b) Was the explanation:
READ OUT
```
                               (48)
        Easy to understand .............1
    or  Difficult to understand ........2
        Neither ........................3
        Don't know .....................4
```
(48)

c) Was the time the practice nurse spent with you ....
READ OUT
```
                               (49)
        Long enough ....................1
    or  Too short ......................2
        Neither ........................3
        Don't know .....................4
```
(49)

d) Was the practice nurse ....
READ OUT
```
                               (50)
        Sympathetic to your
          condition/problem ...........1
    or  Unsympathetic to your
          condition/problem ...........2
        Neither ........................3
        Don't know .....................4
```
(50)

e) Were you able to raise all the issues or problems you wanted to or not?

```
                               (51)
        Yes............................1
        No .............................2
        Don't know .....................3
```
(51)

f) Overall were you satisfied or dissatisfied with the outcome of your visit to the practice nurse?

```
                               (52)
        Satisfied ......................1
        Dissatisfied....................2
        Neither ........................3
        Don't know .....................4
```
(52)

Q78   ASK ALL WHO SAW A RECEPTIONIST (CODE 7 AT Q69). OTHERS GO TO Q79.
Thinking about the last time you saw the receptionist at the surgery or health centre . . . .

(a) Was the receptionist . . . .   READ OUT

(53)

	Friendly	1
or	Unfriendly	2
	Neither	3
	Don't know	4

(53)

(b) Was the receptionist . . . .   READ OUT

(54)

	Helpful	1
or	Unhelpful	2
	Neither	3
	Don't know	4

(54)

(c) Did the receptionist deal with you efficiently or not?

(55)

Efficiently	1
Not efficiently	2
Neither	3
Don't know	4

(55)

(d) Overall were you satisfied or dissatisfied with your dealings with the receptionist?

(56)

Satisfied	1
Dissatisfied	2
Neither	3
Don't know	4

(56)

ASK ALL

Q79   SHOWCARD X (R)   Apart from treatment for illnesses and conditions, what other extra services are available from the surgery or health centre you use, as far as you know? What others?

Q80   SHOWCARD X (R) AGAIN   And which services have you used? What others?

Q81   SHOWCARD X (R) AGAIN   And apart from the services you have actually used, which, if any, would you like to be available at the surgery or health centre you use? What others?

		Q79 (57)	Q80 (59)	Q81 (61)
1	Health promotion services (eg. advice on how to have a healthier lifestyle)	1	1	1
2	Regular check-ups	2	2	2
3	Well woman clinics	3	3	3
4	Well man clinics	4	4	4
5	Immunisation	5	5	5
6	Family planning	6	6	6
7	Child health clinics	7	7	7
8	Support groups/self-help groups	8	8	8
9	Medical social worker	9	9	9
10	Counselling	0	0	0
11	Specialised clinics (eg Diabetic, Asthma)	X	X	X
12	Alternative medicine (eg homeopathy, acupuncture)	Y	Y	Y
		(58)	(60)	(62)
13	Maternity services	1	1	1
14	Counselling for problems with relationships/ marriage	2	2	2
15	Stop smoking sessions	3	3	3
16	Specialist doctors from hospitals	4	4	4
	Other (WRITE IN & CODE 5)			
	....	5	5	5
	None	6	6	6
	Don't know	7	7	7 (57-62)

ASK ALL WHO HAVE BEEN TO SURGERY IN LAST 12 MONTHS (CODES 1–6 AT Q65 OR Q67. OTHERS GO TO Q132 (P46).

Q82   SHOWCARD Y (R)   **In the last year, which of these, if any, have you discussed with a member of staff at the surgery?**

		(63)
1	Diet/healthy food.....................	1
2	Weight control	2
3	Exercise/fitness	3
4	Alcohol	4
5	Smoking	5
6	Stress	6
7	Heart Disease.......................	7
8	Contraception/birth control	8
9	Children's health	9
10	Childhood immunisation	0
11	Cancer	X
12	HIV/AIDS	Y

CONTINUE

(64)

13	Mental or psychological problems (eg. depression, anxiety)	1
14	Emotional problems (eg marital/relationship)	2
15	Sexual problems (eg sexually transmitted diseases)	3
16	Gynaecological problems (eg period problems, cervical smears etc)	4

Other (WRITE IN & CODE 5) .... _____

.... 5

Can't remember.................... 6⎫ GO TO Q131 (P46)
None of these .... 7⎭   (63–64)

DIET/HEALTHY FOOD

Q83   IF NO. 1 AT Q82 (DIET/HEALTHY FOOD) MENTIONED ASK:
       With whom did you discuss diet and healthy food? MULTICODE OK

Q84   ASK FOR EACH PERSON DISCUSSED WITH
       And did you raise the subject yourself, or was it raised by the ... (PERSON) you spoke to?

	Q83 Discussed with (65)		Q84 Resp.	Health pro	Can't remember (65)	
Doctor/GP	1		1 2	 3		(66)
Nurse........................	2		1 2	 3		(67)
Health visitor	3		1 2	 3		(68)
Midwife	4		1 2	 3		(69)
Dietician	5		1 2	 3		(70)
Other (WRITE IN & CODE 6)						
....	6		1 2	 3		(71)
Can't remember...............	7					

Q85 Thinking about the discussion on diet & healthy food

a) Did you find it . . . .
READ OUT

(72)

Helpful	1
or Unhelpful	2
Neither	3
Don't know	4

(72)

b) Was it . . . .
READ OUT

(73)

Easy to understand	1
or Difficult to understand	2
Neither	3
Don't know	4

(73)

c) Did you learn anything new or not?

(74)

Yes	1
No	2
Don't know	3

(74)

d) As a result of the discussion have you made any changes or do you plan to make changes to your lifestyle or not?

(75)

Yes, have made changes	1
Yes, plan to make changes	2
No change made or planned	3
Don't know	4

(75)

e) SHOWCARD Z (R)   Apart from discussing diet and healthy foods which of these if any were you given or recommended to do?

(76)

Asked to keep a special diary/ record sheet	1
Given leaflets/booklets	2
Given a diet sheet	3
Referred to a specialist/other health professional (eg dietician)	4
Recommended to join a special class/ support group (eg weight watchers)	5
Recommended to attend a particular clinic	6
Take (more) exercise	7
Given an exercise/fitness plan	8
Other (WRITE IN & CODE 9)	
	9
Nothing else	0
Don't know	X

(76)

f) Were you asked to return or have you returned to the surgery/health centre for any follow-up checks or advice on diet and healthy food?

(77)

Yes:	for a check up	1
	for advice	2
No, follow-up		3
Don't know		4

(77)

WEIGHT CONTROL

SKIP TO CARD④ 10

Q86 IF NO. 2 AT Q 82 (WEIGHT CONTROL) MENTIONED ASK:
With whom did you discuss weight control? MULTICODE OK

ASK FOR EACH PERSON DISCUSSED WITH
Q87 **And did you raise the subject yourself, or was it raised by the . . . (PERSON) you spoke to?**

	Q86 Discussed with (11)	Q87 Resp.	Health pro	Can't remember (11)	
Doctor/GP	1	1	2	3	(12)
Nurse......................	2	1	2	3	(13)
Health visitor	3	1	2	3	(14)
Midwife....................	4	1	2	3	(15)
Dietician	5	1	2	3	(16)
Other (WRITE IN & CODE 6)					
....	6	1	2	3	(17)
Can't remember..............	7 *GO TO Q88*				

Q88 **Thinking about the discussion on weight control**

a) **Did you find it . . . .**
READ OUT

		(18)	
	Helpful	1	
or	**Unhelpful**	2	
	Neither	3	
	Don't know	4	(18)

b) **Was it . . . .**
READ OUT

		(19)	
	Easy to understand	1	
or	**Difficult to understand**	2	
	Neither	3	
	Don't know	4	(19)

c) **Did you learn anything new or not?**

	(20)	
Yes..............................	1	
No	2	
Don't know	3	(20)

d) **As a result of the discussion have you made any changes or do you plan to make changes to your lifestyle or not?**

	(21)	
Yes, have made changes.............	1	
Yes, plan to make changes..........	2	
No change made or planned	3	
Don't know	4	(21)

e)   SHOWCARD Z (R)   Apart from discussing weight control which of these, if any, were you given or recommended to do?

(22)

Asked to keep a special diary/
record sheet 1
Given leaflets/booklets 2
Given a diet sheet 3
Referred to a specialist/other health
professional (eg dietician) 4
Recommended to join a special class/
support group (eg weight watchers) .. 5
Recommended to attend a particular
clinic 6
Take (more) exercise 7
Given an exercise/fitness plan 8
Other (WRITE IN & CODE 9)

.... 9

Nothing else 0
Don't know X   (22)

f)   Were you asked to return or have you returned to the surgery/health centre for any follow—up checks or advice on diet weight control?

(23)

Yes: for a check up 1
for advice 2

No, follow—up 3
Don't know 4   (23)

EXERCISE/FITNESS

Q89   IF NO. 3 AT Q82 (EXERCISE/FITNESS) MENTIONED ASK:
With whom did you discuss exercise & fitness? MULTICODE OK

Q90   ASK FOR EACH PERSON DISCUSSED WITH
And did you raise the subject yourself, or was it raised by the . . . (PERSON) you spoke to?

	Q89		Q90	
	Discussed with (24)	Resp.	Health pro	Can't remember (24)
Doctor/GP 1		1 .... 2 3		(25)
Nurse 2		1 .... 2 3		(26)
Health visitor 3		1 .... 2 3		(27)
Midwife 4		1 .... 2 3		(28)
Physio–therapist 5		1 .... 2 3		(29)
Other (WRITE IN & CODE 6)				
.... 6		1 .... 2 3		(30)

Can't remember .... 7 *Go To P91*

Q91   **Thinking about the discussion on exercise & fitness**

a)   **Did you find it . . . .**
READ OUT

(31)

Helpful 1
or **Unhelpful** 2
Neither 3
Don't know 4   (31)

b) Was it . . . .
READ OUT

(32)

        Easy to understand 1
or Difficult to understand 2
        Neither 3
        Don't know 4

(32)

c) Did you learn anything new or not?

(33)

        Yes.............................. 1
        No 2
        Don't know 3

(33)

d) As a result of the discussion have you made any changes or do you plan to make changes to your lifestyle or not?

(34)

        Yes, have made changes............ 1
        Yes, plan to make changes.......... 2
        No change made or planned 3
        Don't know 4

(34)

e) SHOWCARD AB (R)   Apart from discussing exercise & fitness which of these, if any, were you given or recommended to do?

(35)

        Asked to keep a special diary/
          record sheet 1
        Given leaflets/booklets.............. 2
        Given a diet sheet 3
        Referred to a specialist/other health
          professional (eg physiotherapist)..... 4
        Recommended to join a special class/
          support group 5
        Recommended to attend a particular
          clinic 6
        Recommended to join a special
          health/sports club 7
        Exercise/fitness plan 8
        Recommended to take (more)
          exercise) 9
        Other (WRITE IN & CODE 0)

        0

        Nothing else...................... X
        Don't know .... Y

(35)

f) Were you asked to return or have you returned to the surgery/health centre for any follow—up checks or advice on exercise & fitness?

(36)

        Yes: for a check up 1
                   for advice 2

        No, follow—up 3
        Don't know 4

(36)

ALCOHOL

Q92 IF NO. 4 AT Q82 (ALCOHOL) MENTIONED ASK:
With whom did you discuss alcohol? MULTICODE OK

Q93 ASK FOR EACH PERSON DISCUSSED WITH
And did you raise the subject yourself, or was it raised by the . . . (PERSON) you spoke to?

	Q92		Q93		
	Discussed with (37)	Resp.	Health pro	Can't remember	(37)
Doctor/GP 1		1 ....2 3			(38)
Nurse.......................2		1 ....2 3			(39)
Health visitor 3		1 ....2 3			(40)
Midwife 4		1 ....2 3			(41)
Dietician 5		1 ....2 3			(42)
Other (WRITE IN & CODE 6)					
...........................6		1 ....2 3			(43)
Can't remember.............7					

Q94 **Thinking about the discussion on alcohol**

   a) **Did you find it . . . .**
      READ OUT

	(44)	
Helpful 1		
or **Unhelpful** 2		
Neither 3		
Don't know 4		(44)

   b) **Was it . . . .**
      READ OUT

	(45)	
Easy to understand 1		
or **Difficult to understand** 2		
Neither 3		
Don't know 4		(45)

   c) **Did you learn anything new or not?**

	(46)	
Yes................................1		
No 2		
Don't know 3		(46)

   d) **As a result of the discussion have you made any changes or do you plan to make changes to your lifestyle or not?**

	(47)	
Yes, have made changes.............1		
Yes, plan to make changes..........2		
No change made or planned 3		
Don't know 4		(47)

e)   SHOWCARD AC (R)   Apart from discussing alcohol which of these if any were you given or recommended to do?

(48)

Telephone a special helpline 1
Given leaflets/booklets............... 2
Referred to a specialist/other health
  professional.........................: 3
Recommended to join a special class/
  support group.................... 4
Recommended to attend a particular
  clinic 5
Other (WRITE IN & CODE 6)

.... 6

Nothing else...................... 7
Don't know......................... 8   (48)

f)   Were you asked to return or have you returned to the surgery/health centre for any follow—up checks or advice on alcohol?

(49)

Yes: for a check up 1
       for advice 2

No, follow—up 3
Don't know.......................... 4   (49)

SMOKING

Q95
IF NO. 5 AT Q82 (SMOKING) MENTIONED ASK:
With whom did you discuss smoking?   MULTICODE OK

Q96
ASK FOR EACH PERSON DISCUSSED WITH
And did you raise the subject yourself, or was it raised by the . . . (PERSON) you spoke to?

	Q95 Discussed with (50)	Q96 Resp.	Health pro	Can't remember (50)	
Doctor/GP 1		1	2	3	(51)
Nurse........................ 2		1	2	3	(52)
Health visitor 3		1	2	3	(53)
Midwife 4		1	2	3	(54)
Dietician 5		1	2	3	(55)
Other (WRITE IN & CODE 6)					
.... 6		1	2	3	(56)
Can't remember.............. 7					

Q97   **Thinking about the discussion on smoking**

**a)   Did you find it . . . .
       READ OUT**

(57)

      Helpful 1
or   **Unhelpful** 2
      Neither 3
      Don't know......................... 4   (57)

b) Was it . . . .
READ OUT

                                    (58)

        Easy to understand 1
or Difficult to understand 2
        Neither 3
        Don't know 4   (58)

c) Did you learn anything new or not?

                                      (59)

        Yes. 1
        No 2
        Don't know 3   (59)

d) As a result of the discussion have you made any changes or do you plan to make changes to your lifestyle or not?

                                      (60)

        Yes, have made changes. 1
        Yes, plan to make changes 2
        No change made or planned 3
        Don't know 4   (60)

e) SHOWCARD AD (R)   Apart from discussing smoking which of these if any were you given or recommended to do?

                                      (61)

        Asked to keep a special diary/
          record sheet 1
        Given leaflets/booklets. 2
        Referred to a specialist/other health
          professional. 3
        Recommended to join a special class/
          support group 4
        Recommended to attend a particular
          smoking clinic 5
        Telephone a special helpline 6
        Recommended to take nicotine
          substitutes 7
        Other (WRITE IN & CODE 8)

        8

        Nothing else. 9
        Don't know 0   (61)

f) Were you asked to return or have you returned to the surgery/health centre for any follow–up checks or advice on smoking?

                                        (62)

        Yes: for a check up 1
              for advice 2

        No, follow–up 3
        Don't know 4   (62)

STRESS

Q98 IF NO. 6 AT Q82 (STRESS) MENTIONED ASK:
Q98 **With whom did you discuss stress? MULTICODE OK**

ASK FOR EACH PERSON DISCUSSED WITH
Q99 **And did you raise the subject yourself, or was it raised by the . . . (PERSON) you spoke to?**

	Q98		Q99		
	Discussed with (63)	Resp.	Health pro	Can't remember	(63)
Doctor/GP 1		1 .... 2 3			(64)
Nurse.......................2		1 .... 2 3			(65)
Health visitor 3		1 .... 2 3			(66)
Midwife 4		1 .... 2 3			(67)
Councellor 5		1 .... 2 3			(68)
Social worker................6		1 .... 2 3			(69)
Other (WRITE IN & CODE 7)					
.........................7		1 .... 2 3			(70)
Can't remember..............8					

Q100 **Thinking about the discussion on stress**

a) **Did you find it . . . .**
READ OUT

	(71)
Helpful 1	
or **Unhelpful** 2	
Neither 3	
Don't know........................4	(71)

b) **Was it . . . .**
READ OUT

	(72)
Easy to understand 1	
or **Difficult to understand** 2	
Neither 3	
Don't know........................4	(72)

c) **Did you learn anything new or not?**

	(73)
Yes...............................1	
No 2	
Don't know........................3	(73)

d) **As a result of the discussion have you made any changes or do you plan to make changes to your lifestyle or not?**

	(74)
Yes, have made changes.............1	
Yes, plan to make changes...........2	
No change made or planned 3	
Don't know........................4	(74)

e) SHOWCARD AE (R)   Apart from discussing stress which of these if any were
you given or recommended to do?

(75)

Asked to keep a special diary/
record sheet 1
Given leaflets/booklets............... 2
Referred to a specialist/other health
professional...................... 3
Recommended to join a special class/
support group..................... 4
Recommended to attend a particular
clinic (eg stress clinic) 5
Recommended to take exercise 6
Other (WRITE IN & CODE 7)

.... 7

Nothing else........................ 8
Don't know......................... 9   (75)

f) Were you asked to return or have you returned to the surgery/health centre
for any follow—up checks or advice on stress?

(76)

Yes: for a check up 1
for advice 2

No, follow—up 3
Don't know......................... 4   (76)

SKIP TO CARD (5) 10

HEART DISEASE

IF NO. 7 AT Q82 (HEART DISEASE) MENTIONED ASK:
Q101 With whom did you discuss heart disease? MULTICODE OK

ASK FOR EACH PERSON DISCUSSED WITH
Q102 And did you raise the subject yourself, or was it raised by the . . . (PERSON) you
spoke to?

	Q101		Q102		
	Discussed with (11)	Resp.	Health pro	Can't remember	(11)
Doctor/GP 1		1 .... 2 3			(12)
Nurse....................... 2		1 .... 2 3			(13)
Health visitor 3		1 .... 2 3			(14)
Midwife 4		1 .... 2 3			(15)
Dietician 5		1 .... 2 3			(16)
Other (WRITE IN & CODE 6)					
.... 6		1 .... 2 3			(17)
Can't remember.............. 7					

Q103 Thinking about the discussion on heart disease

a) Did you find it . . . .
READ OUT

(18)

Helpful 1
or Unhelpful 2
Neither 3
Don't know........................ 4   (18)

b) Was it . . . .
READ OUT

(19)

Easy to understand 1
or Difficult to understand 2
Neither 3
Don't know 4   (19)

c) Did you learn anything new or not?

(20)

Yes 1
No 2
Don't know 3   (20)

d) As a result of the discussion have you made any changes or do you plan to make changes to your lifestyle or not?

(21)

Yes, have made changes 1
Yes, plan to make changes 2
No change made or planned 3
Don't know 4   (21)

e) SHOWCARD AF (R) Apart from discussing heart disease which of these if any were you given or recommended to do?

(22)

Asked to keep a special diary/
    record sheet 1
Given leaflets/booklets 2
Given a diet sheet 3
Referred to a specialist/other health
    professional 4
Recommended to join a special class/
    support group 5
Recommended to attend a particular
    clinic 6
Take (more) exercise 7
Reduce weight 8
Reduce smoking 9
Other (WRITE IN & CODE 0)

. . . . 0

Nothing else X
Don't know . . . . Y   (22)

f) Were you asked to return or have you returned to the surgery/health centre for any follow—up checks or advice on heart disease?

(23)

Yes: for a check up 1
        for advice 2

No, follow-up 3
Don't know 4   (23)

CONTRACEPTION/BIRTH CONTROL

IF NO. 8 AT Q   (CONTRACEPTION/BIRTH CONTROL) MENTIONED ASK:
Q104   With whom did you discuss contraception/birth control?   MULTICODE OK

ASK FOR EACH PERSON DISCUSSED WITH
Q105   And did you raise the subject yourself, or was it raised by the . . . (PERSON) you spoke to?

	Q104		Q105		
	Discussed with (24)	Resp.	Health pro	Can't remember (24)	
Doctor/GP 1		1 .... 2 3			(25)
Nurse.....................2		1 .... 2 3			(26)
Health visitor 3		1 .... 2 3			(27)
Midwife 4		1 .... 2 3			(28)
Dietician 5		1 .... 2 3			(29)
Other (WRITE IN & CODE 6)					
.........................6		1 .... 2 3			(30)
Can't remember.............7					

Q106   Thinking about the discussion on contraception/birth control?

a) Did you find it . . . .
READ OUT
                                      (31)
         Helpful 1
    or   Unhelpful 2
         Neither 3
         Don't know 4   (31)

b) Was it . . . .
READ OUT
                                      (32)
         Easy to understand 1
    or   Difficult to understand 2
         Neither 3
         Don't know 4   (32)

c) Did you learn anything new or not?

                                      (33)
         Yes...............................1
         No 2
         Don't know 3   (33)

d) As a result of the discussion have you made any changes or do you plan to make changes to your lifestyle or not?

                                      (34)
         Yes, have made changes.............1
         Yes, plan to make changes..........2
         No change made or planned 3
         Don't know 4   (34)

e) SHOWCARD AG (R) **Apart from discussing contraception/birth control which of these, if any, were you given or recommended to do?**

(35)

Asked to keep a special diary/
temperature chart 1
Given leaflets/booklets 2
Given free condoms 3
Referred to a specialist/other health
professional 4
Recommended to attend a particular
clinic (eg Family Planning) 5
Other (WRITE IN & CODE 6)

.... 6

Nothing else 7
Don't know 8   (35)

f) **Were you asked to return or have you returned to the surgery/health centre for any follow—up checks or advice on contraception/birth control?**

(36)

Yes: for a check up 1
for advice 2

No, follow—up 3
Don't know 4   (36)

CHILDREN'S HEALTH

IF NO. 9 AT Q82 (CHILDREN'S HEALTH) MENTIONED ASK:
Q107 **With whom did you discuss children health? MULTICODE OK**

ASK FOR EACH PERSON DISCUSSED WITH
Q108 **And did you raise the subject yourself, or was it raised by the ... (PERSON) you spoke to?**

	Q107		Q108		
	Discussed with (37)	Resp.	Health pro	Can't remember	(37)
Doctor/GP 1		1	2	3	(38)
Nurse 2		1	2	3	(39)
Health visitor 3		1	2	3	(40)
Midwife 4		1	2	3	(41)
Dietician 5		1	2	3	(42)
Other (WRITE IN & CODE 6)					
.... 6		1	2	3	(43)
Can't remember 7					

Q109 **Thinking about the discussion on children's health?**

a) **Did you find it ....**
READ OUT

(44)

Helpful 1
or Unhelpful 2
Neither 3
Don't know 4   (44)

b) Was it . . . .
READ OUT

	(45)
Easy to understand	1
or Difficult to understand	2
Neither	3
Don't know	4

(45)

c) Did you learn anything new or not?

	(46)
Yes	1
No	2
Don't know	3

(46)

d) As a result of the discussion have you made any changes or do you plan to make changes to your lifestyle or not?

	(47)
Yes, have made changes	1
Yes, plan to make changes	2
No change made or planned	3
Don't know	4

(47)

SKIP TO COL 49

e) Were you asked to return or have you returned to the surgery/health centre for any follow—up checks or advice on children's health?

		(49)
Yes:	for a check up	1
	for advice	2
No, follow—up		3
Don't know		4

(49)

CHILDHOOD IMMUNISATION

Q110 IF NO. 10 AT Q82 (CHILDHOOD IMMUNISATION) MENTIONED ASK:
With whom did you discuss childhood immunisation? MULTICODE OK

Q111 ASK FOR EACH PERSON DISCUSSED WITH
And did you raise the subject yourself, or was it raised by the . . . (PERSON) you spoke to?

Q110		Q111			
Discussed with (50)		Resp.	Health pro	Can't remember	(50)
Doctor/GP	1	1	2	3	(51)
Nurse	2	1	2	3	(52)
Health visitor	3	1	2	3	(53)
Midwife	4	1	2	3	(54)
Other (WRITE IN & CODE 5)					
	5	1	2	3	(55)
Can't remember	6				

Q112　Thinking about the discussion on childhood immunisation

a) **Did you find it . . . .**
READ OUT

(56)

Helpful 1
or Unhelpful 2
Neither 3
Don't know . . . . 4　　　(56)

b) **Was it . . . .**
READ OUT

(57)

Easy to understand 1
or Difficult to understand 2
Neither 3
Don't know . . . . 4　　　(57)

c) **Did you learn anything new or not?**

(58)

Yes 1
No 2
Don't know . . . . 3　　　(58)

d) **As a result of the discussion have you made any changes or do you plan to make changes to your lifestyle or not?**

(59)

Yes, have made changes 1
Yes, plan to make changes 2
No change made or planned 3
Don't know . . . . 4　　　(59)

e) **SHOWCARD AH (R)　Apart from discussing childhood immunisation which of these if any were you given or recommended to do?**

(60)

Given leaflets/booklets 1
Referred to a specialist/other health
　professional 2
Recommended to attend a particular
　clinic (eg immunisation clinic) 3
Other (WRITE IN & CODE 4)

. . . . 4

Nothing else 5
Don't know . . . . 6　　　(60)

f) **Were you asked to return or have you returned to the surgery/health centre for any follow—up checks or advice on childhood immunisation?**

(61)

Yes:　for a check up 1
　　　for advice 2

No, follow-up 3
Don't know . . . . 4　　　(61)

CANCER

IF NO. 11 AT Q82 (CANCER) MENTIONED ASK:
Q113 **With whom did you discuss cancer?** MULTICODE OK

ASK FOR EACH PERSON DISCUSSED WITH
Q114 **And did you raise the subject yourself, or was it raised by the . . . (PERSON) you spoke to?**

	Q113 Discussed with (62)	Q114 Resp.	Health pro	Can't remember (62)	
Doctor/GP	1	1	2	3	(63)
Nurse	2	1	2	3	(64)
Health visitor	3	1	2	3	(65)
Midwife	4	1	2	3	(66)
Dietician	5	1	2	3	(67)
Other (WRITE IN & CODE 6)					
....	6	1	2	3	(68)
Can't remember	7				

Q115 **Thinking about the discussion on cancer?**

a) **Did you find it . . . .**
READ OUT

(69)
Helpful 1
or Unhelpful 2
Neither 3
Don't know 4   (69)

b) **Was it . . . .**
READ OUT

(70)
Easy to understand 1
or Difficult to understand 2
Neither 3
Don't know 4   (70)

c) **Did you learn anything new or not?**

(71)
Yes................................ 1
No 2
Don't know 3   (71)

d) **As a result of the discussion have you made any changes or do you plan to make changes to your lifestyle or not?**

(72)
Yes, have made changes............. 1
Yes, plan to make changes.......... 2
No change made or planned 3
Don't know 4   (72)

e) SHOWCARD AI (R) **Apart from discussing cancer which of these if any were you given or recommended to do?**

(73)
```
Asked to keep a special diary/
  record sheet ...................... 1
Given leaflets/booklets .............. 2
Given a diet sheet ................... 3
Referred to a specialist/other health
  professional...................... 4
Recommended to join a special class/
  support group .................... 5
Recommended to attend a particular
  clinic ........................... 6
Recommended to a counsellor........ 7
Recommended to contact
  specialist cancer organisation/
  charity........................... 8
Other (WRITE IN & CODE 9)

.................................... 9

Nothing else ........................ 0
Don't know ......................... X        (73)
```

f) **Were you asked to return or have you returned to the surgery/health centre for any follow-up checks or advice on cancer?**

(74)
```
Yes:   for a check up .............. 1
       for advice ................. 2

No, follow-up ...................... 3
Don't know .`....................... 4        (74)
```

SKIP TO CARD ⑥ 10

HIV/AIDS

IF NO. 12 AT Q82 (HIV/AIDS) MENTIONED ASK:
Q116 With whom did you discuss HIV/AIDS? MULTICODE OK

ASK FOR EACH PERSON DISCUSSED WITH
Q117 And did you raise the subject yourself, or was it raised by the . . . (PERSON) you spoke to?

	Q116		Q117		
	Discussed with (11)		Resp.	Health pro	Can't remember (11)
Doctor/GP 1			1.......... 2.......... 3		(12)
Nurse.......................2			1.......... 2.......... 3		(13)
Health visitor 3			1.......... 2.......... 3		(14)
Midwife 4			1.......... 2.......... 3		(15)
Counsellor 5			1.......... 2.......... 3		(16)
Social Worker 6			1.......... 2.......... 3		(17)
Other (WRITE IN & CODE 7)					
...........................7			1.......... 2.......... 3		(18)
Can't remember.............8					

Q118   Thinking about the discussion on HIV/AIDS

a) **Did you find it . . . .**
READ OUT

(19)

Helpful 1
or Unhelpful 2
Neither 3
Don't know 4   (19)

b) **Was it . . . .**
READ OUT

(20)

Easy to understand 1
or Difficult to understand 2
Neither 3
Don't know 4   (20)

c) **Did you learn anything new or not?**

(21)

Yes.............................. 1
No 2
Don't know 3   (21)

d) **As a result of the discussion have you made any changes or do you plan to make changes to your lifestyle or not?**

(22)

Yes, have made changes............. 1
Yes, plan to make changes........... 2
No change made or planned 3
Don't know 4   (22)

e) SHOWCARD AK (R)   **Apart from discussing HIV/AIDS which of these, if any, were you given or recommended to do?**

(23)

Given leaflets/booklets 1
Referred to a specialist/other health
    professional..................... 2
Recommended to join a special class/
    support group................... 3
Recommended to attend a particular
    clinic 4
Recommended to see a counsellor 5
Recommended to contact specialist
    HIV/AIDs organisation or charity 6
Given needles 7
Given condoms 8
Other (WRITE IN & CODE 9)

.... 9

Nothing else....................... 0
Don't know X   (23)

f) **Were you asked to return or have you returned to the surgery/health centre for any follow—up checks or advice on HIV/AIDS?**

(24)

Yes: for a check up 1
        for advice 2

No, follow—up 3
Don't know 4   (24)

MENTAL/PSYCHOLOGICAL PROBLEMS

Q119 IF NO. 13 AT Q82 (MENTAL/PSYCHOLOGICAL PROBLEMS) MENTIONED ASK:
With whom did you discuss mental and psychological problems? MULTICODE OK

Q120 ASK FOR EACH PERSON DISCUSSED WITH
And did you raise the subject yourself, or was it raised by the . . . (PERSON) you spoke to?

	Q119		Q120	
	Discussed with (25)	Resp.	Health pro	Can't remember (25)
Doctor/GP 1				
Nurse.......................2	1 ....2 3			(26)
Health visitor 3	1 ....2 3			(27)
Midwife 4	1 ....2 3			(28)
Councellor 5	1 ....2 3			(29)
Social worker...............6	1 ....2 3			(30)
Other (WRITE IN & CODE 7)	1 ....2 3			(31)
.........................7	1 ....2 3			(32)
Can't remember.............8				

Q121 **Thinking about the discussion on mental and psychological problems**

a) **Did you find it . . . .**
   READ OUT

   (33)
   Helpful 1
   or **Unhelpful** 2
   Neither 3
   Don't know......................4   (33)

b) **Was it . . . .**
   READ OUT

   (34)
   Easy to understand 1
   or **Difficult to understand** 2
   Neither 3
   Don't know......................4   (34)

c) **Did you learn anything new or not?**

   (35)
   Yes.............................1
   No 2
   Don't know......................3   (35)

d) **As a result of the discussion have you made any changes or do you plan to make changes to your lifestyle or not?**

   (36)
   Yes, have made changes............1
   Yes, plan to make changes..........2
   No change made or planned 3
   Don't know......................4   (36)

e) SHOWCARD AL (R) **Apart from discussing mental and psychological problems which of these if any were you given or recommended to do?**

(37)

Asked to keep a special diary/
   record sheet 1
Given leaflets/booklets...............2
Referred to a specialist/other health
   professional (eg psychiatrist) 3
Recommended to join a special class/
   support group 4
Recommended to attend a particular
   clinic 5
Recommended to see a counsellor 6
Recommended to change diet/
   have special diet..................7
Recommended to contact specialist
   organisation/charity................8
Other (WRITE IN & CODE 9)

.................................9

Nothing else........................0
Don't know X   (37)

f) **Were you asked to return or have you returned to the surgery/health centre for any follow—up checks or advice on mental and psychological problems?**

(38)

Yes: for a check up 1
         for advice 2

No, follow—up 3
Don't know........................4   (38)

EMOTIONAL PROBLEMS

IF NO. 14 AT Q82 (EMOTIONAL PROBLEMS) MENTIONED ASK:
Q122 **With whom did you discuss emotional problems? MULTICODE OK**

ASK FOR EACH PERSON DISCUSSED WITH
Q123 **And did you raise the subject yourself, or was it raised by the . . . (PERSON) you spoke to?**

	Q122		Q123		
	Discussed with (39)	Resp.	Health pro	Can't remember	(39)
Doctor/GP 1		1 .... 2 3			(40)
Nurse.........................2		1 .... 2 3			(41)
Health visitor 3		1 .... 2 3			(42)
Midwife 4		1 .... 2 3			(43)
Councellor 5		1 .... 2 3			(44)
Social worker..................6		1 .... 2 3			(45)
Other (WRITE IN & CODE 6)					
.........................7		1 .... 2 3			(46)
Can't remember..............8					

Q124   Thinking about the discussion on emotional problems

   a)   **Did you find it . . . .**
        READ OUT
                                            (47)
                Helpful 1
          or **Unhelpful** 2
                Neither 3
                Don't know.......................... 4   (47)

   b)   **Was it . . . .**
        READ OUT
                                            (48)
                Easy to understand 1
          or **Difficult to understand** 2
                Neither 3
                Don't know.......................... 4   (48)

   c)   **Did you learn anything new or not?**
                                            (49)
                Yes...... 1
                No 2
                Don't know.......................... 3   (49)

   d)   **As a result of the discussion have you made any changes or do you plan to
        make changes to your lifestyle or not?**
                                            (50)
                Yes, have made changes............. 1
                Yes, plan to make changes.......... 2
                No change made or planned 3
                Don't know.......................... 4   (50)

   e)   SHOWCARD AM (R)   **Apart from discussing emotional problems which of these
        if any were you given or recommended to do?**
                                            (51)
                Asked to keep a special diary/
                  record sheet 1
                Given leaflets/booklets.............. 2
                Referred to a specialist/other health
                  professional..................... 3
                Recommended to join a special class/
                  support group................... 4
                Recommended to attend a particular
                  clinic 5
                Recommended to see a counsellor 6
                Recommended to contact specialist
                  organisation/charity............... 7
                Other (WRITE IN & CODE 8)

                8

                Nothing else..................... 9
                Don't know........................ 0   (51)

   f)   **Were you asked to return or have you returned to the surgery/health centre
        for any follow—up checks or advice on emotional problems?**
                                            (52)
                Yes: for a check up 1
                        for advice 2

                No, follow—up 3
                Don't know........................ 4   (52)

SEXUAL PROBLEMS (SEXUALLY TRANSMITTED DISEASES)

Q125   IF NO. 15 AT Q82 (SEXUAL PROBLEMS) MENTIONED ASK:
        With whom did you discuss sexual problems? MULTICODE OK

Q126   ASK FOR EACH PERSON DISCUSSED WITH
        And did you raise the subject yourself, or was it raised by the . . . (PERSON) you spoke to?

	Q125		Q126		
	Discussed with (53)	Resp.	Health pro	Can't remember	(53)
Doctor/GP 1		1	2	3	(54)
Nurse.......................2		1	2	3	(55)
Health visitor 3		1	2	3	(56)
Midwife 4		1	2	3	(57)
Councellor 5		1	2	3	(58)
Social worker...............6		1	2	3	(59)
Other (WRITE IN & CODE 7)					
........................7		1	2	3	(60)
Can't remember.............8					

Q127   **Thinking about the discussion on sexual problems**

a) **Did you find it . . . .**
READ OUT

                (61)
      Helpful 1
  or **Unhelpful** 2
      Neither 3
      Don't know 4   (61)

b) **Was it . . . .**
READ OUT

                (62)
      Easy to understand 1
  or **Difficult to understand** 2
      Neither 3
      Don't know 4   (62)

c) **Did you learn anything new or not?**

                (63)
      Yes................................1
      No 2
      Don't know 3   (63)

d) **As a result of the discussion have you made any changes or do you plan to make changes to your lifestyle or not?**

                (64)
      Yes, have made changes.............1
      Yes, plan to make changes..........2
      No change made or planned 3
      Don't know 4   (64)

e) SHOWCARD AN (R) **Apart from discussing sexual problems which of these, if any, were you given or recommended to do?**

(65)

Asked to keep a special diary/
   record sheet 1
Given leaflets/booklets............... 2
Referred to a specialist/other health
   professional...................... 3
Recommended to join a special class/
   support group 4
Recommended to attend a particular
   clinic (eg genito-urinary)........... 5
Recommended to see a counsellor 6
Other (WRITE IN & CODE 7)

.... 7

Nothing else...................... 8
Don't know 9

(65)

f) **Were you asked to return or have you returned to the surgery/health centre for any follow-up checks or advice on sexual problems?**

(66)

Yes: for a check up 1
         for advice 2

No, follow-up 3
Don't know...................... 4

(66)

GYNAECOLOGICAL PROBLEMS

Q128 IF NO. 16 AT Q82 (GYNAECOLOGICAL PROBLEMS) MENTIONED ASK:
With whom did you discuss gynaecological problems? MULTICODE OK

Q129 ASK FOR EACH PERSON DISCUSSED WITH
And did you raise the subject yourself, or was it raised by the ... (PERSON) you spoke to?

Q128		Q129			
Discussed with (67)		Resp.	Health pro	Can't remember (67)	
Doctor/GP 1		1	2	3	(68)
Nurse...................... 2		1	2	3	(69)
Health visitor 3		1	2	3	(70)
Midwife 4		1	2	3	(71)
Other (WRITE IN & CODE 5)					
.... 5		1	2	3	(72)
Can't remember.............. 6					

Q130   **Thinking about the discussion on gynaecological problems**

a)   **Did you find it . . . .**
     READ OUT

                                           (73)
         Helpful 1
     or **Unhelpful** 2
         Neither 3
         Don't know 4   (73)

b)   **Was it . . . .**
     READ OUT

                                           (74)
         Easy to understand 1
     or **Difficult to understand** 2
         Neither 3
         Don't know 4   (74)

c)   **Did you learn anything new or not?**

                                           (75)
         Yes 1
         No 2
         Don't know 3   (75)

d)   **As a result of the discussion have you made any changes or do you plan to make changes to your lifestyle or not?**

                                           (76)
         Yes, have made changes 1
         Yes, plan to make changes 2
         No change made or planned 3
         Don't know 4   (76)

e)   SHOWCARD AO (R)   **Apart from discussing gynaecological problems which of these if any were you given or recommended to do?**

                                           (77)
         Asked to keep a special diary/
            record sheet/temperature chart 1
         Given leaflets/booklets 2
         Referred to a specialist/other health
            professional 3
         Recommended to join a special class/
            support group 4
         Recommended to attend a particular
            clinic (eg Family Planning,
            infertility) 5
         Other (WRITE IN & CODE 6)

         6

         Nothing else 7
         Don't know 8   (77)

f)   **Were you asked to return or have you returned to the surgery/health centre for any follow–up checks or advice on gynaecological problems?**

                                           (78)
         Yes: for a check up 1
               for advice 2

         No, follow–up 3
         Don't know 4   (78)

                                    SKIP TO CARD (7) 10

ASK ALL WHO HAVE BEEN TO SURGERY IN LAST 12 MONTHS (CODES 1–6 AT Q65 OR Q67). OTHERS GO TO Q132.

Q131   SHOWCARD DD (R)   **From this card, could you tell me please if you are satisfied, or dissatisfied with ...** READ OUT. ROTATE ORDER. TICK START

	Very satisfied	Fairly satisfied	Neither satisfied nor dissatisfied	Fairly dissatisfied	Very dissatisfied	Don't know	
The ease of getting an appointment with your GP at the surgery	1	2	3	4	5	6	(11)
The ease of getting your GP to see you or your family at home at weekends	1	2	3	4	5	6	(12)
The ease of getting your GP to see you or your family at home at night	1	2	3	4	5	6	(13)
The helpfulness of the receptionist/s	1	2	3	4	5	6	(14)
The explanations your GP gives to you	1	2	3	4	5	6	(15)
The amount of time your GP spends with you	1	2	3	4	5	6	(16)
The amount of advice your GP and other surgery staff give to you about how to lead a healthy lifestyle	1	2	3	4	5	6	(17)
The overall service you get from your GP and other surgery staff	1	2	3	4	5	6	(18)
How easy it is to get to the surgery	1	2	3	4	5	6	(19)

ASK ALL

Q132   SHOWCARD EE (R)   **Looking at this card, could you tell me please which, if any, of these you have used in the last 12 months?**

(20)

1	Family planning clinic	1
2	Community midwife	2
3	Health visitor	3
4	Chiropodist	4
5	District nurse	5
6	Optician	6
7	Chiropractor	7
8	Acupuncturist	8
9	Homeopath	9
10	Osteopath	0
11	Aromatherapist	X

Other (WRITE IN AND CODE Y)

.... Y

(21)

Can't remember 1
None of these 2

(20–21)

Q133   SHOWCARD FF (R)   I am going to read out some subjects people might wish to discuss with their GP or other health professionals. Read through the statements carefully and then for each one read out, please tell me from this card how easy you personally find it to discuss with your GP or another health professional based at the surgery or health centre.   Just call out the number. READ OUT. ROTATE ORDER. TICK START

	1 Can discuss without difficulties	2 Can discuss with some difficulty	3 Don't feel I can discuss it with them	4 Have never needed to discuss it	No opinion	
Diet/healthy food	1	2	3	4	5	(22)
Weight control	1	2	3	4	5	(23)
Exercise/fitness	1	2	3	4	5	(24)
Alcohol	1	2	3	4	5	(25)
Smoking	1	2	3	4	5	(26)
Stress	1	2	3	4	5	(27)
Heart Disease	1	2	3	4	5	(28)
Contraception/birth control	1	2	3	4	5	(29)
Children's health	1	2	3	4	5	(30)
Childhood immunisation	1	2	3	4	5	(31)
Cancer	1	2	3	4	5	(32)
HIV/AIDS	1	2	3	4	5	(33)
Mental or psychological problems (eg. depression, anxiety)	1	2	3	4	5	(34)
Emotional problems (eg marital/relationship)	1	2	3	4	5	(35)
Sexual problems (eg sexually transmitted diseases)	1	2	3	4	5	(36)

ASK WOMEN ONLY

	1	2	3	4	5	
Gynaecological problems (eg period problems, infections such as thrush etc)	1	2	3	4	5	(37)

CANCER

Q134 **Now I'd like to ask you some questions about cancer. Which specific types of cancer, if any, have you heard of? DO NOT PROMPT. MULTICODE OK**

(38)

Bladder cancer	1
Breast cancer	2
Bone cancer	3
Bowel cancer	4
Cancer of the kidney	5
Cancer of the lymph/glands/nodes	6
Cancer of the pancreas	7
Cancer of the uterus (womb)	8
Cervical cancer	9
Gullet/oesophagus cancer	0
Leukaemia	X
Liver cancer	Y

(39)

Lung cancer	1
Melanoma	2
Mouth cancer	3
Ovary (ovarian) cancer	4
Prostate cancer	5
Skin cancer	6
Stomach cancer	7
Testicular cancer	8
Throat cancer	9
Other (WRITE IN AND CODE 0)	
....	0
All of these	X
None	Y

(40)

Don't know	1

38– 40

Q135 **And have you personally ever suffered from any cancer? IF YES: What type of cancer?**

Q136 **Has any close member of your family or close friend ever suffered from cancer, as far as you know? IF YES: What type of cancer?**

	Q135 (41)	Q136 (43)
Yes:		
Bladder cancer	1	1
Breast cancer	2	2
Bone cancer	3	3
Bowel cancer	4	4
Cancer of the kidney	5	5
Cancer of the lymph/glands/nodes	6	6
Cancer of the pancreas	7	7
Cancer of the uterus (womb)	8	8
Cervical cancer	9	9
Gullet/oesophagus	0	0
Leukaemia	X	X
Liver cancer	Y	Y
	(42)	(44)
Lung cancer	1	1
Melanoma	2	2
Mouth cancer	3	3
Ovary (ovarian) cancer	4	4
Prostate cancer	5	5
Skin cancer	6	6
Stomach cancer	7	7
Testicular cancer	8	8
Throat cancer	9	9
Other (WRITE IN AND CODE 0)		
....	0	0
No, none	X	X
Don't know	Y	Y

41– 44

Q137 What, if anything, can people do to reduce the risk of bowel cancer? PROBE: What else?

(45)

Not smoke/give up smoking 1
Avoid passive smoking..................... 2
Eat a (more) healthy diet (generally)......... 3
Eat less fat/fewer fatty foods/fatty meat/
    full fat dairy products.................... 4
Eat more fibre/roughage/starchy foods 5
Eat more fruit/vegetables.................. 6
Avoid exposure to radiation 7
Avoid stress 8
Other (WRITE IN & CODE 9)

.... 9

Can't do anything to reduce risk 0
Don't know X   (45)

Q138 What, if anything, can people do to reduce their risk of cervical cancer? PROBE: What else?

(46)

Not smoke/give up smoking 1
Avoid passive smoking..................... 2
Start sexual activity later in life.............. 3
Avoid having a large number of
    sexual partners .... 4 .
Have regular screening/cervical
    smears/tests........................... 5
Use condoms/practice safe sex 6
Improve hygiene.......................... 7
Other (WRITE IN & CODE 8)

.... 8

Can't do anything to reduce risk 9
Don't know 0   (46)

Q139 What, if anything, can people do to reduce the risk of lung cancer? PROBE: What else?

(47)

Not smoke/give up smoking 1
Avoid passive smoking..................... 2
Use special equipment at work
    (eg masks, breathing apparatus).......... 3
Avoid exposure to radiation 4
Avoid polluted areas...................... 5
Reduce atmospheric pollution/
    improve air quality 6
Avoid stress 7
Exercise 8
Diet/better diet/vitamins................... 9
Health checks/screening/X rays 0
Other (WRITE IN & CODE X)

.... X

Can't do anything to reduce risk .... Y
(48)
Don't know 1   (47-48)

Q140 What do you think are the main causes of skin cancer?

(49)

Exposure to sunlight 1
Getting sunburn 2
Using sunbeds/solaria 3
Exposure to radiation 4
Chemicals 5
Pollution 6
Smoking/tobacco 7
The hole in the ozone layer 8
Runs in the families/hereditary 9
It just starts on its own/
    no particular cause 0
Other (WRITE IN & CODE X)

. . . . X

Don't know . . . . Y   (49)

Q141 What, if anything, can people do to reduce the risk of skin cancer? PROBE: What else?

(50)

Avoid the sun 1
Avoid sunburn 2
Protect themselves against the sun
    (eg filter creams/lotions,
    shirt, hat etc) 3
Avoid using sunbeds/solaria 4
Avoid exposure to radiation 5
Avoid polluted areas 6
Avoid contact with chemicals 7
Use special equipment at work 8
Other (WRITE IN & CODE 9)

. . . . 9

Can't do anything to reduce risk 0
Don't know X   (50)

AT Q135
ASK ALL EXCEPT THOSE WHO HAVE CANCER, WHO GO TO Q145
Q142 SHOWCARD GG (R) If you were personally worried about getting cancer, who (if anyone) would you talk to?

(51)

1   Spouse/partner 1
2   Parents 2
3   Other relatives 3
4   Friends 4
5   Colleagues at work 5
6   GP/doctor 6
7   Practice nurse 7
8   Alternative practitioner 8
9   Other health professional 9
10 Social worker 0
11 Telephone helpline X
12 Cancer charities . . . . Y
                                                                                     (52)
13 Hospitals 1
    Other (WRITE IN AND CODE 2)

. . . . 2

No one 3
Don't know 4   (51-52)

Q143 Do you worry about getting cancer yourself, or not? IF YES: Any particular type of cancer, or just cancer generally?

Q144 And do you consider yourself personally at risk from cancer, or not? IF YES: Any particular type of cancer, or just cancer generally?

		Q143 (53)	Q144 (56)
Yes:			
Bladder cancer		1	1
Breast cancer		2	2
Bone cancer		3	3
Bowel cancer		4	4
Cancer of the kidney		5	5
Cancer of the lymph/glands/nodes		6	6
Cancer of the pancreas		7	7
Cancer of the uterus (womb)		8	8
Cervical cancer		9	9
Gullet/oesophagus		0	0
Leukaemia		X	X
Liver cancer		Y	Y
		(54)	(57)
Lung cancer		1	1
Melanoma		2	2
Mouth cancer		3	3
Ovary (ovarian) cancer		4	4
Prostate cancer		5	5
Skin cancer		6	6
Stomach cancer		7	7
Testicular cancer		8	8
Throat cancer		9	9
Other (WRITE IN AND CODE 0)			
....		0	0
Just cancer generally		X	X
No, none		Y	Y
		(55)	(58)
Don't know		1	1	(53–58)

ASK ALL

Q145 SHOWCARD HH (R)   **How well informed do you feel about cancer?**

	(59)
Very well informed	1
Fairly well informed	2
Not very well informed	3
Not at all informed	4
Don't know	5	(59)

Q146 From what sources have you found out most of what you know about cancer? PROBE: What other sources of information? DO NOT PROMPT. MULTICODE OK

Q147 If you wanted more information about cancer generally, or any specific type of cancer, where would you go or where would you look? DO NOT PROMPT. MULTICODE OK

	Q146 (60)	Q147 (63)
Personal experience of cancer	1	1
Talk to/contact with:		
Own GP/doctor	2	2
Nurse at GP surgery	3	3
Doctor/nurse at work	4	4
Well woman/man clinic	5	5
Private medical consultation	6	6
Private screening (eg BUPA)	7	7
Alternative therapist	8	8
Health visitor	9	9
Chemist/pharmacist	0	0
Spouse/partner	X	X
Friends/relatives	Y	Y
	(61)	(64)
Sufferers	1	1
TV:		
Advertising	2	2
Programmes	3	3
Radio:		
Advertising	4	4
Programmes	5	5
Newspapers/magazines:		
Articles	6	6
Advertising	7	7
Posters:		
At GP surgery/health centre/hospital	8	8
At place of work	9	9
In-street	0	0
Get information from work	X	X
Leaflets at GP surgery/health centre/ hospital	Y	Y
	(62)	(65)
Library/books	1	1
Cancer charities	2	2
Hospitals	3	3
Local hospice	4	4
Support groups/women's groups/ men's groups	5	5
Telephone helpline/information line	6	6
Other (WRITE IN & CODE 7)		
....	7	7
None	8	8
Don't know	9	9

(60-65)

Q148 **I'd now like to ask you a few questions about screening. Have you ever had screening for any type of cancer? IF YES: What type of cancer? CODE BELOW**

ASK FOR EACH ONE MENTIONED

Q149 **Was the screening for . . . (TYPE OF CANCER) carried out on the NHS or privately?**

	Q148 (66)	Q149 NHS	Private	Don't know	(66)
Yes:					
Breast cancer 1		1 .... 2 3			(67)
Cervical smear 2		1 .... 2 3			(68)
Skin cancer .... 3 ASK Q149		1 .... 2 3			(69)
Testicular cancer 4		1 .... 2 3			(70)
Other (WRITE IN & CODE 5)					
.... 5		1 .... 2 3			(71)
No, never had screening 6					
Don't know .... 7 SEE Q150					

ASK WOMEN ONLY. MEN GO TO Q155

Q150 **Have you ever had a cervical smear test? IF YES When did you last have a smear test?**

	(72)
In last week.............................. 1	
Within last 6 months 2	
Over 6 months, within last 12 months 3	
Over 1 year, within last 3 years............. 4	
Over 3 years, within last 5 years............ 5	
Over 5 years 6	
Can't remember 7	
Never 8	(72)

Q151 **In the last 12 months, has any health professional suggested you consider having a smear test, or given you an appointment or a written invitation to have a cervical smear test?**

	(73)
Yes 1	
No/don't know 2	(73)

Q152 **How often do you think a woman of your age should have a cervical smear test?**

	(74)
Every 6 months (or more often)............... 1	
Every year (or between 6 months and 1 year)............................ 2	
Every 2 or 3 years 3	
Every 4 or 5 years 4	
Every 6 to 9 years 5	
Every 10 years or more.................... 6	
Women my age don't need to have smears any more 7	
Don't know 8	(74)

Q153 SHOWCARD II (R) **Which of these statements best describes the main purpose of cervical smear tests, as far as you are aware?** SINGLE CODE ONLY

	(75)
1 To let you know you do not have any signs of cervical cancer.................... 1	
2 To let you know whether there are any pre-cancerous changes in the cervical tissue 2	
3 To enable early signs of cancer to be treated 3	
4 To enable the cancer to be treated 4	
None of these 5	
Don't know 6	(75)

ASK IF NEVER HAD SMEAR TEST AT Q150

Q154 Why have you never had a smear test?

	(76)
Never been sexually active.................	1
Never been told/recommended to	2
Embarrassment	3
Scared...................................	4
Doesn't do any good	5
Rather not know	6
Don't think I need one	7
Too busy/never got round to it	8
Other (WRITE IN & CODE 9)	
....	9
Don't know	0	(76)

ASK ALL

Q155 SHOWCARD JJ (R)   How strongly do you agree or disagree with the following statements. READ OUT, ROTATE ORDER AND TICK START

	Strongly agree	Tend to agree	Neither agree nor disagree	Tend to disagree	Strongly disagree	Don't know	
☐ If I was suffering from cancer I would rather not know about it	1	2	3	4	5	6	(77)
☐ One of the things that frightens me most about cancer is the side-effects of the treatments	1	2	3	4	5	6	(78)
☐ These days people can have a good chance of recovering from cancer if they're detected early enough	1	2	3	4	5	6	(79)

SKIP TO CARD (8) 10

SMOKING

ASK ALL

Q156 I would now like to ask you a few questions about smoking. Have you ever smoked a cigarette, cigar or pipe?

	(11)		
Yes	1	ASK Q157	
No...................................	2	GO TO Q189 (P 61)	(11)

ASK ALL WHO EVER SMOKED. OTHERS GO TO Q189 (P   )

Q157 Do you smoke cigarettes at all nowadays?

	(12)		
Yes	1	GO TO Q167	
No...................................	2	ASK Q158	(12)

ASK ALL WHO ARE NOT CURRENT CIGARETTE SMOKERS. OTHERS GO TO Q167 (P57)

Q158 Have you ever smoked cigarettes regularly?

	(13)		
Yes	1	ASK Q159	
No...................................	2	GO TO Q189 (P 61)	(13)

Q159 How old were you when you first tried smoking?

☐☐ years
(14) (15)

(14–15)

Q160 And how old were you when you started to smoke regularly?

☐☐ years
(16) (17)

(16–17)

Q161 How many cigarettes did you smoke in a day when you were a regular smoker?

☐☐☐ cigarettes a day
(18) (19) (20)

(18–20)

Q162 How long ago did you give up smoking?

(21)
In last 6 months............................ 1
In last 12 months........................... 2
In last 2 years.............................. 3 ·
In last 5 years.............................. 4
In last 10 years............................ 5
Longer ago 6
Can't remember 7

(21)

Q163 Why did you give up smoking? PROBE FULLY. MULTICODE OK

(22)
Diagnosis of health problems .... 1⎫ GO
Advice from doctor (but no diagnosis   ⎬ TO
  of health problems)...................... 2⎭ Q165
Pregnancy.................................. 3
Cost/save money........................... 4
General concern about health/fitness 5
Became more aware of health risks
  of smoking (eg read something)........... 6   SEE
Pressure from family 7   Q164
Aesthetic/cosmetic reasons, eg. smell,
  yellow teeth, nicotine stains 8
Pressure from friends/work colleagues 9
Set example for family 0
Worried about effects of passive smoking
  on family................................ X
Because people can't smoke at work .... Y
(23)
No specific reason 1
Other (WRITE IN & CODE '2')

.... 2
Don't know 3

(22–23)

ASK IF CODES 1-3 NOT MENTIONED AT Q163

Q164 **Did anything in particular happen to make you want to give up at that time? IF YES: What was this?**

(24)

No, nothing 1

Yes:

New Year's Resolution 2
Advertising campaign 3
TV programme 4
No Smoking Day 5
No smoking policy at work 6
Smoking–related illness/death
  of relative/friend 7
Cost of cigarettes went up/tax on
  tobacco increased/budget day 8
Talked to smoking advice/
  counselling phone line.................. 9
Other (WRITE IN & CODE 0)

.... 0

Don't know X   (24)

ASK ALL EX-SMOKERS (CODE 1 AT Q158)

Q165 **SHOWCARD KK (R)   Here is a list of things some people have used to give up smoking. Could you tell me please which, if any, you used? MULTICODE OK**

(25)

1	Help and support from family 1
2	Help and support from friends 2
3	Help and support at work 3
4	Advice from doctor 4
5	Prescription from doctor 5
6	Aids bought from chemist (eg. nicorettes) 6
7	Special clinics or 'stop smoking' groups 7
8	Booklets with advice and practical tips on how to stop smoking 8
9	Individual counselling and advice 9
10	Quitline/telephone helpline/advice line 0
11	"How to quit" videos X
12	Alternative treatments such as hypnosis or acupuncture . Y

(26)

Other (PLEASE SPECIFY & CODE 1)

.... 1

None of these....................................... 2
Don't know 3   (25-26)

Q166 **About how many times did you attempt to give up smoking before you succeeded?**

(27)

Succeeded first time 1
Twice 2
3–4 times 3
5–9 times 4   NOW GO TO Q189
10–14 times 5
15–19 times 6
20+ times 7
Can't remember 8   (27)

ASK CURRENT SMOKERS ONLY (YES AT Q157). OTHERS GO TO Q189

Q167 Do you smoke cigarettes regularly nowadays?

(28)

Yes 1   ASK Q168
No...................................... 2   GO TO Q189 (P6|)   (28)

Q168 How old were you when you first tried smoking?

☐☐ years
(29) (30)   (29–30)

Q169 And how old were you when you started to smoke regularly?

☐☐ years
(31) (32)   (31–32)

Q170 How many cigarettes do you smoke in an average day?

☐☐☐ cigarettes
(33) (34) (35)   (33–35)

Q171 Did you smoke any cigarettes yesterday?

(36)

Yes 1   ASK Q172
No...................................... 2   GO TO Q173   (36)

Q172 How many cigarettes did you smoke yesterday?

☐☐☐ cigarettes
(37) (38) (39)   (37–39)

NB. IF "ROLL YOUR OWN" GIVE AMOUNT OF TOBACCO USED

☐☐ grammes OR ☐☐ ounces
(40) (41)   (42) (43)   (40–43)

ASK ALL CURRENT REGULAR SMOKERS (YES AT Q167)

Q173 Do you ever smoke in your own home, or not?

(44)

Yes 1
No 2   (44)

Q174 Do you want to continue being a smoker or do you want to give up smoking?

(45)

Continue 1   GO TO Q176
Give up 2   ASK Q175
Don't know 3   GO TO Q176   (45)

ASK IF GIVE UP AT Q174

Q175 Do you have any firm plans to give up smoking in the future, or not?

(46)

Yes...................................... 1
No/not sure 2   (46)

ASK ALL CURRENT REGULAR SMOKERS
Q176 **Have you ever tried to give up smoking?**

```
                                                   (47)
       Yes ....................................... 1    ASK Q177
       No........................................ 2    GO TO Q183 (P 60)   (47)
```

Q177 **About how many times have you tried to give up smoking?**

```
                                                   (48)
       Once .................................... 1
       Twice ................................... 2
       3–4 times ............................... 3
       5–9 times ............................... 4
       10–14 times ............................. 5
       15–19 times ............................. 6
       20+ times ............................... 7
       Can't remember ......................... 8              (48)
```

Q178 **Why did you try to give up smoking?** PROBE FULLY. MULTICODE OK
```
                                                   (49)
       Diagnosis of health problems .............. 1
       Illness/too sick to smoke ................. 2
       In hospital .............................. 3
       Advice from doctor (but no diagnosis
          of health problems)..................... 4
       Cost/save money .......................... 5
       Pregnancy................................ 6
       General concern about health/fitness ....... 7
       Pressure from family ..................... 8
       Aesthetic/cosmetic reasons,
          eg. smell, yellow teeth, nicotine
          stains................................. 9
       Pressure from friends/work colleagues ...... 0
       Set example for family ................... X
       Worried about effects of passive smoking
          on family ............................. Y
                                                   (50)
       Because people can't smoke at work ........ 1
       No specific reason ...................... 2
       Other (WRITE IN & CODE '3')

       ........................................ 3
       Don't know ............................. 4              (49-50)
```

Q179 **What factors or events made you take up smoking again?** MULTICODE OK
```
                                                   (51)
       Weight gain ............................. 1
       Stress................................... 2
       Lack of will–power ...................... 3
       Encouragement by friends/colleagues/
          peer group pressure .................... 4
       Encouragement by family members ......... 5
       Withdrawal symptoms, eg. headaches
          shakes, irritability .................... 6
       Loss of enjoyment ....................... 7
       Loss of social prop/need something
          to do with hands....................... 8
       Other (WRITE IN & CODE 9)

       ........................................ 9

       Nothing in particular..................... 0
       Don't know ............................. X              (51)
```

Q180   SHOWCARD KK (R) AGAIN   **Here is a list of things some people have used to give up smoking. Could you tell me please which, if any, you have used?** MULTICODE OK

Q181   SHOWCARD KK (R) AGAIN   **And which, if any, did you find most useful in helping you to give up smoking?** MULTICODE OK

		Q180 Used (52)	Q181 Most useful (54)
1	Help and support from family	1	1
2	Help and support from friends	2	2
3	Help and support at work	3	3
4	Advice and support from doctor	4	4
5	Prescription from doctor	5	5
6	Aids bought from chemist (eg. nicorettes)	6	6
7	Special clinics or 'stop smoking' groups	7	7
8	Booklets with advice and practical tips on how to stop smoking	8	8
9	Individual counselling and advice	9	9
10	Quitline/telephone helpline/ advice line	0	0
11	"How to quit" videos	X	X
12	Alternative treatments such as hypnosis or acupuncture	Y	Y
		(53)	(55)

Other (PLEASE SPECIFY & CODE 1)

.... 1 ⎤ -------- 1
None of these .... 2 ⎬ GO TO 2   52–
Don't know .... 3 ⎦ Q182 3   55

ASK ALL WHO HAVE TRIED TO GIVE UP (YES AT Q176)
Q182   SHOWCARD KK (R) AGAIN   **Which, if any, of these would you find useful in helping you to give up smoking?** MULTICODE OK

		(56)
1	Help and support from family	1
2	Help and support from friends	2
3	Help and support at work	3
4	Advice and support from doctor	4
5	Prescription from doctor	5
6	Aids bought from chemist (eg. nicorettes)	6
7	Special clinics or 'stop smoking' groups	7
8	Booklets with advice and practical tips on how to stop smoking	8
9	Individual counselling and advice	9
10	Quitline/telephone helpline/ advice line	0
11	"How to quit" videos	X
12	Alternative treatments such as hypnosis or acupuncture	Y
		(57)

Other (PLEASE SPECIFY & CODE 1) ....

.... 1
None of these 2   56–
Don't know 3   57

<u>NOW GO TO Q184</u>

Q183 ASK THOSE WHO HAVE NEVER TRIED TO GIVE UP (NO AT Q 176)
What do you think would be the main disadvantages of giving up smoking, for you personally? DO NOT PROMPT. CODE BELOW

(58)

Weight gain 1
Stress 2
Withdrawal symptoms eg headaches,
   shakes irritability 3
Loss of enjoyment 4
Loss of social prop/need something
   to do with hands 5
Friends smoke/would feel left out 6
Other (WRITE IN & CODE 7)

.... 7

None (no disadvantages) 8
Don't know 9

(≤8)

Q184 ASK ALL CURRENT REGULAR SMOKERS (*YES AT Q167*)
What do you think would be main advantages of giving up smoking, for you personally? DO NOT PROMPT. CODE BELOW

(59)

Current health would improve 1
Improve fitness 2
Other people's health (eg. family, children).......... 3
Saves money................................. 4
Smell on self/hair/clothes/breath 5
Increased attractiveness to other people............ 6
More socially acceptable 7
Less worry about health in future 8
Free of pressure from other people (nagging) 9
Other (WRITE IN & CODE 0)

.... 0

None (no advantages)............................ X
Don't know .... Y

(59)

Q185 SHOWCARD LL (R) **How much, if at all, do you think the amount you smoke affects your health now?**

(60)

A great deal............................... 1 ⎫
A fair amount .... 2 ⎬ ASK Q186
Just a little .... 3 ⎭
Not at all .... 4 ⎫ GO TO
Don't know............................... 5 ⎭ Q187

(60)

Q186 ASK IF CODES 1–3 AT Q185 . OTHERS GO TO Q187
In what ways do you think it affects your health now? PROBE: What others?

(61)

Breathlessness 1
Coughing 2
Wheezing 3
Prone to chest infections.................... 4
Less fit than I used to be.................... 5
Worry about serious illnesses................ 6
Other (WRITE IN & CODE 7)

.... 7

Don't know................................ 8

(61)

ASK ALL CURRENT REGULAR SMOKERS

Q187 SHOWCARD LL(R) And how much, if at all, do you think the amount you smoke will affect your health in the future?

```
                                            (62)
       A great deal .............................. 1 ⎤
       A fair amount ............................. 2 ⎬
       Just a little ............................... 3 ⎦  ASK Q188
       Not at all ................................. 4 ⎤  GO TO
       Don't know................................ 5 ⎦  Q189        (62)
```

ASK IF CODES 1–3 AT Q187

Q188 In what ways do you think it will affect your health in the future? PROBE: What others?

```
                                            (63)
       Likely to get heart disease ................... 1
       Likely to get chest infections/bronchitis ....... 2
       Likely to get lung cancer ..................... 3
       Likely to get other cancer .................... 4
       Likely to get cancer (unspecified) ............ 5
       Likely to get lung problems (unspecified) ....... 6
       Likely to get problems with breathing/
         coughing/wheezing ........................ 7
       Likely to get breathlessness .................. 8
       Likely to become less fit .................... 9
       Likely to get a serious illness (unspecified) ..... 0
       Other (WRITE IN & CODE X)

       ............................................. X

       Don't know................................. Y        (63)
```

ASK ALL

Q189 In an average day, do you spend any time in places where you are inhaling other people's cigarette smoke, or not?

```
                                    (64)
       Yes ..................... 1  ASK Q190
       No....................... 2 ⎤ SEE
       Don't know .............. 3 ⎦ Q192              64
```

ASK IF YES AT Q189

Q190 In an average day, would you spend any time exposed to other people's cigarette smoke ... READ OUT

	Yes	No	Don't know	Not applicable	
at home	1	2	3	4	(65)
at work....................	1	2	3	4	(66)
in shops	1	2	3	4	(67)
in pubs or restaurants........	1	2	3	4	(68)
in other places you go socially	1	2	3	4	(69)
while travelling	1	2	3	4	(70)

Q191 And how much time would you say you spend in an average day, in places where you are inhaling other people's cigarette smoke?

```
       ☐    ☐   hours  ☐    ☐   minutes
      (71) (72)       (73) (74)

       Don't know ................. Y                 (71–74)
```

CHECK IF RESPONDENT WORKS (FULL–TIME OR PART–TIME) AT Q19. IF WORKING, ASK Q192. OTHERS GO TO Q196

ASK : WORKING SMOKERS AND WORKING NON–SMOKERS

Q192 **At your place of work, are people allowed to smoke anywhere or in special sections only, or is smoking banned?**

	(75)	
Allowed anywhere 1	GO TO Q194	
Special sections only 2	ASK Q193	
Banned 3	GO TO Q194	(75)

ASK IF SMOKING ALLOWED IN SPECIAL SECTIONS ONLY

Q193 **Is smoking allowed in ...? READ OUT**

	Yes	No	Some	Not applicable	Don't know	
All open work areas	1	2	3	4	5	(76)
Private offices	1	2	3	4	5	(77)
Catering/eating areas	1	2	3	4	5	(78)
Conference/meeting areas ...	1	2	3	4	5	(79)
Customer/visitor areas	1	2	3	4	5	(80)

SKIP TO CARD 9 10

CHECK IF RESPONDENT SELF–EMPLOYED AT Q19. IF YES, GO TO Q196
IF NOT SELF–EMPLOYED ASK:

Q194 SHOWCARD MM (R)   **Which, if any, of these does your employer do about smoking at work?** MULTICODE OK

Q195 SHOWCARD MM (R) AGAIN   **And which, if any, of these would you like your employer to do, or to do more?** MULTICODE OK

		Q194 Current provision	Q195 Desired provision
		(11)	(13)
1	Leaflets on how to stop smoking	1	1
2	Posters on how to stop smoking....................	2	2
3	A complete ban on smoking at work	3	3
4	No smoking signs	4	4
5	A smoking room...............................	5	5
6	Advice from works doctor/nurse.................	6	6
7	Advice from personnel officers	7	7
8	Advice from outside counsellors.................	8	8
9	Work with trade unions to promote smoking bans/control.................	9	9
10	Contact with self-help groups (eg stop smoking groups)	0	0
11	Run stop smoking groups	X	X
11	Support from management to reduce work stress	Y	Y
		(12)	(14)
12	Time off for counselling or treatment	1	1
	Other (WRITE IN & CODE '2')		
	....	2	2
	None of these	3	3
	Don't know	4	4

(11–14)

ASK ALL
Q196 **Which diseases or conditions are smokers more likely to suffer from?** DO NOT PROMPT. PROBE **Which others?** CODE ALL MENTIONED

Q197 SHOWCARD NN (R) **And from this card, which other diseases or conditions, which you may not have mentioned before, do you think smokers are more likely to suffer from? Which others?** MULTICODE OK

Q198 SHOWCARD NN (R) AGAIN **Which three or four of the diseases or conditions on this card do you think are most strongly linked to smoking?**

		Q196 (15)	Q197 (17)	Q198 (19)
1	Asthma	1	1	1
2	Cancer of the mouth/throat	2	2	2
3	Chronic bronchitis/wheezing/emphysema	3	3	3
4	Dandruff	4	4	4
5	Diabetes	5	5	5
6	Gangrene	6	6	6
7	Hardening of the arteries	7	7	7
8	Heart attack/disease	8	8	8
9	Jaundice	9	9	9
10	Lung cancer	0	0	0
11	Senile dementia	X	X	X
12	Strokes	Y	Y	Y
		(16)	(18)	(20)
13.	TB (Tuberculosis)	1	1	1
14	Wrinkles/skin ages more quickly	2	2	2

Chest/lung diseases/infections
  (unspecified) 3

Cancer (unspecified) 4

Other heart/circulation conditions
  (WRITE IN & CODE 5)

....5

Other chest/lung (WRITE IN & CODE 6)

....6

Other cancer (WRITE IN AND CODE 7)

....7

Other (WRITE IN & CODE 8)

....8 ....8 8

None ....9 ....9 9
Don't know ....0 ....0 0

(15 - 20

ASK ALL

Q199 I would now like to ask you where, in your opinion, smoking should be allowed and where not.

SHOWCARD OO (R) Do you think smoking should be allowed everywhere, allowed in special smoking sections only, or banned completely . . . . . .
READ OUT. ROTATE ORDER. TICK START.

	Allowed everywhere	Allowed in special smoking sections only	Banned completely	Don't know	
On public transport	1	2	3	4	(21)
In restaurants and cafes	1	2	3	4	(22)
In shops	1	2	3	4	(23)
In pubs	1	2	3	4	(24)
In banks and post offices	1	2	3	4	(25)
In cinemas	1	2	3	4	(26)
In hospitals or clinics	1	2	3	4	(27)
In offices or workplaces	1	2	3	4	(28)

Q200 SHOWCARD PP (R)   There are a number of things the Government could do to discourage people from smoking. For each item I read out, please tell me how strongly you personally would support or oppose the Government doing this.
READ OUT, ROTATE ORDER AND TICK START

	Strongly support	Tend to support	Neither support nor oppose	Tend to oppose	Strongly oppose	Don't know	
a) A total ban on the advertising of tobacco products	1	2	3	4	5	6	(29)
b) Increasing the prices of tobacco products through higher taxes	1	2	3	4	5	6	(30)
c) Stricter enforcement of the rules on under age sales	1	2	3	4	5	6	(31)
d) More Government funds for anti-smoking education	1	2	3	4	5	6	(32)

INTERVIEWER: NOW HAND OVER SELF–COMPLETION QUESTIONNAIRE, CHECKING FOR MEN'S/WOMEN'S VERSION.   DO NOT GIVE THE QUESTIONNAIRE TO RESPONDENTS AGED 55+ (THESE GO STRAIGHT TO Q201).

SAY "This questionnaire is designed for you to complete on your own. Please read the instructions on the front page carefully and then try to answer the questions. When you have finished, put the questionnaire into the brown envelope and hand it back to me"

THEN WHEN SELF–COMPLETION QUESTIONNAIRE DONE COME BACK TO Q201.

Q201 **We have almost come to the end of the questionnaire now, in which we have covered a number of different health issues. Are there any other health concerns you have which have not been covered? IF YES, PROBE. And what concerns have not been covered?** PROBE FULLY

(33)

	(33)
No additional concerns	1
Additional concerns	2

WRITE IN

. . . .

. . . .

. . . .

. . . .

(33)
3 4
5 6 4 8
9 0 X Y
(34)
1 2 3 4
5 6 4 8
9 0 X Y
(35)
1 2 3 4
5 6 4 8
9 0 X Y
(36)
1 2 3 4
5 6 4 8
9 0 X Y

Q 202 **Is there anything which you wish to add about your health or how to be healthy?** IF YES PROBE

(37)

	(37)
No additional concerns	1
Additional concerns	2

WRITE IN

. . . .

. . . .

. . . .

. . . .

(37)
3 4
5 6 4 8
9 0 X Y
(38)
1 2 3 4
5 6 4 8
9 0 X Y
(39)
1 2 3 4
5 6 4 8
9 0 X Y
(40)
1 2 3 4
5 6 4 8
9 0 X Y

Respondent Feedback

I would like to end the interview by asking you what you thought about the interview.

Q203 How interesting did you find the interview? Would you say . . .
READ OUT. ALTERNATE & TICK START

(41)

☐ . . . very interesting 1
. . . fairly interesting 2
. . . not very interesting 3
☐ . . . not at all interesting 4
Don't know 5   (41)

Q204 Were there any sections which you found difficult to answer?

(42)

Yes 1   ASK Q205
No 2   GO TO Q206   (42)

IF YES, ASK Q112b
Q205 And what one(s) was that/were they?

(43)

Health concerns 1
Food labelling 2
Environment 3
Psycho–social 4
Social support 5
Health services 6
Cancer 7
Smoking 8
Sexual health (self–completion) 9
Other (WRITE IN & CODE '0')

. . . . 0   (43)

ASK ALL
Q206 And how long did you find the interview? Would you say . . .
READ OUT. ALTERNATE & TICK START

(44)

☐ . . . much too long 1
. . . a little too long 2
. . . about right 3
☐ . . . too short 4
Don't know 5   (44)

Q207 **Did you think the questions were difficult to understand or not? Would you say they were . . .**
READ OUT. ALTERNATE & TICK START

(45)

☐ . . . very difficult 1
   . . . fairly difficult 2
   . . . not very difficult 3
☐ . . . not at all difficult........................ 4
   Don't know 5   (45)

Q208 **Finally, how interested would you be in participating in future surveys on similar subjects? Would you be . . .**
READ OUT. ALTERNATE & TICK START

(46)

☐ . . . very interested 1
   . . . fairly interested......................... 2
   . . . not very interested...................... 3
☐ . . . not at all interested 4
   Don't know 5   (46)

INTERVIEWER CODE:

This interview was carried out:

(47)

In total privacy throughout 1
With someone else present for part of
   the interview 2
With someone else present for most of/
   all of the interview 3   (47)

IF SOMEONE ELSE WAS PRESENT (CODES 2 OR 3)

The other person/people present was/were:

(48)

Respondent's spouse/partner 1
Respondent's child/ren 2
Respondent's parent/s or other relatives 3
Other.. 4
Don't know 5   (48)

INTERVIEWER ASSESSMENT:

This respondent's level of literacy seemed:

(49)

Good.. 1
Average 2
Poor 3   (49)

Length of Interview write in ☐☐☐ minutes
                             (50) (51) (52)   (50-52)

THANK RESPONDENT & CLOSE

MORI/6638
(1-4)

Health & Lifestyle Questionnaire

Self—Completion Section

WOMEN

The next set of questions are in this booklet. It is probably easier for you to read them and to tick the answers which apply to you.

It is important that you answer accurately and honestly. Place the completed questionnaire in the envelope and seal it before returning it to the interviewer. When the envelope is opened, together with thousands of other envelopes, all the answers will be analysed together anonymously.

Q1   Below is a list of topics to do with sexual health. Please read the list carefully, and for each topic put a tick in the box which best describes how informed you feel. How well informed do you feel about . . . .

TICK ONE BOX IN EACH LINE

	Very well informed	Fairly well informed	Not very well informed	Not at all well informed	Don't know	
. . . contraception and birth control	☐ 1	☐ 2	☐ 3	☐ 4	☐ 5	(14)
. . . menstruation (periods)	☐ 1	☐ 2	☐ 3	☐ 4	☐ 5	(15)
. . . pre-menstrual tension (PMT)	☐ 1	☐ 2	☐ 3	☐ 4	☐ 5	(16)
. . . the menopause (the change)	☐ 1	☐ 2	☐ 3	☐ 4	☐ 5	(17)
. . . abortion	☐ 1	☐ 2	☐ 3	☐ 4	☐ 5	(18)
. . . the risks of HIV/AIDS	☐ 1	☐ 2	☐ 3	☐ 4	☐ 5	(19)
. . . the risks of other sexually transmitted diseases	☐ 1	☐ 2	☐ 3	☐ 4	☐ 5	(20)
. . . the emotional side of sexual relationships	☐ 1	☐ 2	☐ 3	☐ 4	☐ 5	(21)

Q2 **Have you ever had vaginal sexual intercourse with a man?**
(by this I mean a man's penis entering a woman's vagina)

Yes	☐ 1	CONTINUE WITH Q3
No	☐ 2	NOW GO TO Q14 ON PAGE 6 (22)

The next section is for women who have had vaginal sexual intercourse with men. If this does not apply to you, please go to Q14 on page 6.

Q3 **How long ago did you last have vaginal sexual intercourse with a man?**

TICK
ONE BOX

Within last week	☐	1
Within last 2 weeks	☐	2
Within last 3 weeks	☐	3
Within last 4 weeks	☐	4
Within last 6 weeks	☐	5
Within last 3 months	☐	6
Within last 6 months	☐	7
Within last 9 months	☐	8
Within last 12 months	☐	9
Within last 2 years	☐	0
Within last 5 years	☐	X
More than 5 years ago	☐	Y
Cannot remember	☐	1

(23–24)

Q4 **At the time you last had vaginal sexual intercourse with that person, how long had you known him?**

TICK
ONE BOX

Less than a week	☐	1
Less than a month	☐	2
Less than 3 months	☐	3
Less than 6 months	☐	4
Less than a year	☐	5
Less than 2 years	☐	6
Less than 5 years	☐	7
Less than 10 years	☐	8
Less than 15 years	☐	9
Less than 20 years	☐	0
Over 20 years	☐	X
Can't remember	☐	Y

(25)

Q5 **Is/was the person you last had vaginal sexual intercourse with your . . .**

TICK
ONE BOX

Husband	☐	1
The man you live with	☐	2
Your regular boyfriend	☐	3
An occasional boyfriend	☐	4
Someone you just met/casual encounter	☐	5
Someone else	☐	6

(26)

Q6 Approximately how many times altogether have you had vaginal sexual intercourse with that person? If you can't remember exactly please give your best estimate.

TICK
ONE BOX

Once only	☐ 1
Twice	☐ 2
3 times	☐ 3
4 times	☐ 4
5 times	☐ 5
6 times	☐ 6
7 times	☐ 7
8 times	☐ 8
9 times	☐ 9
10 times	☐ 0
11–20 times	☐ X
21–100 times	☐ Y
Over 100 times	☐ 1 (27–28)

Q7 And which of the following took place, when you last had sexual contact with that person?

TICK ALL THE BOXES
WHICH APPLY

Vaginal sexual intercourse
(by this I mean a man's penis entering a woman's vagina) ☐ 1

Anal sexual intercourse
(man's penis entering partner's anus/back passage) ☐ 2

Oral sex – on man by woman
(woman's mouth on man's genital area/sex organs) ☐ 3

Oral sex – on woman by man
(man's mouth on woman's genital area/sex organs) ☐ 4

Masturbation – of man by woman
(woman stimulating man's genital area/sex organs by hand) ☐ 5

Masturbation – of woman by man
(man stimulating woman's genital area/sex organs by hand) ☐ 6

Cannot remember ☐ 7 (29)

Q8 On the last occasion when you had vaginal sexual intercourse, did you and your partner talk about using a condom for . . .

PLEASE TICK ONE BOX IN EACH LINE

	Yes	No	Can't remember	
Contraception	☐ 1	☐ 2	☐ 3	(30)
Prevention of HIV (the AIDS virus)	☐ 1	☐ 2	☐ 3	(31)
Prevention of other infections	☐ 1	☐ 2	☐ 3	(32)

Q9 **When you last had vaginal sexual intercourse with a man, which of these, if any, were used?**

TICK ALL THE BOXES
WHICH APPLY

Condom	☐ 1
Cap/diaphragm	☐ 2
Contraceptive pill	☐ 3
Contraceptive sponge	☐ 4
Emergency contraception/'Morning after' pill	☐ 5
Coil/IUD	☐ 6
'Barrier' creams (foam tablets, jelly, creams, suppositories, etc)	☐ 7
Withdrawal	☐ 8
Rhythm method/safe period	☐ 9
Douching/washing	☐ 0
Something else (PLEASE WRITE IN & TICK BOX)	

.... ☐ X

Nothing ☐ Y

Can't remember ☐ 1 (33–34)

IF CONDOM WAS USED, CONTINUE WITH Q10. OTHERS GO TO Q11

Q10a **If a condom was used on the last occasion you had vaginal sexual intercourse with a man, please indicate which of the following was the most important reason for using a condom?**

Q10b **Which (if any) was another reason for using a condom?**

	Q10a Most important (TICK ONE BOX)	Q10b Other reason (TICK ONE BOX)
Contraception	☐ 1	☐ 1
Prevention of HIV (the AIDS virus)	☐ 2	☐ 2
Prevention of other infections	☐ 3	☐ 3 (35–36)

Q11 **These days, if you have sex with a new partner do you use a condom . . .**

TICK ONE BOX

Always	☐ 1
Most times	☐ 2
About half the time	☐ 3
Occasionally	☐ 4
Never	☐ 5
Does not apply to me	☐ 6 (37)

Q12   In the last 12 months, with how many men have you had vaginal sexual intercourse? Please include every man you have had vaginal sexual intercourse within the last 12 months, even if only once. Please remember to include your present partner (if you have had vaginal sexual intercourse with him). If you can't remember exactly please give your best estimate.

TICK
ONE BOX

Number of partners

Number of partners		Code		Number of partners		Code
None	☐	0		13	☐	2
1	☐	1		14	☐	3
2	☐	2		15	☐	4
3	☐	3		16	☐	5
4	☐	4		17	☐	6
5	☐	5		18	☐	7
6	☐	6		19	☐	8
7	☐	7		20	☐	9
8	☐	8		21–25	☐	0
9	☐	9		26–30	☐	X
10	☐	X		31–40	☐	Y
11	☐	Y		41–50	☐	1
12	☐	1		51–100	☐	2
				More than 100	☐	3

(38–40)

Q13   In the last **5 years**, with how many men have you had vaginal sexual intercourse even if only once? Please include those you have already counted in the last 12 months, and remember to include your present partner (if you have had vaginal sexual intercourse with him). If you can't remember exactly please give your best estimate.

TICK
ONE BOX

Number of partners

Number of partners		Code		Number of partners		Code
None	☐	0		16	☐	5
1	☐	1		17	☐	6
2	☐	2		18	☐	7
3	☐	3		19	☐	8
4	☐	4		20	☐	9
5	☐	5		21–25	☐	0
6	☐	6		26–30	☐	X
7	☐	7		31–40	☐	Y
8	☐	8		41–50	☐	1
9	☐	9		51–100	☐	2
10	☐	X		101–200	☐	3
11	☐	Y		201–300	☐	4
12	☐	1		301–400	☐	5
13	☐	2		401–500	☐	6
14	☐	3		More than 500	☐	7
15	☐	4				

(41–43)

Q14 **Do you agree or disagree with the following statements?**
TICK ONE BOX FOR EACH STATEMENT.

	Strongly agree	Tend to agree	Tend to disagree	Strongly disagree	Don't know	
I don't think I'll ever get HIV (the AIDS virus)	☐ 1	☐ 2	☐ 3	☐ 4	☐ 5	(44)
If someone I worked with had HIV (the AIDS virus), it would be my right to be informed about it	☐ 1	☐ 2	☐ 3	☐ 4	☐ 5	(45)
Condoms are too unreliable as a method of contraception	☐ 1	☐ 2	☐ 3	☐ 4	☐ 5	(46)
Easy availability of condoms is harmful for young people	☐ 1	☐ 2	☐ 3	☐ 4	☐ 5	(47)
The risk for people like me of getting HIV (the AIDS virus) has been exaggerated by Government and health officials	☐ 1	☐ 2	☐ 3	☐ 4	☐ 5	(48)
The age at which two men can legally have sex should be the same as for a man and a woman	☐ 1	☐ 2	☐ 3	☐ 4	☐ 5	(49)
It can sometimes be right for a GP to provide contraception to people under 16 without informing their parents	☐ 1	☐ 2	☐ 3	☐ 4	☐ 5	(50)
Women often do not suggest using a condom with a new partner because they are afraid of being rejected by that partner	☐ 1	☐ 2	☐ 3	☐ 4	☐ 5	(51)
You don't need to use a condom for protection against HIV (the AIDS virus) if you are careful about the sexual partners you choose	☐ 1	☐ 2	☐ 3	☐ 4	☐ 5	(52)
Sex education in schools should include information on how to use a condom	☐ 1	☐ 2	☐ 3	☐ 4	☐ 5	(53)
Most parents don't talk openly to their children about sexual matters	☐ 1	☐ 2	☐ 3	☐ 4	☐ 5	(54)
AIDS educational advertising on TV should show how condoms should be used	☐ 1	☐ 2	☐ 3	☐ 4	☐ 5	(55)

Q15 **What do you think are the chances on average these days of people in this country getting HIV (the AIDS virus) from sexual intercourse without a condom between men and women?**

TICK ONE
BOX

Very high	1
Quite high	2
Moderate	3
Quite low	4
Very low	5

(56)
SKIP TO COL 60

Q16 **Have you ever seriously considered having the HIV (AIDS) blood test?**

Yes	1
No	2

(60)

Q17 **Have you ever been offered the HIV (AIDS) blood test?**

Yes	1
No	2

(61)

Q18 **Have you actually had the HIV (AIDS) blood test?**

Yes	1 ANSWER Q22
No	2 SKIP TO Q23

(62)

Q19 **How helpful was any counselling you received concerning the HIV test?**

TICK ONE
BOX

Did not get any counselling	1
Not at all helpful	2
Not very helpful	3
Fairly helpful	4
Very helpful	5

(63)

Q20 **Compared to other women of your age living in this country, do you feel that your chances of getting HIV (the AIDS virus) from vaginal sexual intercourse without a condom are . . . .**

TICK
ONE BOX

Much less than average	1
Slightly less than average	2
About average	3
Slightly greater than average	4
Much greater than average	5

(64)

Q21   **Are there any other concerns you have about HIV, AIDS or other matters of sexual health?**

PLEASE WRITE BELOW

(65)
1234
5678
90XY
(66)
1234
5678
90XY
(67)
1234
5678
90XY
(68)
1234
5678
90XY

....

....

....

....

....

THANK YOU FOR COMPLETING THE QUESTIONNAIRE

THE INFORMATION YOU HAVE GIVEN US WILL HELP TO PROVIDE A NATIONAL PICTURE OF PEOPLE'S HEALTH AND HEALTH CONCERNS.   YOUR ANSWERS ARE COMPLETELY CONFIDENTIAL.

NOW PLACE THE BOOKLET IN THE ENVELOPE, SEAL IT AND RETURN IT TO THE INTERVIEWER.

MORI/6638
(1–4)

· · · · · · · · · · · · (5–12)
②   13

Health & Lifestyle Questionnaire

Self—Completion Section

MEN

The next set of questions are in this booklet. It is probably easier for you to read them and to tick the answers which apply to you.

It is important that you answer accurately and honestly.   Place the completed questionnaire in the envelope and seal it before returning it to the interviewer. When the envelope is opened, together with thousands of other envelopes, all the answers will be analysed together anonymously.

Q1   Below is a list of topics to do with sexual health. Please read the list carefully, and for each topic put a tick in the box which best describes how informed you feel. How well informed do you feel about . . . .

TICK ONE BOX IN EACH LINE

Very well informed	Fairly well informed	Not very well informed	Not at all well informed	Don't know	
☐ 1	☐ 2	☐ 3	☐ 4	☐ 5	(14)
☐ 1	☐ 2	☐ 3	☐ 4	☐ 5	(15)
☐ 1	☐ 2	☐ 3	☐ 4	☐ 5	(16)
☐ 1	☐ 2	☐ 3	☐ 4	☐ 5	(17)
☐ 1	☐ 2	☐ 3	☐ 4	☐ 5	(18)
☐ 1	☐ 2	☐ 3	☐ 4	☐ 5	(19)
☐ 1	☐ 2	☐ 3	☐ 4	☐ 5	(20)
☐ 1	☐ 2	☐ 3	☐ 4	☐ 5	(21)

Q2   **Have you ever had vaginal sexual intercourse with a woman?**
(by this I mean a man's penis entering a woman's vagina)

Yes	☐	1 CONTINUE WITH Q3
No	☐	2 NOW GO TO Q14 ON PAGE 6 (22)

The next section is for men who have had vaginal sexual intercourse with women. If this does not apply to you, please go to Q14 on page 6.

Q3   **How long ago did you last have vaginal sexual intercourse with a woman?**

TICK
ONE BOX

Within last week	☐	1
Within last 2 weeks	☐	2
Within last 3 weeks	☐	3
Within last 4 weeks	☐	4
Within last 6 weeks	☐	5
Within last 3 months	☐	6
Within last 6 months	☐	7
Within last 9 months	☐	8
Within last 12 months	☐	9
Within last 2 years	☐	0
Within last 5 years	☐	X
More than 5 years ago	☐	Y
Cannot remember	☐	1

(23–24)

Q4   **At the time you last had vaginal sexual intercourse with that person, how long had you known her?**

TICK
ONE BOX

Less than a week	☐	1
Less than a month	☐	2
Less than 3 months	☐	3
Less than 6 months	☐	4
Less than a year	☐	5
Less than 2 years	☐	6
Less than 5 years	☐	7
Less than 10 years	☐	8
Less than 15 years	☐	9
Less than 20 years	☐	0
Over 20 years	☐	X
Can't remember	☐	Y

(25)

Q5   **Is/was the person you last had vaginal sexual intercourse with your . . .**

TICK
ONE BOX

Wife	☐	1
The woman you live with	☐	2
Your regular girlfriend	☐	3
An occasional girlfriend	☐	4
Someone you just met/casual encounter	☐	5
Someone else	☐	6

(26)

Q6   Approximately how many times altogether have you had vaginal sexual intercourse with that person? If you can't remember exactly please give your best estimate.

TICK
ONE BOX

Once only	1
Twice	2
3 times	3
4 times	4
5 times	5
6 times	6
7 times	7
8 times	8
9 times	9
10 times	0
11–20 times	X
21–100 times	Y
Over 100 times	1

(27–28)

Q7   And which of the following took place, when you last had sexual contact with that person?

TICK ALL THE BOXES
WHICH APPLY

Vaginal sexual intercourse
(by this I mean a man's penis entering a woman's vagina)   1

Anal sexual intercourse
(man's penis entering partner's anus/back passage)   2

Oral sex – on man by woman
(woman's mouth on man's genital area/sex organs)   3

Oral sex – on woman by man
(man's mouth on woman's genital area/sex organs)   4

Masturbation – of man by woman
(woman stimulating man's genital area/sex organs by hand)   5

Masturbation – of woman by man
(man stimulating woman's genital area/sex organs by hand)   6

Cannot remember   7   (29)

Q8   On the last occasion when you had vaginal sexual intercourse, did you and your partner talk about using a condom for . . .

PLEASE TICK ONE BOX IN EACH LINE

	Yes	No	Can't remember	
Contraception	1	2	3	(30)
Prevention of HIV (the AIDS virus)	1	2	3	(31)
Prevention of other infections	1	2	3	(32)

Q9 When you last had vaginal sexual intercourse with a woman, which of these, if any, were used?

TICK ALL THE BOXES
WHICH APPLY

Condom	☐	1
Cap/diaphragm	☐	2
Contraceptive pill	☐	3
Contraceptive sponge	☐	4
Emergency contraception/'Morning after' pill	☐	5
Coil/IUD	☐	6
'Barrier' creams (foam tablets, jelly, creams, suppositories, etc)	☐	7
Withdrawal	☐	8
Rhythm method/safe period	☐	9
Douching/washing	☐	0

Something else (PLEASE WRITE IN & TICK BOX)

.... ☐ X

Nothing ☐ Y

Can't remember ☐ 1 (33–34)

IF CONDOM WAS USED, CONTINUE WITH Q10. OTHERS GO TO Q11

Q10a If a condom was used on the last occasion you had vaginal sexual intercourse with a woman, please indicate which of the following was the most important reason for using a condom?

Q10b Which (if any) was another reason for using a condom?

	Q10a Most important (TICK ONE BOX)	Q10b Other reason (TICK ONE BOX)	
Contraception	☐ 1	☐ 1	
Prevention of HIV (the AIDS virus)	☐ 2	☐ 2	
Prevention of other infections	☐ 3	☐ 3	(35–36)

Q11 These days, if you have sex with a new partner do you use a condom . . .

TICK ONE
BOX

Always	☐	1
Most times	☐	2
About half the time	☐	3
Occasionally	☐	4
Never	☐	5
Does not apply to me	☐	6

(37)

Q12 In the last 12 months, with how many women have you had vaginal sexual
intercourse? Please include every woman you have had vaginal sexual
intercourse within the last 12 months, even if only once. Please remember to
include your present partner (if you have had vaginal sexual intercourse with her).
If you can't remember exactly please give your best estimate.

TICK
ONE BOX

Number of
partners

None	0		13	2
1	1		14	3
2	2		15	4
3	3		16	5
4	4		17	6
5	5		18	7
6	6		19	8
7	7		20	9
8	8		21–25	0
9	9		26–30	X
10	X		31–40	Y
11	Y		41–50	1
12	1		51–100	2
			More than 100	3

(38–40)

Q13 In the last 5 years, with how many women have you had vaginal sexual
intercourse even if only once. Please include those you have already counted in
the last 12 months, and remember to include your present partner (if you have
had vaginal sexual intercourse with her). If you can't remember exactly please
give your best estimate.

TICK
ONE BOX

Number of
partners

None	0		16	5
1	1		17	6
2	2		18	7
3	3		19	8
4	4		20	9
5	5		21–25	0
6	6		26–30	X
7	7		31–40	Y
8	8		41–50	1
9	9		51–100	2
10	X		101–200	3
11	Y		201–300	4
12	1		301–400	5
13	2		401–500	6
14	3		More than 500	7
15	4			

(41–43)

Q14   How strongly do you agree or disagree with the following statements?
TICK ONE BOX FOR EACH STATEMENT.

	Strongly agree	Tend to agree	Tend to disagree	Strongly disagree	Don't know	
I don't think I'll ever get HIV (the AIDS virus)	☐ 1	☐ 2	☐ 3	☐ 4	☐ 5	(44)
If someone I worked with had HIV (the AIDS virus), it would be my right to be informed about it	☐ 1	☐ 2	☐ 3	☐ 4	☐ 5	(45)
Condoms are too unreliable as a method of contraception	☐ 1	☐ 2	☐ 3	☐ 4	☐ 5	(46)
Easy availability of condoms is harmful for young people	☐ 1	☐ 2	☐ 3	☐ 4	☐ 5	(47)
The risk for people like me of getting HIV (the AIDS virus) has been exaggerated by Government and health officials	☐ 1	☐ 2	☐ 3	☐ 4	☐ 5	(48)
The age at which two men can legally have sex should be the same as for a man and a woman	☐ 1	☐ 2	☐ 3	☐ 4	☐ 5	(49)
It can sometimes be right for a GP to provide contraception to people under 16 without informing their parents	☐ 1	☐ 2	☐ 3	☐ 4	☐ 5	(50)
Women often do not suggest using a condom with a new partner because they are afraid of being rejected by that partner	☐ 1	☐ 2	☐ 3	☐ 4	☐ 5	(51)
You don't need to use a condom for protection against HIV (the AIDS virus) if you are careful about the sexual partners you choose	☐ 1	☐ 2	☐ 3	☐ 4	☐ 5	(52)
Sex education in schools should include information on how to use a condom	☐ 1	☐ 2	☐ 3	☐ 4	☐ 5	(53)
Most parents don't talk openly to their children about sexual matters	☐ 1	☐ 2	☐ 3	☐ 4	☐ 5	(54)
AIDS educational advertising on TV should show how condoms should be used	☐ 1	☐ 2	☐ 3	☐ 4	☐ 5	(55)

Q15 **What do you think are the chances on average these days of people in this country getting HIV (the AIDS virus) from sexual intercourse without a condom between men and women?**

TICK ONE
BOX

Very high	☐ 1
Quite high	☐ 2
Moderate	☐ 3
Quite low	☐ 4
Very low	☐ 5

(56)

Q16 **Which of these best describes you?**

TICK ONE
BOX

a) I have absolutely never felt (sexually) attracted towards another man ☐ 1

b) I have felt (sexually) attracted towards another man, but never had any sexual contact with another man ☐ 2

c) I have had sexual contact with another man, but only once or very rarely ☐ 3

d) I have had sexual contact with another man more often than this ☐ 4

(57)

IF YOU ANSWERED a OR b (NOT HAD SEXUAL CONTACT WITH ANOTHER MAN) GO TO QUESTION 19 ON PAGE 8

IF YOU ANSWERED c OR d (HAD SEXUAL CONTACT WITH ANOTHER MAN) CONTINUE WITH QUESTION 17

Q17 **When did you last have sexual contact with a man?**

TICK
ONE BOX

Within last week	☐ 1
Within last month	☐ 2
Within last 2 months	☐ 3
Within last 4 months	☐ 4
Within last 6 months	☐ 5
Within last year	☐ 6
Longer ago	☐ 7
Cannot remember	☐ 8

(58)

Q18 **On the last occasion you had sexual contact with a man, which of these (if any) took place?**

TICK ALL THE BOXES
WHICH APPLY

Anal intercourse using a condom	☐ 1
Anal intercourse without a condom	☐ 2
Oral sex using a condom	☐ 3
Oral sex without a condom	☐ 4
Masturbation	☐ 5
None of these	☐ 6

(59)

Q19 **Have you ever seriously considered having the HIV (AIDS) blood test?**

Yes ☐ 1
No ☐ 2 (60)

Q20 **Have you ever been offered the HIV (AIDS) blood test?**

Yes ☐ 1
No ☐ 2 (61)

Q21 **Have you actually had the HIV (AIDS) blood test?**

Yes ☐ 1 ANSWER Q22
No ☐ 2 SKIP TO Q23 (62)

Q22 **How helpful was any counselling you received concerning the HIV test?**

TICK ONE
BOX

Did not get any counselling ☐ 1
Not at all helpful ☐ 2
Not very helpful ☐ 3
Fairly helpful ☐ 4
Very helpful ☐ 5 (63)

Q23 **Compared to other men of your age living in this country, do you feel that your chances of getting HIV (the AIDS virus) from vaginal sexual intercourse without a condom are . . . .**

TICK
ONE BOX

Much less than average ☐ 1
Slightly less than average ☐ 2
About average ☐ 3
Slightly greater than average ☐ 4
Much greater than average ☐ 5 (64)

Q24 **Are there any other concerns you have about HIV, AIDS or other matters of sexual health?**

(65)
1234
5678
90XY

PLEASE WRITE BELOW

. . . .

(66)
1234
5678
90XY

. . . .

(67)
1234
5678
90XY

. . . .

. . . .

(68)
1234
5678
90XY

. . . .

THANK YOU FOR COMPLETING THE QUESTIONNAIRE

THE INFORMATION YOU HAVE GIVEN US WILL HELP TO PROVIDE A NATIONAL PICTURE OF PEOPLE'S HEALTH AND HEALTH CONCERNS. YOUR ANSWERS ARE <u>COMPLETELY CONFIDENTIAL</u>.

NOW PLACE THE BOOKLET IN THE ENVELOPE, SEAL IT AND RETURN IT TO THE INTERVIEWER.

Computerised tables

In addition to this published report a complete set of data tables is available on electronic fiche. These disk-based reports contain over 1500 data tables which break down the questionnaire variables by sex, age, social class, household type, region, and other appropriate variables.

Additionally, background notes on the survey and a complete set of questionnaires are included for reference.

Using a package called Ite Electronic Fiche for Windows these reports can be easily installed on any PC with the Windows operating system.

A user friendly indexing system allows easy and rapid retrieval of any table, while tables can be imported directly into word processing or spreadsheet packages.

Further details about the electronic fiche can be obtained from either Keith Bolling – telephone: 0171 413 1837 or Dominic McVey – telephone: 0171 413 1809.